Bright
WITH
Silver

Kathrene Pinkerton

WILLIAM SLOANE
ASSOCIATES, INC.
Publishers -- New York

Revised Edition

Manufactured in the United States

BRIGHT WITH SILVER

I AM INDEBTED TO SO MANY FOR HELP IN THE PREPARA-
tion of this book it is impossible to name them all.
Generous with time and effort were the Fromm brothers,
Edward, Henry, John, and Walter; John A. Fromm,
Arthur's son; Dr. Robert G. Green, Harry J. La Due,
and Dr. W. A. Young, pathologist of the Fromm farm
clinic. Also, men and women on the Fromm farms, fur
breeders, buyers, manufacturers, and other people in
the industry have given me valuable information.

K.G.P.

Chapter One

Henry Fromm had always liked foxes. The hardwood land of north central Wisconsin was famous for them, and before Henry knew A from B he could read the story of their footprints in the snow. The forest pressed close around the few cleared acres of his pioneer farm home, and its creatures were as familiar to Henry and his brothers as were their father's horses, cows, and pigs. They were even more important, for only by trapping could they obtain the things all boys want.

Henry, youngest of four brothers who grew up together, couldn't remember when he had not heard talk of fur, and before he was able to set his first weasel trap he roamed the woods with John, two years older. They were a strange pair, Henry intense and eager, and even at six a husky chunk of a lad; John shy and remote, and as niggardly with words as an Indian. John loved the forest. He knew it better than the others, and sometimes disappeared in it for two or three days. His traps earned as much as those of his two older brothers.

The four depended for their income on skunk and

weasel but caught an occasional raccoon and mink, and there was always the possibility of a red fox. Even grown men got only three or four in a winter, but John and Henry talked more of foxes than other animals. John, a born trapper, was challenged by their craftiness, Henry fascinated by the creatures themselves. Since he was old enough to hold a pencil he had drawn pictures of them, and imagined how wonderful it would be to have a fox of his own. Then he could be near it and watch it, really know it. He never followed a fox track without thinking of this, and although he knew that he and John could never overtake one, he always hoped to catch a glimpse of a red coat.

"Maybe we could find young ones and keep them," he said.

John walked a hundred yards before he spoke.

"You couldn't put collars on 'em, like on a dog," he said.

"We could keep them in a box with chicken wire," Henry said. "You and I'd shoot birds and snare rabbits for them. And I'd take care of them."

John considered the suggestion. "Maybe it would work," he agreed at last.

Henry was thinking only of a fox, any fox, a creature of sagacity and of pride too, with eyes of intelligence and ears alert for the faintest warning. Having such an animal would be exciting, but later he became aware that there were even more glorious foxes than the reds which lived in their forests. He learned this when, with weasel pelts of his own to sell and fur prices of vital interest, he listened as the older boys read fur buyers' price lists. Always at the top was the incredible sum of fifteen hundred dollars offered for the rare black

4

silver fox. This never failed to arouse the wonder of the Fromm boys. It was exciting even to think that so fabulous a creature existed.

They always read the placards that itinerant fur buyers tacked on trees, and whenever they could afford it they bought a copy of *Hunter-Trader-Trapper*, a monthly magazine that was the trappers' Bible. Walter, oldest of the four, always looked first at market reports. He worked hard at trapping because he wanted things, and in summer he added to his income by hoeing corn and potatoes for neighbors at fifty cents a day. He was no more industrious than the others, but he had learned what money could accomplish, and he always knew which fur buyers offered the best prices.

Weasel was usually quoted at fifty cents, and to Henry four skins from a winter's work meant that he could buy more traps for next year. The other three were concerned with bigger sales. A double-striped skunk might be quoted as low as a dollar but a single-stripe brought more, and a short-stripe was worth three times as much. Raccoons did not bring much, mink varied, and a red fox might go as high as five dollars, although a trapper was prepared to take less. Buyers and trappers always differed on grading pelts. After the boys compared fur prices, guessed at the quality of their skins, and estimated the winter's income, their eyes always went to the offer for a black silver fox. None of the boys believed a trapper would get that much, Edward least of all. He was the next oldest, but surer in his opinions than the others. He knew that the fur was precious and that only a few were caught each year, but buyers who haggled over the size and quality of a skunk were not merchant princes.

"Those fellows would never pay fifteen hundred dollars for one skin," he said. "If I caught a black silver I'd take it right to St. Louis where you could find out what it was worth. What do you suppose it would really be?"

The boys spent hours talking about how a man would feel and what he'd do if he caught a silver fox. A discussion of the most dramatic event possible in any trapper's life held a vicarious thrill for the older three. Henry listened, and wondered what a black silver would look like.

In 1901, when Henry was seven, he became sure that the silver fox must be the most beautiful creature in the world. *Hunter-Trader-Trapper* printed a picture and story of the pelt that had topped the London auction at twelve hundred dollars. Edward read it aloud after the chores were done that evening. Another skin had brought the record figure, eighteen hundred, the previous year.

"Don't you wish you'd got that one!" Walter said. "We're lucky if we get four dollars for a red."

John, now nine, had already caught a red fox, and Walter, thirteen, had two to his credit. Edward trapped as industriously as the others, but he was not an instinctive hunter. Already he was strongly set apart from his brothers. His features were finer, he was not so shy, and he looked ahead of the moment. His eyes, of the same intense blue, kindled as did Henry's to an idea. In many ways these two were alike, and yet strangely different.

When Edward finished reading, Henry reached for the picture of the famous pelt. More than the record price, it proved how wonderful such a creature must be.

Walter wished he knew where the fox was caught. "Probably 'way up north in Canada," he said. "No one around here ever got one, and that's funny when we have so many foxes."

"But there could be one," Edward said.

The boys knew what he meant and now, with the picture before them, they thrilled to this possibility. Only recently they had read that it was definitely established that silver foxes could be born of red parents. Trappers still spoke of them as "freaks," and Charles Darwin had pronounced them a separate species, but at the turn of the century evidence had piled up that the two were of the same family. It had been nature's whim to make the lowly commoner, the red fox, capable of producing the aristocrat of fur land, while the cross fox, with its curious markings of red, black, and silver, was merely a red fox showing silver blood.

Much proof of this had been uncovered. A Nescape Indian in Labrador found a litter of one silver, one red, and two cross pups. Similar accounts came from trappers who wrote of their experiences to local newspapers and to *Hunter-Trader-Trapper*. Men saw reds running with silver mates, found mixed litters, and even trailed what appeared to be a silver and a fortune to dig out pups that were cross, or common red. Despite this simple explanation of its origin, the silver continued to be rare. In 1901, when the Hudson's Bay Company sold 5,446 red and 1,534 cross fox pelts, it offered only 325 silvers, and these were of all grades. Some brought as little as five dollars. The rarity of a perfect black silver was one reason for its being so precious. A pelt could be marred by many factors — fur not prime, damage to a skin in capture, a red tinge in what should be lustrous black, a pepper-and-salt coat instead of veiled and gleaming silver or a long hard winter's wear by the original owner.

But to the Fromm boys the article in *Hunter-Trader-Trapper* proved that eighteen hundred dollars actually had been paid for a single pelt. They could talk of nothing else that evening until their father said boys who had work to do in the morning should get some sleep. Their mother had long since gone to bed with their baby sisters. The little girls slept in their parents' room, and through eighteen years of marriage the small cot beside the bed of Frederick and Alwina Fromm had always had an occupant. The boys went upstairs to the unfinished half-story where the cold usually ended any desire to talk, but tonight the news of the silver fox kept them excited.

Such a price seemed fantastic. In their pioneering farm life they had known only frugality, self-denial, and the need to work. A large family and a partially cleared homestead could mean nothing else. The farm had good land, but it was a farm in the making. Alwina's father, Joachim Nieman, had given her the quarter-section in Hamburg township when she married. A forester in Germany and a Social Democrat, he came to America in the political exodus of 1848, and recognized the fine soil of the hardwood country of northern Wisconsin. Alwina's wedding gift was an untouched wilderness. Frederick built a small log cabin and began to chop a farm out of the forest. It was hard and slow work but eventually he achieved tilled fields, a barn, and a farm-house of logs hewed foursquare and sheathed with siding. The acres were claimed so slowly that when Frederick's father gave him rich cleared Iowa land he wanted to move his family to it, but Alwina, with an obstinacy rare in her, had clung to her farm, her forests, the people she had always known, and the Lutheran church she loved. Frederick, usually a man of stubbornness, did not persist, and now the land he had won was as dear to him as to Alwina.

The homestead was built by ceaseless and driving toil. Ease and comfort were unknown. Each year another field was added, and another child must be cared for. Not an hour, not a penny, could be wasted. Wool from the sheep was carded, spun, and woven, to be made into clothing for the boys. Produce was traded for groceries. Trees felled in clearing were cut into cordwood, hauled twenty-two miles by oxen, and sold to pay the yearly taxes. Barley grown for a brewery was the cash crop. As on all pioneer farms, the table depended largely on the forest. Rabbits were snared, small streams yielded fish, and roadsides and clearings were filled with wild berries. In autumn butternut trees were laden, and in spring maple sap was boiled to make syrup for the year.

Always the four younger boys turned to the forest for the money they needed, and carrying on this serious business of making a living welded a close-knit group. As early as they began to roam the woods, they called themselves "The Wolves" because they ran in a pack and believed they were invincible. There had always been an age-cleavage between them and their older brothers, Arthur and Herbert, and it had widened when these two went away to study for teachers' certificates. Frederick Fromm had encouraged this ambition. A few pioneer acres could not support so many boys, and he would never be able to leave each of his sons a piece of land, as his father and Alwina's had done before them. Teaching offered a thrifty way to education and independence, for with savings from a country school position a boy could go to normal school and equip himself to escape the drudgery of farming. Frederick was already looking forward to the time when Walter and Edward would follow their older brothers.

"I want you boys to get your feet out of the mud," he said.

If at times Frederick seemed inexorable about farm tasks — and he expected every boy to earn his keep — it was understandable to The Wolves. They had known the necessity of work and a serious purpose since they could remember, but they were aware that their father was capable of strange contradictions. To his people music was a part of living, and as a young man he had played the violin for square dances as well as on Sundays when neighbors gathered. He gave violins to the older boys and taught them to play, and when six sons made family concerts possible he bought a cottage piano, horns, and flutes, and on trips to town he took the boys along for music lessons. The instruments and occasional instruction made inroads on a scanty cash crop, but Frederick gave them to his sons at a time when a new pair of shoes would have been a major purchase. The little orchestra practiced winter evenings, and Alwina spun or knitted as she listened, surrounded by her sons. She did not worry about their future. That was for men to think of. To be sure, life was hard when so little must be spread so far, but this was only to be expected when people married and had children. She was a happy woman, for she knew no mother had finer sons.

As music was an expression of the family's self-sufficiency, so the activities of the four younger Fromm boys set them apart from their fellows. To be one of The Wolves entailed achievement. They bought corduroy to replace the homespun clothing made by their mother. They bought traps, ammunition, guns, a tent for camping trips, and at last bicycles to ride when others walked, an undeniable mark of success. Fur supplied their wants, and when their wants increased they thought more and more of what the forest offered.

Trapping pelts which brought only a few dollars had limitations, but they had never accepted these. Trapping was also a gamble. A clever set took a poor pelt as surely as a valuable one, and a trap baited for a red fox might catch a silver. It could happen, and they talked of it as they did their chores, roamed the woods, and hoed in the field. A Fromm boy catching the greatest prize in fur land! He might even dig out a litter in the spring and find a black silver among the reds. They talked of this, too.

"We'd keep it until it was grown and the fur was prime," Walter said. "If other trappers can, there's no reason why we couldn't."

Several instances had been related in *Hunter-Trader-Trapper* of men carrying over a young or late-spring-caught silver to pelting time.

"But if we had a silver why couldn't we raise some more?" Henry asked. "What if we were lucky and got two pups?"

"We'd be dumb if we didn't try to raise a litter," Edward said.

They talked of this more and more, and the dazzling idea received new impetus each time *Hunter-Trader-*

Trapper carried news of silver foxes, or a price list quoted fifteen hundred dollars. At last the boys no longer spoke of a pair of foxes, but of dozens of pairs. They had never heard of anyone who had attempted to raise them; but doing so would have the thrill of an untried venture and seemed as practical, they thought, as expecting an increase from any pair of farm animals. The greatest difficulty was that a silver had never been caught in their district.

"Maybe we could start with a red and a cross fox," Walter said. "Then we'd keep on breeding until we got pure silvers."

They talked of this, too, and how it might happen. It was nature's method.

"And we'd have to study how to raise foxes," Henry said.

He had thought more about foxes than the others; for him foxes never would be creatures to be cared for like horses, cows, and sheep. He was sure they must be fed the same food they ate in the wilds, and live as nearly as possible as in the forest.

They discussed all these matters endlessly, and finally what had been at first only a wish became so real that in their minds they no longer doubted but that some day they would raise silver foxes. Although they didn't have even a common red fox or money to build a pen in which to keep it, never did the idea seem preposterous. It grew year after year as its scope and daring caught them. Always they had been seeking ways to lift themselves above the neighborhood level, and now the dream of silver foxes became a plan, as the four boys schemed and argued until fantasy was hammered into a fixed purpose. If silver foxes could be raised and bred, they would be the owners of a herd of the most precious fur in the world.

Having determined on this they ceased to refer to themselves as The Wolves. They needed something significant to mark a solidarity the dream had brought, and since they bought traps from one company, sold fur to another, and read advertisements of many companies, they began to ship fur and buy traps as a company. "The Company" had more than a fine sound in the ears of teen-age boys. To them it meant maturity and permanence, and an impersonal power behind which they could move onward against any obstacles. "The Company" it became.

In 1904 they recognized how tremendous these obstacles were. Walter was sixteen, Edward fourteen, John twelve, and Henry ten. They knew they could not depend on so frail a hope as finding a litter with silver foxes.

"There's only one other way," Edward said. "We've got to get money to buy a pair, and we'll never make enough by trapping."

"How much would we need?" Walter asked.

They didn't know. They had no way of knowing. For a time the boys did not talk so much of silver foxes. The forest had closed in upon them. It had been their friend when they needed little, but it could not give what they needed now. This was in their minds one Sunday afternoon when they took a stroll with their father to estimate the fall butternut crop. The first tree at the edge of the woods was usually heavily laden, and Frederick looked at the upper branches.

"We'll have plenty of nuts if the neighbors don't get them first," he said and started on, only to stop and poke at a plant with his toe and chuckle. "Here's the thing Reinhold Dietsch is going to get rich on."

Edward bent over the plant. It had broad, bright green leaves and a stalk of red berries.

"How can he make money out of this?" he asked.

"I don't know," his father said, "but to hear Dietsch talk he's already got the money in the bank. He's even built a house of laths to grow it in."

Walter examined the plant. "We've seen this all through the woods," he said. "What is it?"

"Ginseng, Dietsch calls it. He claims Chinamen pay so much for it that he can make twenty thousand dollars an acre."

Frederick had his sons' entire attention. They had read price quotations for ginseng root on every fur list.

"Does Dietsch say he can grow this in a garden?" Walter asked. "Did he get seeds from the berries?"

"He dug up plants. Went all around these woods to find them. He says it will be five years or longer before he can dig the crop."

"What kind of soil did he use?" Walter asked.

"How would I know?" his father said. "I didn't ask him. I've got something better to do than listen to such crazy ideas."

He was through with the subject, and they walked on to another tree. Butternuts at least supplied good food for a family, and when the crop had been inspected Frederick returned to the farmhouse. The Company did not go with him. The four boys went back to the plants with the broad leaves and red berries.

Chapter Two

As they stared at the bright green foliage and the stalk of handsome berries, they marveled that so conspicuous a plant had not caught their attention long before. Walter brought some dry branches and propped them carefully above a plant.

"We've got to cover every one," he said. "The cows might get them."

The plants had survived all summer despite cows, but no one spoke of that, for now they had become company treasure. As they carried brush and built barricades against browsing cattle, John suggested they dig the ginseng at once to insure possession.

"We can't move them until we have a place to put them," Walter said. The oldest, and with a natural aptitude for growing things, he had taken charge. "Besides, we should wait until the seeds are ripe."

They had no idea when that would be, and they were dismayed at how little they knew about ginseng. The plants they'd found grew in deep shade, and Reinhold Dietsch had built an arbor. Walter sifted a handful of black porous earth through his fingers.

"We can scrape all the loam we'll need from under trees," he said. "Tomorrow we'll bring grain sacks."

"We'd better hunt more plants first," Edward said. "We can spot them easy while the berries are red, unless Dietsch got them all."

Already Mr. Dietsch was a competitor. As they walked home they planned the arbor. They would need lumber, and wondered how much the sawing would cost. Nails were no problem. For years the burned ruins of a sawmill had supplied the boys with odd bits of hardware.

"Think Pa will let us have the timber?" Henry asked.

They knew he wouldn't. Good building timber must be saved for the stable Frederick Fromm intended to have some day, and trees cut in the work of clearing as they pushed the farm farther into the forest were sold as cordwood to pay the yearly taxes.

"He can't say anything if we take dead balsam and hemlock," Walter said.

Resources were at hand but their greatest need, information, would be more difficult. It was unfortunate they had not seen Dietsch's garden, but a visit now would arouse suspicion, since he would know rival growers were searching for the plant. Nor could he be expected to reveal the secrets of ginseng culture to competitors. He might even lead them astray.

"I wonder how he found out you could grow it," Edward said. "I never knew he was that smart. And what if he isn't right about its growing in a garden?"

It always bothered Edward to be outthought by others. They'd read the prices of ginseng root in fur lists and knew medicinal plants provided summer pin money for trappers, but it had never occurred to the Company that ginseng could be cultivated. Now, if

Reinhold Dietsch were right, the possibilities were dazzling. How dazzling, they discovered at home when they looked up the market reports in *Hunter-Trader-Trapper*. Dried ginseng root from the north central states, the most valuable of all, was listed at six dollars a pound. While the boys had been searching desperately for a way to own a herd of silver foxes, a neighbor had gathered a fortune from their own forest. Edward quoted the price at the supper table.

"It'd have to be worth a lot more than that before I'd fuss with a crop that takes five years to grow," his father said. "By the time Dietsch gets his harvest, probably the Chinese won't want it."

The Company did not argue this, and it was no time to tell him that ginseng was about to invade his farm. Nor did they know how long the sale of the root had existed, nor why the Chinese desired it. It was only much later, and little by little, that they learned that for centuries the people of China had venerated the plant and that the mystical value they ascribed to it, and the astounding prices they were willing to pay, had placed it among the conspicuous flora of the world. It was a strange and exotic plant for four farm boys to seize upon as a way to earn a herd of silver foxes, but silvers were almost as exotic.

The Company's attack was intensely practical. The boys searched the woods for miles around and carefully observed the habits of the plant. Success would depend on the fidelity with which they reproduced natural conditions, and the forest could be their only guide in making the bed and arbor.

They were nagged by the need of money and time. Soon Walter, graduated from the little log schoolhouse down the road, must go to Wausau, twenty-two miles away, to prepare to become a teacher. This had been talked of for so many years that now it was not even questioned. Arthur and Herbert had already proved how practical was this thrifty way to an education, and were attending normal school with money saved by teaching country school. Frederick realized that the initial two years in training school necessary for a teacher's certificate meant a cash outlay, and he would pay Walter's room rent and bring food from the farm for his bachelor housekeeping. Books, clothing, and incidentals must be earned by odd jobs.

Now Walter was eager to complete the garden before departure, and he dared not cut too deeply into his savings. His father would not be willing to replace funds wasted on such folly as ginseng.

The boys hauled hemlock lath bolts and windfalls to the neighboring mill for sawing. The price for this was more than they had expected, and they held a consultation and counted their money.

"Let's have it sawed into wide boards," Edward said. "Then we can rip them to what we need."

John had a truly inspired idea when they built the arbor. He suggested that the lath walls and roof be made in sections, so that if the first bed proved a failure the structure could be dismantled and moved without wasting precious lumber. This idea, although no one realized it at the time, was one of the soundest notions a boy ever had.

The first ginseng bed, five by sixteen feet, was shaded by the woodshed, and because all the plants had been found in dry places the bed was raised. It held 150 plants; not as many as they had hoped to find, for

Dietsch's earlier search had made their own the harder. The creamy spindle-shaped roots had an odor that reminded the boys of licorice, and deep encircling wrinkles gave the appearance of great age. When they counted stalk scars on the neck of the root, they found that the years varied. Those with a bud which were sufficiently young to promise greater size were used as nursery stock. Ancient roots that had ceased growing — and they found some of thirty and fifty years, and even a grandfather root of seventy-five — were put aside for sale. These were washed and dried on strings hung above the kitchen stove, and lost two-thirds of their weight in the drying process. When the prongs and fibers had been removed the Company had one pound to send to market. Hunting ginseng was less profitable than trapping, but ginseng culture, which Dietsch had said would produce twenty thousand dollars an acre, would be vastly different.

To get even a small part of an acre they must learn to raise plants from seed. In a second bed, each of the three hundred small flat seeds extracted from berry pulp was dropped into a separate hole made with a stick. This was Walter's last task before departure. But he considered ginseng his responsibility, and as he and Frederick were ready to start to town in the wagon with Walter's boxes behind them, he called a last direction on the winter protection of the garden when leaves fell in the forest.

"Be sure you rake leaves from under the same kind of trees where we found the plants," he said. "Maybe those leaves are the only kind we should use."

Later, when this was done and the roof of the arbor removed to prevent damage from weight of snow, ginseng work was finished. Henry and John, anxious to get out their traps, found Walter's absence made a difference. There was one less pair of hands to help with farm chores. Next year Edward would be gone. But Henry at ten was as strong as, and even bigger than, John and a hard worker.

"I chose the two huskiest of the lot to be farmers," Frederick often said. A powerful man himself, he admired strength.

The three members of the Company still at home went on their annual October camping trip, and carried tent, quilts, food, and dishes to a spot they had discovered years before and called their own. It was almost a day's tramp away, and they remained two nights, which was as long as Frederick was willing to do their chores. But they had two days of exploring and hunting in distant woods, and of talking around a camp fire. Edward was the cook and made potato pancakes which, with plenty of maple syrup, tasted even better over a camp fire than when made at home. It was the boys' favorite food. This year they talked often of the herd of silvers, for even finding a possible means to earn them had brought them nearer.

"We could begin with two pairs, or even one," Edward said. "We'd have twice that number in a year."

"Do you suppose all the young ones would be silvers?" John asked.

"Why not?" Edward said. "If you breed purebred horses and cattle, you get purebred colts and calves. Of course we'd have to wait until we could buy some pure silvers. And we'd have to build pens to keep them in. All that would cost money."

"We could hunt enough game to feed them," Henry said.

"And for a year or so we couldn't sell any fur," Edward said. "We'd have to keep the young to get a big herd started."

When they talked thus the herd of silvers sounded real, and because a distant goal never seemed impossible to Edward, he could make it sound very real to others. But many times that winter Henry stopped on his way home from school to stare at the small bed of ginseng and wonder if the plant could ever earn silver foxes. He doubted it, yet when anyone wanted anything as passionately as Henry wanted silver foxes, any means was worth trying.

In the spring, when green shoots appeared, they knew they had brought the transplanted ginseng through the winter. But the seeded bed had not sprouted. They weeded it as zealously as they did the young shoots of ginseng. No sprouts had appeared when Walter returned from school.

"Maybe I planted them a little deep," he said. "Let's give them a chance. Seeds take longer than roots."

His tone was less cheerful as weeks, then months, went by, and the seed bed remained a blank. Still they weeded, always hoping. Every free hour was spent searching for more wild ginseng, but the plants had to be left in the forest until the seeds had ripened, for these were even more important than the plants. Other farmers were now starting ginseng gardens and were rival hunters, and finders were keepers. It was desirable, however, that no one should discover that anyone had so valuable a plant on his land, and the Company reconnoitered, studied neighbors' habits, and learned what each might be doing at any hour of the day. A few apples, a melon, or handful of berries have always been a farm boy's loot, and a wild ginseng plant was not different.

But the Company was horrified on learning that a farmer's ginseng bed had been raided and a whole planting stolen. Thieves might plunder the Fromm garden, for the bed, though close to the house, was vulnerable at night, so they contrived a burglar alarm. The burned mill supplied wire which they stretched around the lath house and hooked to a battery and electric cell. They felt safe until John demonstrated its inadequacy by stepping over it.

"Any thief would expect a wire," he said.

A second and higher wire was installed, so that if jarred or broken it would not only ring a bell but flash a light. Walter backed up the alarm system by sleeping in the woodshed with a shotgun at his side, but they overlooked night-flying birds. When a night hawk or owl struck the wire a bell rang, a light flashed, Walter rushed out with a gun, and three boys dashed from the house. Frederick and Alwina wistfully recalled the old days when they had raised only such commonplace crops as turnips, barley, and potatoes.

At the end of the summer hundreds of plants waited in the forest. Blazed trees, broken branches, heaps of brush, and maps, were guides to the treasure. A new arbor would draw heavily on company capital, but land was the greater problem. In the first transplanting, roots had rotted in soggy soil; higher land, or any land, must be obtained from their father.

The boys laid their case before him. Ginseng culture

had become a nuisance to Frederick Fromm. It threatened to encroach on a farm of orderly fields and traditional crops, and whenever a boy was needed he was off trailing ginseng or weeding the useless plant.

"Cleared land is valuable," he said.

"So is ginseng," said Walter, who had become spokesman for its rights.

Frederick scowled. "Yes, to hear you boys talk you'd think — "

"But Pa!" Alwina said, "the boys work hard to grow it." Almost never did she interfere between them, and no one knew better how hard Frederick had worked to clear those fields. Now she finished mildly, "Besides, their small gardens take so little land."

Her husband didn't answer for a moment. He knew his refusal would hurt Alwina, for her faith in her sons was unbounded, but if he gave land freely he would be retreating from his position.

"A boy who wants good cleared land should be glad to earn it," he said. "You can have the ground under the pile of rocks behind the barnyard, but I want those rocks carried to the woods."

The rocks had been there since he had dragged them off the field on a stoneboat, and the woods were a quarter of a mile away. His proposal was infuriating. Land for oats, barley, or any other farm crop would have been given gladly, but this was a contrived slur on ginseng. The boys knew their father was no man to argue with and, angry though they were, they carried away the rocks. Being angry they worked the harder, and as they saw the good land they uncovered — rich, cleared, free from weeds and as virgin as the forest — they laughed. This was better than they had expected. In the struggle between farm crops and ginseng, the strange wild root had won.

The new bed held four hundred plants. This forest booty was brought home in an oilcloth-covered box so that if, by some misjudgment, they encountered the real owner, he would not see what they carried. From the berries they extracted three hundred seeds, although not one of the previous planting had sprouted. The day for Walter's and Edward's departure for school in Wausau was drawing close and time was precious. Also there was much to do, and they had wasted a summer's weeding on an empty bed.

"Anyhow, it's ready for seeds now," Henry said.

He was beginning to be annoyed by the eccentric demands of ginseng. Such a plant was a frail hope for silver foxes. The Company considered this suggested economy in effort.

"But we've waited only a year," Edward said.

"And we still aren't sure those seeds won't come up," Walter added.

The next spring even Henry began to believe ginseng might bring silver foxes. After eighteen long months seeds in the first bed sprouted; it didn't seem possible they could take so long to germinate. Ginseng must indeed be a plant of leisurely habits. Some seeds had died from lying too long in the soil. This undoubtedly happened in the forest too, but nature could be more wasteful than boys who had extracted three hundred small seeds, washed, dried, and planted them one at a time in holes. They wondered if there were facts about ginseng culture the forest could not teach them.

"Maybe I'd better join the ginseng association," Walter said.

"It wouldn't cost much," Edward said, "and might be worth while for the Company."

Local growers had formed an organization for mutual aid and were affiliated with the National Cultivated Wild Ginseng Growers' Association. They knew the county might become an important center, and plans to interest eastern capital were already under way. Although Walter feared men might resent an eighteen-year-old, he found himself welcomed.

The Association offered a reward for the apprehension of ginseng thieves, but this service did not impress Walter. Now, to supplement the burglar alarm and shotgun, all four boys slept on the arbors. A sheepskin coat and a folded quilt made a comfortable bed on the springy lath roof. High enough to be above mosquitoes, it was a pleasant place to spend the night, and under a starlit sky a boy could contemplate his treasures. The Company would never have to call on the Association to catch a thief. The boys laughed when Walter reported the reward.

But at the first meeting Walter learned the answer to seed trouble. Eastern growers had discovered that seeds should be stratified in layers of moist sand for a year before the outer shells were ready to open, and that during this period they must have the same protection and ventilation as in porous forest loam. This was accomplished in boxes sunk in the ground. Other information was funneled through the local organization from experienced eastern growers. Young nursery stock required little space, and could be transplanted to a permanent bed after two years. This was an economy in land and arbors, and the Company adopted the idea with enthusiasm.

More astonishing was the practice of spraying to protect wild plants from the hazards of domestication. Herded together, they were vulnerable. Blight spores from the foliage traveled down the stems, might cause root rot the next season, and most certainly would infect new stock. To prevent this, all new growth must be covered with a spray of slaked lime and blue vitriol. Blight, Walter's fellow members said, was the greatest hazard and, if unchecked, would wipe out a garden.

Walter had never heard of the evil, but he wrote down the formula and directions for testing the strength of the spray by dropping a bit of the mixture into corrosive sublimate. The Company listened to this report with reservations, and inspected its garden. The plants were beautiful. Growing sturdily, the mass of bright green foliage, bathed in the subdued sunlight of a lath house, imparted a sense of tranquillity. The plants, lovelier and more exotic than any they had ever seen, spoke of far lands and ancient peoples. It seemed dreadful to mar such perfection.

"Maybe our plants are healthier than theirs," John said.

"We can wait till the blight comes," Edward added, "but it's a good thing we heard about it."

Walter learned much about blight. Because the disease left spores in the soil, ginseng could not be grown twice on the same land, and eastern growers were experimenting with chemicals and live steam as disinfectants. China, faced with the same problem centuries earlier, had turned to other lands. Further mysteries were cleared up as Walter attended meetings. He was taking a place in the community as a young ginseng grower.

Any doubts the Company might have had concerning

the permanence of the Chinese ginseng market were completely set at rest as they learned the history of the plant. Ginseng had been exported from America since 1713. The earliest Chinese literature had testified to the virtues of the root. The Chinese used it not only in sickness, but in health to retain vigor, and it was considered an effective specific against all nervous diseases and the debilities of age. In some measure this was due to the great age the plant attained — specimens ninety years old had been found in the forests of North America — but the original reason for its unique position was the root's strange resemblance to the form of man. This parsnip-like root was often split and had curious prongs and fibers, and those specimens that most faithfully resembled the human figure were so highly prized as talismans against the inevitable weaknesses of age that they brought incredible prices. This resemblance had given the plant its name. Ginseng, like the fountain of youth, promised to banish the universal dread of age.

The first description of ginseng reached Europe in letters from China written by one of the French Jesuit priests. Another Jesuit, Père Lafitau, working among the Iroquois of North America, read them, and recognized the plant as one the Indians called *Garent-oguen*, signifying the representation of a man's thighs and legs. They, too, believed that the plant insured the user a vigorous old age. Ginseng was plentiful in America while China's supply was diminishing, because it cannot be grown more than once on the same land. Samples of the North American root were sent to China, and a Canadian company was formed to export it. Iroquois were hired to dig the root, and for a time the commerce threatened to rival that of the fur trade.

Later ginseng was discovered in the Himalayas of Nepal, and hunters climbed ten thousand feet in search of the fabled root. In the United States it was found in many districts, and "cheng," "chang," or "shang" hunters — the vernacular differed with the locality — made a precarious living. Superstitions grew up among these hunters, for a plant capable of living undetected for almost a century was awesome, and they believed it would refuse to work for man if he tried to tame it. In the south shang hunters bestowed almost human attributes on the plant, maintaining that, although it was of a wild and wayward nature, it would indicate the existence of other roots to those of sympathy and understanding; but only people of deep wisdom could read the direction indicated by one cluster of broad palmated leaves.

Intensive search almost brought about extinction, and as early as 1877 a farmer in Wisconsin spent hundreds of dollars in a futile attempt to grow the plant from seed. In the late eighties George Stanton, a ginseng hunter in New York State and an instinctive horticulturist, succeeded in transplanting the wild root to his garden. He became the founder of the cultivated wild ginseng industry, which later spread to the Middle West.

The Company eagerly awaited reports of visits to other gardens, and the evening was filled with shoptalk. Men the other boys had never seen were now familiars and associates, for at each meeting a different member talked on ginseng.

"All of them complain about the cost of arbors," Walter said. "It's expensive to build a lath house for only one crop."

"Did you tell them we can take ours apart without losing lumber?" Edward asked.

"No, and I didn't tell them our roofs are flat. They build theirs peaked, like a house."

This gave the Company a chuckle. Older minds, set in the traditional pattern of fixed structures, had contrived roofs to carry off rain and snow. It had never occurred to them to duplicate forest shade and an equal distribution of both rain and sunlight. The Company was pleased to learn it had evolved an original and superior model.

"Won't you have to tell them when it's your turn to talk?" John asked. "And what will you do when they want to come here to see how we grow ginseng?"

This was a threat they had not considered. Their methods, learned by hard work and by years of watching wild things in the forest, were company secrets.

"My turn is coming soon," Walter said.

"Then you'd better quit now," Edward said. "Let them find things out for themselves the way we did."

The Association lost its youngest member and the four resumed their isolated existence, finding ginseng plants where they could and spending hot summer days weeding. When the weeds were checked they carried loam from the woods to make ready for the fall garden.

This year they would not lose Walter entirely. With his new certificate he had found a position that permitted a compromise between his ideas and those of his father. His salary was forty dollars a month, he could board at home, ride a bicycle to his school, and have Saturdays in the ginseng garden. Edward would be in Oshkosh Normal. A job as janitor, thrifty bachelor meals, and a little help from his father had made this possible, and if he had to teach to make a living until ginseng could lead to silver foxes, he intended to earn a better salary in a high school. The way of John and Henry was easy. Frederick's selection of them as the farmers of the family made trapping a possible means to a living until the Company was on its feet.

Ginseng was a summer job, but even then it could not have all the Company's time. Although the older brothers, Arthur and Herbert, were at home to help in vacations, there was still need for all of Frederick's sons. The farm was operated largely by man power. The forest still left its mark on the small clearing. Stumps of trees with deep roots which defied grubbing had been left to rot in tilled fields and made it impossible to use mowing-machine, binder, or tedder. Hay was cut with scythes and turned over with pitchforks; oats, wheat, rye, and barley were cut with cradles and bound by hand; peas for hog feed were hand-harvested and hand-threshed.

And always the forest must be pushed back. Every season more land was to be cleared, and two acres was the best a farmer could hope to gain in a year. Trees must be felled and cut for cordwood and the brush burned; the acrid smoke of smoldering fires hung in the air. Frederick was justified in his belief that cleared land was precious, and with misgiving he watched preparations for a larger ginseng arbor.

These unsightly structures were becoming an eyesore, and four boys who could be useful on a farm were wasting time and energy. But the Company was untouched by parental disapproval and, as they searched for new plants, weeded, collected loam and timber from the forest, the boys talked of silver foxes. Such talk was a prod to tired bodies and an escape for flagging spirits. Weeds were less depressing as they considered how glamorous would be their foxes.

"We could improve them like farm stock," John said. "A trapper has to take what he can catch."

"If we fed them game and the kind of food they're used to, they ought to get along all right," Henry said.

"Foxes aren't any wilder than ginseng," Walter said. "We're growing that. We'll have to build pens for foxes, though, and that will mean money. All we have to spend on arbors is the cost of sawing lumber."

"One fox is worth more than all the ginseng we can grow in five years," said Henry. He had never given his allegiance to the strange root. For him it was only a back breaking means to an end, and he wanted to make sure no one would mistake the route for the destination. But he was generous and he added, "I suppose we'll be glad we found ginseng when the Company raises the finest silver foxes in the world."

"If we make them fine enough, everyone will know a Fromm fox when he sees one," Edward said, for he had a natural awareness of horizons. "Ever think we might be the only company in the world that raises them?"

These hours when they talked of silver foxes held for John and Henry all the splendor of shining dreams. They had no second route to achievement or did they wish one, for silver foxes had taken early possession of their thoughts and their desires. To them life without silver foxes would be only failure.

Chapter Three

Henry was fourteen, and the company seemed as far from its goal as ever. Now, in 1908, he was appalled to realize that while they had talked of silver foxes and of how they must learn to raise them by experimenting with common reds, others had actually started silver fox farms. He read this in an article in *Hunter-Trader-Trapper* written by an official in the U.S. Department of Agriculture.

"Of some twenty parties known to have engaged in breeding them," Henry read, "one began fifteen years ago, another eight, while the others have undertaken the business within the past five years. Those who have persevered in spite of early failures have attained some success. Some have become discouraged while others are just beginning, and their experience is too slight to be of much value in determining the practicability of the business."

The Company had let years slip by, and if it didn't get foxes soon the boys would be old men before they even began the real business of the firm. With such articles giving not only directions for building pens and feeding, but assuring readers that the rare silver was a color phase of the red, any number of fox farms would be started.

Henry showed the article to John, who was equally disturbed.

"We should have begun with reds five years ago," John said. "But you can't keep foxes without pens."

Henry did not let that deter him, and answered a classified advertisement in the magazine in which a trapper offered four live red foxes. The signature bothered him. The company name, "Fromm Brothers," would be more impressive but might inflate the price, and he signed the letter, "Henry Fromm." The trapper replied asking five dollars for each pup, money in advance, and expressage to be paid by purchaser. The terms ended negotiations.

The Company was still financing itself precariously. Walter, after one year of teaching, had decided forty dollars less board money did not permit white-collar splendor, and he abandoned the profession for a business course at Wittenberg Academy. At least a business training would have some value to the Company, and he answered his father's protests by paying his own expenses with savings from his teacher's salary and earnings as a photographer. Modest prices — fifty cents for a mounted five-by-seven print — brought work with country school classes, new babies, and family reunions. Rumors of a neighborhood festivity sent him pedaling on his bicycle. Edward was in normal school and would not have a high school teacher's certificate until the following June. John and Henry were depending on traps. Skunk and weasel provided a small but steady income, and an occasional mink or fox was a windfall. Fur bought clothes, ammunition, and hunting gear, but the trap lines had to be fitted in with school and farm chores, which was not always easy. Henry occasionally played hooky to visit his sets, and once swaggered past the schoolhouse with a red fox slung over his shoulder.

Ginseng had not brought the returns the Company expected. Each fall the crop was larger. In the past four years it had outgrown the string method of drying, and was taken care of on a rack set above the stove. But the product still barely supported the new enterprise. The Company had learned not to expect the top price because ginseng, like fur, was graded. Through the centuries the Chinese had become discriminating buyers, and roots must be round, of good body structure, deeply furrowed, with the appearance of a vigorous old age. Dried, they must not be soft and never bonelike. Few roots in the company's harvest met all these requirements, and expenses also were increasing. Each fall lumber must be sawed for a new arbor; the supply of nails in the burned mill was exhausted; always a necessary purchase swept away resources. An orchard sprayer was imperative when blight at last came to the Company's gardens. Vigorous plants suddenly drooped, and must be sprayed zealously to avert disaster.

A company with all these problems could not afford to buy red foxes or build pens. Henry regretfully laid aside the trapper's offer, but he somewhat assuaged his disappointment by reflecting that five dollars was too much to pay for a red fox. When the Company could afford wire netting he and John would catch their own. They had often talked of how they could do this. In midwinter during breeding season they must watch for the finer tracks of the female, study her habits and the district in which she chose her den. Tracking must be cautious, and after whelping season neither parent fox must know that the retreat had been discovered. The young could be dug from the den before they were old enough to go forth into the world.

"It'll take a lot of time," John said, "but I bet you and I could get a few litters."

These would be useless without pens, but hopes ran high the next fall when the ginseng crop was the largest they had yet dug, roots of those first forest plants brought to their garden. Even more exciting, the Company planted a half acre from two-year-old nursery stock grown from seeds they had stratified. They estimated this would bring ten thousand dollars. The dazzling sum was reckoned on maximum production, and no one spoke of the five years of weeding, mulching, raking forest leaves, and constant battle against blight which lay between them and harvest.

It was triumph enough to plant a half acre. They had scraped the forest floor of the Fromm quarter section for loam, and looked with envy on the loam of neighbors. Even nursery stock had cost weeks of toil. Almost seven pounds of ginseng seeds, which ran eight thousand to the pound, had first been planted in seedbeds. The boys had progressed from the hole-and-stick method and now worked in pairs. One raked the soil from a trench, the other knelt on a board and dropped seeds in one by one, while the raker used displaced earth to cover the trench behind. They were beginning to think in assembly-line methods. They had to. Speed and effectiveness could be the only answer to what four boys must accomplish.

Soon after planting, Edward went to his first teaching

job on a high school faculty of three, salary sixty-five dollars a month. This marked for Frederick the final launching of another son, but his satisfaction was short-lived. A few weeks later Walter returned from the academy to announce he intended to grow ginseng, and with this news ginseng fell into complete disrepute. Not only did it take good land and timber and mar an orderly farmstead with untidy arbors, but now the root had dragged a son back to the soil. If Walter had never heard of ginseng he would have been a teacher like Edward. And if it wasn't ginseng it was foxes! All John and Henry thought of was how men were raising the filthy creatures.

"Crazy dreams!" Frederick said. "Ginseng and foxes! What kind of a farm is that?"

Almost at once his two foes struck again. Edward came home and said he was through with teaching. The school principal drew a larger salary, but left his work to assistants. At the end of the first month Edward protested, at the end of the second he acted. His abrupt departure shut off the possibility of teaching in that school or any other, but Edward felt completely justified. He was a member of a company with property to be looked after. It was time to give his whole attention to that.

Now the Company was together again in the fall of 1909, and doing exactly what it always had intended to do. John and Henry set out trap lines and the others prepared to advance ginseng culture. The new half-acre garden would need an arbor in the spring, and since it would be unwise at this time to ask their father for more timber, Walter and Edward found a job clearing land. In payment they received hemlock bolts for laths, balsam for support posts, and a few tamarack logs for sideboards for the beds. This arrangement opened a new avenue to a supply of lumber, which was well, for the less said to their father about ginseng the better.

In December the Company heard of a litter of live red foxes in a nearby township. John Wittkop, a farmer, had bought six males and one female from an Indian for fourteen dollars, and asked twenty-five dollars. The Company had sold its ginseng and Walter, as treasurer, said it had sufficient funds to buy the litter and a roll of netting. Edward urged the purchase.

"After we've raised reds we'll be sure we can take care of silvers," he said.

"But Wittkop's making nine dollars on the deal," Walter said. "Next spring we can dig out our own litter."

"But by next spring these foxes would have young," Henry said. "We'd be a year ahead. And if we don't find a litter next spring we'd be two years ahead. What are we weeding ginseng for if it isn't to buy foxes?"

Impatience was apt to make Henry reckless but now John, who was never swung from caution, pointed out that foxes in their own neighborhood could be inspected before buying.

"They're almost nine months old," he said. "We can be sure we'd raise them."

The Company decided on the investment and the next day, when their father made his regular trip to town, was a desirable time for the purchase, as awkward arguments with him could thus be avoided.

Henry wakened early that morning. Sometimes he had doubted if the day would ever come when they would start their fox farm. Even after his brothers had gone downstairs he lay for a time contemplating the dazzling possibilities. These foxes were red, to be sure, yet reds had been known to throw cross foxes and even silvers. Anything might happen. But, red, cross, or silver, he wanted these foxes more than anything he had ever wanted in his life.

Town days were always rushed, and the boys hurried to harness the team and load barley for the brewery. If Frederick was startled when no boy appeared in his best clothes he made no comment, and the Company managed to conceal its excitement. The wagon was scarcely out of sight before the boys had a horse hitched to the buggy. Walter had the money, and he took precautions to have small bills in case they were able to strike a better bargain. They had grain sacks in which to carry the foxes, and when they reached Wittkop's farm these may have revealed their determination. Although the haggling was lengthy, the Company won some sort of victory when it bought the litter for twenty-four dollars. A dollar was important.

The foxes did not have the predominance of black markings that might indicate the possibility of cross or silver offspring. They were the rich fulvous hue typical of the district, in good winter fur, and had full brushes with white tips. But even red foxes were a beginning, and the return home was a journey of pure enchantment.

The litter was housed in a large box covered with wire netting, and Alwina came out to admire it. She knew how much it meant to her sons, and she and the Company were standing before the box when Frederick Fromm drove through the gate. He stared, but until he climbed down from the wagon and looked through the netting he did not believe the box contained seven foxes.

He had thought fur farm talk was merely the chatter of sheep-headed boys, and it had never occurred to him that foxes might become as great a nuisance as unsightly ginseng arbors. And when he learned that they actually paid money for the animals, he knew the time had come to stop such nonsense.

"You'll not keep those miserable creatures on my land," he said.

The boys knew he meant it. Ginseng may have won after five long years of struggle, but foxes did not have a chance.

No one thought of Alwina. In the years of ginseng quarrels over land and timber she had remained apart. Those were problems for men to settle. Her world was the home and the care of her family. But now she stepped forward.

"Put them on my land, boys," she said.

It was the first reference she had ever made to the actual ownership of the quarter section.

Chapter Four

THE PENS WERE BUILT CLOSE TO THE HOUSE AS A precaution against theft. It was December, the ground was frozen, and for days the Company worked with pickaxes to set poles and wire netting in the earth. Hollow logs were used for houses, since foxes chose them in the forest.

From the first Henry was the official "fox man." The article in *Hunter-Trader-Trapper* had emphasized the importance of a regular keeper, and the Company knew from watching wild creatures that foxes, nervous and distrustful, must not be disturbed. Custody of the Company's herd was a big responsibility for a fifteen-year-old, but Henry liked foxes, liked hunting small game and snaring rabbits for them, and became adroit in getting extra tidbits from the kitchen. The job of keeper, however, changed Henry's life. No matter how exciting a forest expedition, the foxes' supper hour was a must.

He spent hours watching them from his special lookout on the roof. He watched in daytime and in moonlight, and because foxes behave naturally only when

40

they think they are not observed, he learned many things about them. Some were only interesting bits of nature lore, such as the fact they never ran alongside the netting but always described a figure eight. Yet everything he saw was of interest to Henry, for a good keeper must be able to think as foxes think.

His first effort in fox thinking brought tragedy. The animals fought the netting, and he believed they had too much leisure in which to resent captivity. Finding busy work for penned foxes was difficult, and Henry's scheme to hang meat on wires, so that they must jump to get it, seemed inspired. He was confident that he would have tired and contented foxes, but next morning he found one hanging from a wire, strangled. It had caught its head in a loop holding the meat.

The Company lost more than one fox. The victim was the only female, and unless another could be had before breeding season there would be no increase. The four boys had been searching for wild foxes, and now John worked hard with his snares. To everyone's astonishment he brought in a live female a short time later. He refused to reveal his technique, calling it a trade secret and claiming that skill enabled him to catch a fox by both forelegs and neck to avoid strangling. He proved this by catching a second female a week later. The Company had begun to believe John really had a secret method when Walter saw a fox lying in the woods, apparently asleep. He decided he, too, would be a hero, the only man who had sneaked up on a fox and captured it with his bare hands. He crept forward by inches, only to find the fox was dead. One of John's snares was around its neck.

The females John caught gave the Company a chance

for two spring litters, or so they thought until Henry saw one was growing thinner. They knew nothing of fox diseases and the mystery was not solved until a few days later, when she died of abdominal strangulation. A snare wire had caught around her body and had gone unnoticed in the thick fur. John's technique had imperfections, and again they had six males and a female.

Henry began to understand why fox farmers failed, and still all the usual hazards — sickness, escape, lost litters and infertility — were ahead. This job required more than forest thinking and he needed help. Since the article on fur farming had been written by a member of the Department of Agriculture Henry wondered if the government had not issued bulletins for fur farmers as it had done for others. He wrote and received one.

It became his Bible. He found directions for feeding, warnings against excitement in breeding and whelping seasons, and diagrams of pens and houses. The bulletin stressed the need of proper nesting boxes and large pens, thirty by forty feet. Many fox farms had failed through ignoring a fox's need for space.

Netting for such pens would cost more than the Company's treasury held. The next ginseng harvest could not be sold before fall, and in any event the hastily-built winter pens must be replaced and construction finished while the ground was soft. Even now the posts had begun to lean at drunken angles, and the only reason the foxes were still inside was that they found it as difficult to dig in the frozen soil as had the boys. The situation appeared hopeless until one of the boys saw an advertisement in *Hunter-Trader-Trapper*. Funsten Brothers, St. Louis fur buyers, offered fifty dollars for the best picture and story of the successful use of their "Trail Scent and Animal Bait." Henry had a bottle of the bait, and the directions read:

"Foxes are the most cunning of all wild animals to trap. The traps should be boiled in hemlock water, or sprinkled with blood to which has been added a few drops of Funsten Trail Scent. In setting the traps, be sure to sprinkle a half-dozen drops of Funsten's Animal Bait. The powerful odor, which is irresistible, will draw the animals from long distances right to your traps and into them. Every trapper knows that animals continually sniff and smell in their prowling, and once they smell an odor or strike a trail that appeals to their passions they will follow it to the end."

A bait for which the manufacturer made such claims demanded a spectacular picture, and it was reasonable that Fromm foxes should earn their own housing. Not one fox lured to death, but seven! If they were tied in traps and a bottle of animal bait were set in the foreground, a picture of the scene must certainly win the fifty dollars. An outer fence of netting (not showing in the photograph) would prevent escape.

Next morning the seven foxes, in grain sacks, lay outside the door while the boys gathered equipment. John looked up to see a sack was empty. Walter picked up a rifle and ran out as a fox went down the road. After two miles he decided a pelt was better than no fox, and a pelt was all he brought back. The Company lost interest in posing the herd for pictures.

But the dead fox gave the boys a new idea. By freezing it and others they might trap, they would have enough dead models; but this, too, was abandoned. Pelts might be damaged through delay in skinning. The even-

tual scheme was depressingly unexciting. The skins of
a winter's hunt were draped over Walter's shoulders.
His look of maturity might add weight to the claim that
all the foxes had been caught in a single morning as a
result of using the Animal Bait. Henry signed the picture, as he was the only member who'd had financial
dealings with Funsten Brothers, and that too might be
considered in the award. The picture and a fulsome
account of the miraculous properties of Animal Bait
were mailed. For a month the Company waited, and
then gave up hope.

In April the question of greatest moment was what
might be happening in the nesting log of the only pair
of foxes. The Company had no way of knowing. The
bulletin warned that if fox mothers were upset or frightened they might destroy the pups in an ill-advised
attempt to save them. Henry, attuned to fox thinking,
could not follow this fox reasoning, but he took care
not to vary his feeding routine by an incautious step.
From his outlook post he saw the pair carry meat to the
hollow log, which must mean young were being fed;
but that could not be confirmed until the pups should
come out, when they were about four weeks old. The
Company must endure the suspense as best it could.

Waiting was hard because of the electrifying news of
the winter sale in London. For the first time rumors and
conjectures as to the possibilities of fox raising were
settled. The Dalton fox farm on Prince Edward Island
in Canada had sent twenty-five ranch-bred black silver
pelts to the London auction, a dramatic proof that the
rare creature could be bred and reared in confinement.
With these foxes, which were unusually fine, man had

carried an experiment of nature to new standards. Buyers paid $34,000 for the twenty-five skins, and one brought $2,600, a record price for a silver fox. The pelts were well furred, the guard hairs were long and glossy, the color was good, the black had no tinge of rust, and the silver was well veiled. The farm had successfully competed with the forest.

The last was the most exciting news of all. Until 1910 the fox farms of Prince Edward Island had been operated in secrecy. A few pelts were sent to London and sold by C. M. Lampson and Company under a pledge not to reveal their source. Charles Dalton had been experimenting since the late eighties, and in the middle nineties was joined by Robert Oulton. To these two men is given the credit for pioneering fox farming on a commercial basis. Others had made contributions to the domestication of the fox, and eventually six Canadian firms combined in what was virtually a monopoly. They owned all the breeding stock and refused to reveal their methods. Finally a member broke the agreement not to sell and, the secret out, Charles Dalton sent twenty-five pelts to London.

This meant many things. Not only was the silver fox, once wholly a creature of luck and accident, now an established strain, but the future of a fur threatened with extinction was assured. The animal had been growing rarer until in the previous decade the supply had fallen off 45 per cent. Similar decreases had been recorded in other fur bearers. The world's traffic in raw pelts, which had grown into ninety-five million dollars annually, was threatened by the inevitable dwindling of supply due to greater areas of settlement, more skillful tools for hunting, aggressive trapping, and clearing of forests.

The hunter-trapper era in North America had passed its peak, but man's ingenuity had rescued the fur trade. Until now good pelts had come only from the wilderness, and it was still believed that if animals were confined the quality of fur must suffer, be of poor color and, more important, lack luster. Thus the sale of twenty-five ranched silver fox pelts, acknowledged to be as beautiful as those taken in the wilds, was of far greater significance than the mere fact a few men had discovered a way to fortune. It was a signpost to the great fur trade itself. A new and profitable industry had been founded, and already it was being called the "Industry of the Golden Pelt."

To the Fromms in Wisconsin this was confirmation of the soundness of a boyish dream. Men had succeeded in raising silver foxes by the same methods the boys had planned, but this priority did not affect the Fromms' purpose. Their goal was still ahead, still as tempting, and now could be even more audacious. If selective breeding could produce pelts that as a whole were better than those from the wilds where nature often fumbled, then the Company could by the same process produce an even finer strain of silvers, and become owners of the most beautiful silver foxes the world had ever known.

News of the Dalton sale quickened the Company's eagerness to know what was happening in the hollow nesting log, but all Henry could report was that both parents had been carrying in food. At last, when whelping season was long past and pups should be taking the air of a morning, Henry investigated.

There were no pups. There never had been. A heap of gnawed bones filled the den. What Henry had presumed to be parental solicitude was merely a desire for mealtime seclusion, and the Company's first breeding season was a blank. It was little comfort to know this was an old story in fox farming. With one female, a hollow log, and pens so near the house, the boys should not have expected an increase, but they determined to have proper equipment and more females before another breeding season. Additional stock was the immediate problem. They had searched in vain for dens, and their only hope lay in purchase from a luckier trapper.

"We might get an answer from my advertisement in *Hunter-Trader-Trapper*," John said.

This was the first the others had heard of it. Caution had made John less sanguine about the explanation of the secret meals, and he had not wanted to risk missing a spring litter. It would be June before he could expect replies to his ad, but Edward began to figure on the probable cost of pups and measures to raise the money.

"We may not have to buy a litter," Walter said. "We've still got a chance if it snows in May."

A May snowstorm was capricious. It might be only a light powder, gone by noon and of no value to a tracker, or it might lie on the ground a day or two and give the Company one last chance to hunt a den. Again, it might not snow at all.

But a promise of snow was in the air one day when Walter entered the forest, and an hour later lazy flakes floated down. Before dark he not only found a den, but had seen the tracks of pups in fresh snow at the entrance.

Next morning the wagon delivered Walter to a place from which he could pack his gear to the nest. One hunter could be more quiet than two or more, and it might take three days to capture a litter. The pups, he learned, had not emerged since the previous day, and after he had made camp he prepared his traps, padding the jaws with cloth so they would not break the pups' legs. Before dark he set them at the entrance and through the night he waited in the tent. In the morning the traps were as he had left them, and there were no fresh tracks. The foxes had smelled man at their front door. All day he watched and not a fox appeared. The second night he dozed and was wakened by a shrill scream. He had caught a pup.

It was not injured by the padded trap, but Walter had not realized how trying the lamentations of his tent mate would be. Through that night and all the next day the pup whimpered. It refused to eat or be consoled, and its constant cries began to break down Walter's resolution. More than anything else he wanted to restore the pup to its mother and go away, leaving her family unmolested. He knew he would not have minded the usual method of getting pups — chopping a litter from a hollow log. The zest of discovery and the need for speed would carry a hunter through. But now he could only wait, listening to the pup and watching the entrance. He hoped the job would soon be over.

That night he caught the four remaining pups. Scarcely would he get one in a grain sack than another screamed in fright. Swiftness of events made the wait easier, and it was wonderful to show the Company five pups, three males and two females, when the boys called for him in the morning. Their admiration and rejoicing helped enormously, but Walter was glad when he left the camp site.

"Did you see the old ones?" John asked.

"No," Walter said, "and I'm glad I didn't. But at least we won't have to buy red foxes this year."

Ginseng absorbed the Company through the spring. Lath arbors were mended or replaced and a new seed-bed put under cover, but before shoots showed above ground the weeds took possession and, with larger bed area, presented a serious problem. Ginseng and farm tasks were a full time job for four, and often one robbed the other.

But the boys still took time to hunt new nursery stock. When they began ginseng culture they had set the round sum of one thousand wild plants as their final goal. But this summer when they reached the figure they realized the goal had been too easy, and they knew they would miss the fun of looting plants from neighbors' forests, and competition with the many shang hunters. So they had lifted the mark to 1,100, an eye-filling number. Now the oilcloth-covered box went forth on quick and furtive forays until they were well advanced in the last hundred. Walter kept the tally. Ginseng had become his department.

The Company's treasury still did not have money for woven wire fencing of new pens. It was useless to ask their father, although the Iowa farm had yielded enough for the purchase of an automobile. He had hesitated before buying a car. It would save hours in deliveries to the creamery or shopping trips to Wausau, twenty-two miles away, but he said a man whose four sons elected to grub about with ginseng and filthy foxes should save money against the inevitable day when this waste of time and energy must be reckoned. The Company had answered this with spirit; not only would it care for the present but it would provide for the future, and after such a reply it could scarcely try to borrow money for fencing.

Yet by midsummer no one had found a way to raise money. The boys were weeding in the garden when John brought a letter from Funsten Brothers addressed to Henry. Henry was always writing for bulletins, catalogues, and price lists, and the others paid no attention until he held up five new ten-dollar bills. Their picture and fulsome account of "one morning's haul" had won the prize.

Weeds grew unchecked the rest of the day. The Company was too busy choosing a site for pens and making out an order for netting. Lumber and peeled balsam poles were estimated, but roofing and paint were beyond the budget. This distressed Henry, for he wanted the first fox houses to be of special excellence.

The next day, for the first and last time in his life, Henry Fromm became a wage slave. A neighbor agreed that, big for his age and unusually strong, he was worth a dollar a day. Thirty dollars was needed for paint, roofing, and feed pans, and he worked exactly thirty days. When this economic servitude was ended he drove to town and spent the money on ornamentation of fox houses. A white enamel feeding pan at sixty cents, almost a day's work, distressed him, but he had the satisfaction of knowing that no foxes on any farm would eat from better dishes.

When the woven wire netting arrived, John and Henry drove to town and brought it home. The wagonload of rolls seemed some sort of a miracle; they had pitted their wits against the makers of Animal Bait and now had fencing for proper yards of thirty by forty feet — enough space to keep any pair of foxes healthy and contented. The pens were made exactly as the bulletin specified. A ditch was dug and netting sunk two feet in the ground, and a wire overhang was set at the top to prevent foxes from climbing over. The boys changed only one detail.

"There's no reason to build those walls ten feet high," Henry said. "Maybe the bulletin is right about some places where the snow is deep and the foxes could get away over the drifts. We shouldn't build ours over eight feet."

"We'd save netting," Walter said.

"Besides, I've watched 'em," Henry said. "A fox can't jump more'n eight feet without hurting himself." Henry was becoming a fox man.

He and John built the houses. Plans were elaborate after the hollow nesting log and were not exactly forest thinking — or perhaps were forest thinking adapted to man's world. Each house had an insulated nest box and an outside spout or tunnel to permit a fox to make a cautious survey before emerging. The boys followed the specifications. Innovations could come later when they knew more about the home life of foxes, and as they sawed and hammered they talked of the day when these very houses might shelter silvers. It wasn't impossible that one might hold a silver next spring.

A short time later they heard of a silver that an Indian at Star Lake had caught in a trap the previous winter. This proved silvers did appear in their district, and the Company caught fire. The boys couldn't buy it but at least they could see it, could know if it was as beautiful as they imagined. Silvers had become so real to them

51

that they were shocked by the realization they had never actually seen one, and they decided to send a member of the firm to look at it. Henry could not go, with foxes to feed, and Walter was busy with ginseng. Edward was accustomed to dealing with the outside world. Normal school and two months of teaching in a high school had given him assurance, and he was elected.

Henry drove him to Merrill, where he could take a train to Star Lake, and next morning he would return to tell exactly what a silver looked like. The others were still talking of how exciting this would be when they saw Edward coming down the road. The round-trip fare, he said, was three dollars, and when he counted his money he was short sixty cents.

Sixty cents! It had made all the difference between a firsthand account of the color, bearing, and habits of a live silver fox and looking at a picture of pelts.

"I'd have got there if I'd had to walk!" Henry blazed, and he meant it.

When he'd had time to cool his anger and recover from the disappointment, he realized that he might have done as Edward did. Ninety miles was a long way, but he still resented that sixty cents. It was so little, and yet it had been an obstacle to a company which intended to make world history in silver foxes. That morning, somehow, the herd of silvers seemed far away.

The summer narrowed the age gap between Herbert and the four, and Arthur's absence left Herbert the only older brother still at home. His violin helped family concerts, especially when their old music teacher came to spend a few days in a small log cabin Frederick Fromm had built for him. Then concerts lasted into the late evening; with either the two violins and Edward at the piano playing popular classics, or the entire family orchestra — Walter's clarinet, Henry's flute, and John's cornet — in Strauss waltzes or arias from German operas. Even when their teacher was not with them the boys still had music, if only a half hour snatched at noon, and ginseng weeding went the better for the interruption.

The last weeks of the ginseng search were exciting. Early in August they had found the eleven hundredth plant and again success was strangely disappointing. The tedium of a completed mission led John to suggest the change of each cipher to a digit. Eleven hundred and eleven pleased their fancy, but the last eleven plants were hard to find. Aggressive shang hunters had been everywhere, and only just before the first frost did Edward bring in the final plant.

For the first time the ginseng harvest made an impressive pile, so impressive that Walter snapped a picture as Edward carried the last armful to the heap. It was not all first-grade root, but the sale in December warranted a bank account; Walter opened it, and the pass book showed a balance of $175.

The Company was on its way, and it did not need to use bank funds to buy foxes. John and Henry had captured three live females. This raised the fox population; but so many hungry foxes presented a food problem that could no longer be met with game alone. Henry scouted the countryside for old horses. Frederick Fromm scowled when he saw these tired beasts brought home. His farm not only harbored filthy foxes, but now a Fromm went about buying cast-off animals, the final humiliation. When a neighbor asked him to tell the boys he had an old horse to sell, Frederick drew himself up in wrath.

"The boys don't want it!" he said. "If I had my way, they'd never need any man's old horses."

Perhaps the father's uncompromising attitude was a good tonic against the madness which now seized the fur world. Almost overnight the boom started. The boys heard of it from fur buyers and read of it in outdoor magazines and in *Hunter-Trader-Trapper*. Raising silver foxes had become the new and easy way to fortune. The rush of those eager to get in the game sent prices of breeding stock soaring, and pairs of pups brought six thousand dollars. Large companies were being capitalized, and investors were exhorted to get into this newest bonanza before the price of breeding stock went higher. Clerks mortgaged homes, school teachers invested savings, and men and women who had never seen a live fox computed paper profits. Promotion literature made it sound so easy! Each pair of foxes would bear four young. A pair of pups, worth six thousand dollars, undoubtedly would be worth twice that sum next season, and each pair of pups would produce four more foxes. An investor couldn't lose. Silver foxes bought now while prices were at rock bottom might be the foundation of a fortune.

All this meant nothing to the Fromm boys, except as each advance in the price of breeding stock put the possibility of purchase further off. They didn't stop talking about their future herd of silvers, but they began to lean on luck. Henry spent hours studying the markings of their foxes, trying to find some indication of silver blood. When whelping season arrived he made no effort to conceal his excitement, for he was certain there were young in the houses. He was beginning to know foxes.

While the Company awaited the outcome it searched the forest for litters, and because the boys had become skillful they were able to get several. All were red, but no boy admitted his disappointment. Their own foxes, they felt certain, would produce at least a cross, and five of the six females had families, a far better record than that of most inexperienced breeders.

Gradually the mothers began to bring out the young. Each litter was large and healthy. And every pup was red. Not until the very last pup of the very last litter had appeared did Henry give up hope. Even then he couldn't believe it. In spite of the mysterious workings of the silver strain and the lucky breaks of others, the Company had failed to produce a single silver hair.

But at least Henry had proved he could raise foxes.

Chapter Five

THEIR SECOND FAILURE TO GET A SILVER PUP, OR EVEN a cross, ended the Fromms' hope of obtaining silvers from native stock. They became impatient — or as impatient as a Fromm ever permitted himself to be. It would be years before ginseng money could buy a pair of silvers. Now there was no such thing as finding a bargain in a silver fox. Henry, reading the news of the industry with despair, knew that the price of six thousand for a pair of silvers was already a thing of the past. Walter was not so irked as the others, for he liked ginseng culture; but no matter what the Company accomplished in ginseng, the advance in the price of breeding stock would still carry foxes beyond their reach.

Henry knew this when he answered the advertisement of James A. Kane in *Hunter-Trader-Trapper*. Kane was a dealer in cross and silver foxes. Henry had to talk to someone about silver foxes, and it was the informality of Kane's advertisement in the classified columns of the familiar magazine that led him to hope for an answer, for he feared the large eastern ranches would not bother with him. He did not ask for prices nor pretend to be a potential customer; neither did he mention the existence of a company. His earnest letter told — lest the dealer consider him a young amateur asking idle questions — of the many years he had been planning to raise silver foxes and of his two failures, and it asked if there were any way for a boy with no money to obtain breeding stock.

James Kane answered promptly. The fervor of one fanatic had made touch with another. Kane believed in silver foxes, and he, too, knew failure. His own fox farm had not succeeded. As a buyer of western foxes for eastern ranches he was often absent on extended field trips and the Kane farm, entrusted to the custody of others, had been neglected. Henry's ardor and determination therefore held an appeal.

The two exchanged long letters. James Kane, a man of importance in the industry, was in a position to tell Henry the news and gossip about fox farming. He regularly visited the Canadian ranches, talked with breeders, and knew what fox men were doing; he was aware that fur farming was fast becoming a business ruled by speculation and promotion. Though some of his clients, interested in the future of the industry, were purchasing foxes to experiment with the infusion of fresh blood, others thought only of easy profits and bought for resale. Even at the 1911 high prices, demand for breeding stock had outrun supply, and eastern ranches were building up their herds with importations from the wilds of northwest Canada. There were rumors of ranches where a wild fox might enter the back door at night to leave the next morning as a registered member of the herd. Customers eager to start ranches, and knowing nothing about silver foxes, had been easy prey to such swindles.

But more important to Henry than the shoptalk of the industry were the theories about the silver strain. Kane knew the work of pioneers, men of practical experience who had reached conclusions by breeding foxes. Test matings had proved that a red pup of one silver parent might carry silver blood and in turn, when mated to a silver, produce one, or even half a litter, of silver offspring. These reds, carriers of silver blood, were referred to by Kane as "outcastes"; they were valuable as breeders, and ranchers had even paid five hundred dollars for them. Outcastes, a longer but much cheaper route to a silver herd, suggested a possible means for Henry, and should he want to try it Kane would find him a bargain in an outcaste and a silver mate.

Henry was elated, but he knew that even if they managed the price of an outcaste red there was no hope of buying a silver mate. He refused the offer with deep regret, and still made no mention of a company. It would be too humiliating to admit that a firm organized to raise silver foxes could not purchase even a single silver — and in a year when eastern companies were being capitalized at fifty, and even one hundred thousand dollars. It was absurd for a seventeen-year-old boy with no money to be writing to a leading dealer, and Henry was afraid the correspondence would end there.

But Kane had become emotionally involved in Henry's venture. Something in the boy's letter had caught him. He continued to write and, as a fellow breeder, to discuss problems of fox raising. Henry was delighted to be able to refer his questions to an authority, and he had an important one at the moment. The government bulletin said the male fox should be separated from the litter since he might destroy the young, or his presence might make the mother nervous and drive her to kill the pups. But Henry and John had discovered that both parents grieved when they were separated. They talked it over. Wild foxes lived a family life, and while some fathers might destroy the young, others helped in the care of pups. The matter was referred to Kane and he agreed with Henry; he also pointed out how much the boy was learning by housing reds before he attempted the more costly silvers. When Henry restored the fathers to their families, pen life was again peaceful. But it was just as gratifying that a practical breeder had approved his and John's conclusions.

The autumn of 1911 had arrived when Kane finally suggested an even less costly way for Henry to get silvers. He had found a fine male cross, which he referred to as a "double-cross" because its black coat had a reddish flash only on a flank and shoulder. This, mated to an outcaste, should produce at least one silver pup. He warned Henry that the male was not prepossessing; puppyhood rickets had broken down its front legs. But this defect did not harm its breeding value and was, moreover, the reason for the exceedingly low price of $350. Another two hundred would buy an outcaste female, and with the outlay of only $550 Henry would have a start toward a silver herd. One silver pup was the least Henry might expect, and the male's black coat, showing a predominance of silver blood, justified even higher hopes.

The Company shared Henry's excitement. A double-cross must be almost a pure silver! It was miraculous good fortune — but not within their reach. Apparently Kane had not taken Henry's financial statement quite as literally as Henry had intended it. The Company's funds of earnings from the traps, red fox hunting and a spring sale of ginseng fiber and second-grade root, fell far short of $550. The fall harvest of ginseng could not be dug until late October, and then would take two months to dry and market. But they could not afford to wait. Delay or temporizing would lose the bargain, might even forfeit Kane's interest. It was useless to try to borrow from their father; foxes, red, silver, cross, or outcaste, were obnoxious to him. In the midst of this crisis their older brother Herbert, home from teaching for a week end, offered his savings to make up the deficit. Never was a new stockholder welcomed more warmly.

With the money in hand, the Company now considered its business relations with James Kane, who was under the impression that his sympathy had been extended to one boy yearning for foxes. It was doubtful that this warm interest would stretch to include a whole company of yearners. The obvious course — not to tell him — was hazardous. Should he deliver the foxes in person, he would surely discover the other brothers. The proposed strategies to prevent this became as elaborate, and as diverting, as in the old days when the four had plundered the land of neighbors. But in the meantime Henry's name must be used in making the purchase. Edward argued that this slight deception was really a kindness, since finding out there were four boys instead of just Henry would be a disappointment, if not an emotional loss, to James Kane; the rights of a benefactor were important. Edward had a keen sense of the reactions of others.

But a deal involving so large a sum as $550 had become real business, and company transactions were usually executed by Edward. Older, and already beginning to show ability as a coordinator, he had good ideas that were generally accepted by the others, and he handled correspondence easily. So Edward took over the purchase and managed a fair imitation of Henry's writing, which must have been successful, for Kane continued to address the firm as "Dear Henry." The partners figured that if Edward changed gradually to his own penmanship, the dealer would never notice. The more simple expedient of having Henry transcribe the letters did not occur to them. The Fromm boys liked their obstacles.

Fortunately for their peace of mind, Kane wrote that the foxes would arrive by express. The Company had already started a new block of pens in the woods where shade and trees would give the animals a sense of forest life. The pens would house the new pair and the spring increase, and now the cost of pennage in money and labor must be added each year to increased ginseng gardens.

The pens were finished when the pair arrived. The double-cross male was a disappointment. He looked almost like a silver, but his front legs were worse than they had imagined. The boys were appalled to see that the sire of their herd walked on his elbows. But the red female was a fine large fox, light, with black lips and a tinge of black on the feet proving she was an outcaste, although the term seemed a sorry one for the carrier of proud silver blood.

Now at last, after two years of effort, the silver herd seemed just around the corner. The Company plunged into the rush of the fall season. Not only must a farm be harvested and made ready for the winter, but ginseng seeds were to be planted, roots dug, leaves raked, arbors dismantled, and plants mulched against the winter. When these tasks were finished a log icehouse must be built to provide safe storage for fox food. Sometimes cattle were killed by lightning or Henry was able to buy several horses, and the Company must be ready to avail itself of lucky windfalls. The meat was to be kept in the center of the icehouse, in a hollow square walled with cakes of ice and reached through an ice tunnel. It would be crude refrigeration, but was the best they could devise.

Winter brought another problem. The new pair of foxes must be guarded. In summer both ginseng and foxes could be watched from the beds on the tops of the ginseng arbors, but this comfortable arrangement was no longer possible when the arbors were dismantled. A lookout tent was the simplest answer. They found three trees growing in such a position as to make corner posts. By sinking a fourth post they were able to build a high platform for a tent that commanded a view of the fur farm.

Edward and Henry slept in the tent through the winter. On cold mornings their damp footwear was so stiff and frozen that a barefoot dash to the house was a lesser test of their endurance. But no member of the Company doubted for a moment that this watch should be maintained. Eastern ranches were equipped with day and night guards and often with burglar alarm systems to protect famous foxes and, while the pair of cross and outcaste would hardly tempt a thief, the Company would not have liked to admit this. A secretive boyhood existence, isolation, group allegiance to a goal, and years of struggle, had deepened an instinctive sense of misgiving about outsiders into actual distrust.

Bright With Silver

The outcaste female was a forthright creature and did not keep her owners in suspense longer than was necessary. In late March her nest box held young; Henry distinctly heard pups whimper. Now the Company was safely past three of the hazards of fox farming — infertility, abortion, and a lost litter. The last is the most maddening to a keeper, for there is no evidence to tell him what has happened to the young. Keepers have learned to recognize the implications when a fox mother drags the straw out of her nest box. They call it "cleaning house" and know it to be the bad sign of a blank, a whole year's work lost. But only the fox mother knows whether a crime has been committed, and she can't be made to tell.

The good news of a litter was written to James Kane. He was as pleased as the Company. No one doubted that there would be one silver pup. Kane, counting on the preponderance of silver blood in the double-cross, was even more sanguine about the number. Edward was inclined to share the dealer's opinion. John held out for one silver. Henry merely waited. And the Company knew now how necessary it was to wait without investigation.

Nervous fox mothers are one of the main griefs of fox farming. Fright will cause them to drag the young from a nest box into the pen yard, hide them, bury them, leave them exposed to damp and cold, or in a complete panic destroy and eat them. Quite as unreasonably a mother, having dined off the litter, may resume her anxious worrying about the lost young. The unpredictability of maternal solicitude is still one of the major problems of fox farming. A fox mother, terrified for the safety of a pup that has escaped the yard, will try to drag it home through the fencing, and in so doing may tear its leg off. Whereupon she is very apt to stop and eat the leg before she returns to her truly earnest and well-meant rescue efforts. Generations of domestication, however, have now accustomed mothers to a keeper's inspection. When the pups are about a week old a good keeper always puts his ear to the outside of the house and listens. If the low whimperings are only those of contentment he does nothing, but if there is continuous whining registering discomfort he investigates, and perhaps saves the litter. In the early days when foxes were much wilder, even listening led to loss of litters. Maternal distrust demanded that a keeper adhere to a set pattern and never threaten intrusion by even one incautious step.

Henry knew this, and resisted the great temptation to find out how many silver pups there were. But at last the period of waiting was over. One sunny April morning Henry saw the family. He stared for a long moment, unable to believe his eyes. Three pups, and all red! To Henry they looked as red as the Wisconsin native foxes. Henry reported the incredible fact to the others, and they, fully as shocked as Henry, rushed out to verify. Everyone had been so confident. Wasn't the sire almost a silver?

The news was written to James Kane, and his reply was filled with genuine astonishment and dismay. Outcaste matings produced silvers for other breeders, and he had made sure this female was an outcaste. Yet she must have been the parent at fault. There could be no uncertainty about the double-cross, for his coat carried visible proof of silver blood.

The dealer made two suggestions. Henry could send

back the disgraced outcaste when her nursing duties were over and he would replace her with another outcaste. Or if Henry, discouraged by the loss of a whole year, had abandoned the idea of a herd of silvers, he could have his money back. Nothing could be fairer than this. The Company did not for an instant question Kane's sincerity and friendship, nor had it occurred to them not to persist in raising silver foxes. But at the moment, still so close to the sudden end of high hopes, they did not want another outcaste. They wrote Kane that they were returning the female and would wait until winter before deciding what to do about a mate for the double-cross. In that fox at least they had a fine male; they had now, in fact, begun to speak of him as a silver. In a way they were justified, for a rusty patch on one flank and shoulder could be considered only a blemish. Kane had truly given them a bargain.

The double-cross was now an even better bargain than when they had bought him, for the price of silvers was soaring. Pairs of spring pups had jumped to ten thousand dollars, and offspring of famous foxes brought still more. The fur world had gone mad in the new bonanza. Companies that had foreseen the sudden rise of prices and acquired breeding stock in the early boom days were reporting spectacular profits. And there were the get-rich-quick stories. A group of clerks had cleared forty thousand dollars in a year, and three sisters had made thirty-five thousand in their venture as fox farmers. Apparently the only requisite for success was capital for a half-dozen pairs of foxes; natural increase and ascending prices would pile up a fortune. Glib salesmanship and specious promises of quick and easy money were finding naive victims, and the silver fox industry was fast taking on all the excitement and inflated values of a land boom or a gold strike. With each week and month hope grew slenderer that the Fromm boys could buy anything but another outcaste. Yet they hesitated. They did not doubt Kane's wisdom, but they could not bear to risk the loss of another breeding season. Their silver male — and now they never referred to him in any other way — deserved a silver mate.

In midsummer luck appeared to nod in their direction. They heard of a silver owned by a farmer named Herman who lived outside the village of Polar, over sixty miles away. The fox had been trapped, and was not only a silver, but a female. Mr. Herman wished to sell, and while purchase by the Company was out of the question, a partnership might be profitable to both Mr. Herman and the Fromms. The Company discussed the possibilities. It decided that representatives should visit Mr. Herman and propose the alliance, and Henry and Edward were chosen. They would walk fifteen miles to Marathon City, take the train to Polar and then walk ten miles to Mr. Herman's farm. The boys wore their best clothes so that Herman's prospective partners would appear impressive. Their best shoes would be uncomfortable for walking, but were an important evidence of prosperity. Alwina packed a lunch of fried chicken, her way of wishing them luck. Frederick listened to the elaborate plans for this partnership in one silver fox and found them humorous. He had gone to the stable when the boys walked toward the gate and he came to the wide door to watch them.

"Go!" he said, and the one word carried his contempt and ill opinion of their errand.

Late that afternoon Henry and Edward arrived at Polar and walked to the farm of Mr. Herman. They saw the fox and stared at it for a long time without speaking. Neither wanted to admit his disappointment. The fox was black, but the unkempt summer coat had none of the glorious guard hairs they had imagined.

"So that's a silver fox," Edward said at last.

"We shouldn't have expected it to look good in summer," Henry said a bit wistfully. "She'll be a different fox when she gets her winter coat."

Mr. Herman said he would sell the fox for three thousand dollars, and he wanted cash. The price was not out of line with the times. Edward began to talk about a partnership. Mr. Herman shook his head, walked into the barn and began the evening milking. Edward and Henry followed and talked about the next spring's increase, which could be halved between them. Mr. Herman did not answer and went on milking. The two boys stood at either side and, as the jets squirted into the pail, argued the benefits of partnership. Never had any promoter of a fox ranch spoken more persuasively of the dazzling profits in the industry of the golden pelt. They summoned every fact they had read or that James Kane had told them, but Mr. Herman remained unmoved. He carried the milk pails to the house and started the separator, a small one of quart capacity.

The separating process lasted a long time, but the boys never stopped talking above the clatter. Mr. Herman was still unconvinced. He remained so through the evening, and when at last he went to bed the boys departed for the barn, where they slept in the hayloft.

They arose early in the morning to resume their arguments. The owner of the fox continued to be obdurate. The price was three thousands dollars.

At ten o'clock the boys gave up. Mr. Herman was becoming irritable. They returned to Polar, so dejected by the failure of their salesmanship that they decided at the station to save the money for their fare. It was sixty-two miles to Hamburg. They walked all day and all night. Their shoes hurt their feet, and when they tried walking barefoot, stones cut their soles. They finished the journey in their heavy woolen socks, and arrived home in time for the morning milking.

When the chores were done the Company held a conference; it had not yet abandoned the idea of the Polar fox. Walter, bookkeeper for the firm, had a brilliant idea. Their father had three thousand dollars in a savings account, profits of the Iowa farm, which he might loan if the Company gave a note and paid bank interest. Walter presented the idea to his father, and to everyone's amazement Frederick Fromm agreed. The note was written that morning. Then Frederick Fromm realized that withdrawal from the bank at this particular time would penalize him for three months' interest. The note was redrawn to cover this loss.

It was noon before negotiations were finally concluded. Henry and Edward had hoped to make up lost sleep during their father's visit to the bank to draw the money, but Frederick Fromm told the boys to get the car. He had sufficient cash on hand to bind the bargain, and no man could be expected to carry three thousand dollars around the country. An immediate departure had at least one advantage; their father would have less time to change his mind.

Bright With Silver

The three drove to Polar, and again they reached the Herman farm at milking time. The boys showed the silver fox to Frederick Fromm. He made no effort to conceal his opinion; he believed a creature worth three thousand dollars should look wonderful in any season. The boys explained about a fox's summer coat and opened transactions with Mr. Herman, who was still determined but no longer irritable, since Frederick Fromm's arrival had proved the purchasers to be in earnest. The price was argued through the evening, and again the Fromms slept in the hayloft.

In the morning Frederick awoke with deep misgivings. Three thousand dollars was a lot of money. He knew how big the sum was from having worked for it, and the boys would discover how large it was when they had to work to pay it back. Mr. Herman was a hard man in a bargain and besides, this fox did not look like anything a man should pay three thousand dollars to possess. Frederick knew that other fox farmers had paid even more for silver foxes, but fox farming was a wildcat business anyway. He was deeply troubled, and also mystified at finding himself involved in such a transaction.

The boys made a last desperate effort for better terms. Mr. Herman was still obdurate and finally, convinced that it was three thousand dollars or nothing, they turned to their father for the cash to bind the bargain.

Frederick Fromm was not in sight. The boys ran to the car. Although their father could not drive, he might be threatening departure in order to force Mr. Herman to close the deal. But the car was empty. They stared down the road. Large footprints, one so directly ahead of another and so firmly impressed that they meant fixed purpose, led over the hill toward town. The boys feared the worst, but they rushed back to Mr. Herman and told him negotiations would be resumed when they found their father.

They followed the footprints and from the top of the hill saw a stubborn figure plodding down the road. They overtook him, held the car door open. Frederick Fromm climbed into his accustomed seat beside the driver. He said nothing. The boys asked no questions. Everyone knew the episode was finished, and on the drive home no one spoke.

Chapter Six

FREDERICK FROMM'S DISTRUST OF SILVER FOXES RECEIVED wholly unexpected confirmation when news of the Polar fox reached Hamburg. Mr. Herman had sold it for three thousand dollars to a Canadian dealer. This news had been depressing to the Company though no comment had been made in the family. But later, in the fall fur-making months when the fox should have emerged a glamorous creature of beauty, it had proved to be a Sampson, of no value as a breeder or a pelt. A Sampson is a fox which does not fur out properly. Such foxes have been known since the early fur days, when it was assumed that they were merely poorer foxes — inferior examples of the species. But when foxes were raised in pens Sampson characteristics grew steadily worse. A mildly Sampson fox might merely have curly hair. Then animals would appear that failed to grow guard hairs, then others with dry and thin undercoats, and finally foxes with no brushes. If allowed to breed indefinitely, Sampsons might even become hairless. In any of its stages a Sampson is a miserable-looking fox, and unfortunately it is the toughest fox of all. Nothing kills it except its owner.

Since a dealer had not recognized a Sampson, boys who had never even seen silver foxes could not have been expected to recognize its early characteristics, and their faith in the beauty of the silver fox made them charitable toward summer coats. The skepticism of Frederick, who had no such feeling of charity, had saved them from a crippling blow. The three thousand dollars would have had to be repaid from ginseng profits, thus ending all but the most distant hopes of a silver herd. Shaken by this close brush with disaster, the Company was in no mood to argue with Frederick. His position was unassailable. He might even prove to be right about ginseng.

The Company could only go on working, with the problems of the ranch constantly increasing. Each spring's crop of fox pups required more pens; more pens meant more posts, lumber, and netting; posts and lumber meant more work at clearing; more grown foxes ate more small game. As the ginseng gardens grew in area, more mulch had to be carried from the forest, more sideboards staked around beds, more arbors built. As the number of plants increased, spraying became a problem; the small, hand-driven orchard spray demanded terrific toil. The Company's first change from man to machine power came with the purchase of a gasoline power spray. This more effective weapon in the constant warfare against blight would eventually save many dollars but, like any improvement, it put a strain upon the treasury.

There were difficulties, too, in the scheme to duplicate ginseng's natural environment, for nature sometimes worked against it. The necessity for dry leaf mulch had always been an anxiety. Leaves must fall before tender plants were exposed to cold, and since leaf raking was a long job the boys operated on a timetable over which they had no control. This autumn, 1912, nature contrived a real threat. A heavy snowstorm on October 4th covered the ground and the trees, when foliage had only begun to color. The ginseng gardens, which had been sprayed and weeded and which comprised the Company's entire capital, were without protection.

It looked as though Frederick's dismal warnings were to be justified, and there was nothing the Company could do; one really cold night would wipe them out. Day after day no leaves fell. A week of dreadful waiting and watching was spent, and then all the leaves in the forest let go at once. Leaves red and yellow and glorious bronze worked magic on the white forest floor. The sight was beautiful; the boys recognized its beauty even though it still spelled danger. Through every hour of daylight they worked, scraping the precious mulch from the snow, and at last every plant was protected. They had succeeded in spite of nature, but it had been a harrowing victory.

Washing roots was the hardest task in ginseng culture, for the crop could not be dug before late October when it ripened, and then the washing, which was done in the stream, was an icy job. The water chilled the hands, and the rough roots wore down fingernails until they were sore and tender. Various methods of speeding the operation were tried, such as placing the roots on racks and using a hand-driven barrel spray. Manning the pressure pump demanded a lot of muscle power, but it was less arduous than hand scrubbing. This year, however, there was more root than ever. The first seed-bed, planted eight years before, was ready to harvest. It had been a long time since the boys poked three hundred small flat seeds into holes made with a stick, and the present harvest fell far short of those first brave plans, but it was large enough to increase the dread of the washing and to make it a real problem.

The morning they began Edward noticed the family car standing in the shed, and thought of its motor, idle while they toiled. It should be made to work. He suggested that they drive the car to the stream, jack up the rear end and rig it up with a belt to drive the pump. The extemporized power plant was clumsy, but it was a beginning. They planned improvements. Next year they would buy a better pump and bring the root to the stream in a wagon that had a screen bottom to let the soil escape, thus making a second handling unnecessary. And "Some day," Henry said, "we'll have stationary motors working for us." They were started on the route of planning instead of plodding.

In November the double-cross fox was still living mateless in solitary grandeur when the boys heard of another silver trapped in their own district. That such luck should have struck three times in their neighborhood and yet have passed them by was beginning to seem incredible, for they had trapped dozens of red foxes. The local agent of the express company told the Fromm boys that more than a year earlier Henry Moreland of Iron Mountain had trapped two silvers, a male and a female. He had refused offers from the Dalton Silver Black Fox Company of Prince Edward Island because he intended to start his own farm. But after his first breeding season proved a failure, with no litter or no indication whether a litter had been born and destroyed by the parent foxes, he had reopened negotiations with the Dalton firm. A representative had come to Wisconsin and purchased the male for five thousand dollars. Now Mr. Moreland wished to sell the female. The agent had seen the fox and reported her beautiful, if a three-legged fox could be considered beautiful. She had lost the fourth leg in the trap.

It was almost a duplication of the Polar fox situation, except that the boys now knew it was hopeless to try to borrow from their father. They decided against a personal visit to the owner until they had first sounded him out by letter. Edward wrote a carefully worded proposal of partnership and since Mr. Moreland, through dealing with the Dalton firm, must already be well aware of the profits in fox farming, Edward dwelt principally on the fine qualities of their own silver male and on the Company's success with large litters. The agent of the express company also wrote Mr. Moreland, saying that he had known the Fromm boys for years. The two letters were only the opening guns in the negotiations, and the Company watched the mails for an answer.

To their astonishment the Moreland fox arrived by express. To have been entrusted with the sister of a fox which had brought five thousand dollars, and by a man who had never seen them, was a startling show of faith. The boys were slightly stunned by the ease with which the partnership had been managed; it had been like bracing for a tug at a spike and having a shingle nail come loose in the hand. Moreland's faith put a great responsibility upon them, and two silver foxes, one their own and one belonging to a stranger, demanded vigilance.

They built a watchtower which bristled with an air of threat. The structure was called "Fort Moreland." It had portholes for rifle fire, living quarters for a night guard, and withal a very militant aspect reminiscent of the blockhouses erected in days of Indian warfare. But the Company saw no humor in these extreme measures. Defensiveness was now the set pattern, and the 1913 breeding season must be made a success. Safety, care, and seclusion were the Company's solemn obligations. The rest was up to the foxes. And they couldn't miss. The female was a beautiful silver and the male was almost, though not quite, a silver.

The pair got on comfortably together. Perhaps the cross fox's broken-down front legs made him charitable about the three-legged condition of his consort. Two weeks before the whelping date in mid-April, there was no doubt of an increase; the Moreland female was heavy. In view of her history as a careless, if not an actually cannibalistic, mother, Henry redoubled his precautions for seclusion. If quiet would develop maternal instincts he was determined to provide it, and he tiptoed when he brought the food. Events in the nest box remained a mystery except for one morning after whelping time, when Henry was sure he heard pups whimper. The weeks of seclusion crawled by, and when the litter was about a month old John and Henry made occasional stealthy visits to the pen. The two boys were together when they first saw the litter. For a moment neither spoke. "Mrs. Moreland" was delighted with her family. She suffered no loss of pride whatever because she had mothered two cross pups and two reds.

There was no possible explanation of her failure to produce a silver. She was undoubtedly a silver. The sire showed a preponderance of silver blood. By all known laws of breeding, silver offspring should have resulted. It began to look as though bad luck had fastened on the Fromm boys in earnest; for the second time proper matings had failed them.

John looked at the double-cross sire doubtfully. "Maybe that outcaste red female wasn't to blame for those red pups," he said.

It was the first time suspicion had fastened on the double-cross, and even now it seemed unwarranted. Any fox with a black coat, silver guard hairs and only a slight blemish on the flank and shoulder must be almost silver. John's comment was unfortunate, however, for when the Company considered the grim possibility, they were even more distressed by what Moreland might think of them than by the fact of their own disaster. He had sent his fox in good faith. They had told him their male was a silver. He could only conclude that the Company was concealing silver pups. But the news of a litter of cross and red foxes must be broken to him. Edward wrote the letter, and it required all the statesmanlike tact the Company's "front man" could muster.

Mr. Moreland arrived at the end of the nursing period. The boys exhibited the silver sire and expressed their regret and dismay. They never knew what Mr. Moreland's real conclusions were. He made no accusations — simply departed with his silver female. On one point only he was definite; he absolutely refused to take his share of pups, red or cross. He was through with fox breeding forever.

The fiasco of the Moreland mating cast a shadow on the summer. Henry worried about it. He could not bear to think that a man who had shown such faith in the Company might now consider it dishonest. He brooded until he became really ill. A doctor diagnosed the trouble as a digestive ailment and suggested treatment at Battle Creek Sanitarium; a few weeks of care should put a strong boy of nineteen on his feet. Henry protested at such needless expense, but a thoroughly frightened Company insisted upon it. Although the treasury was in its usual summer doldrums, the poor health of a partner was an emergency.

To Henry the journey, his first into the outside world, was absorbing, but neither the excitement of travel nor the novelty of sanitarium life freed him of depondency. He continued to brood about the litter from the Moreland mating, then finally decided he could never find peace until he himself had made a statement of the honesty of the Company. He wrote a long letter to Mr. Moreland, assuring him it had not stolen silver pups, had none on the ranch, and was still mystified why there were none. When the letter was mailed he began to feel better. Undoubtedly the doctors were astonished at his abrupt recovery.

Completely cured Henry started home, stopping in Chicago for one errand. He visited the fur salon in the Marshall Field store. He'd not known stores had such thick carpets and luxurious appointments, but he did not permit awe to distract him. He asked to see a silver fox scarf. The saleswoman stared at him for a moment and then went to get one. It was priced at nine hundred dollars. Henry examined it carefully, handed it back to the saleswoman, thanked her, and went away. It never dawned on him that he left her mystified. He had seen a silver fox scarf, so much desired by women. The pelt was dark, lustrous, soft, and silky; but Henry thought it should have had more silver to make it brighter.

He returned to Hamburg. During his absence several letters had arrived from James Kane. The dealer was thoroughly baffled by the two unsuccessful matings of the double-cross. He was sure the fox was a western fox, and the term "double" had been his own invention to describe the evident preponderance of silver blood. He agreed, however, that it would be unwise to continue to depend on such a fox to sire a silver herd. Perhaps it was a Jonah.

But the Moreland mating had at least cleared the good name of the outcaste female, and Kane was now more sure than ever of the breeding value of such outcastes. In the previous two years ranchers had discovered many facts about them. Outcastes, mated with each other, produced silvers. And the outcaste offspring of outcaste parents might in their turn produce a silver pup in a litter of mixed foxes. Kane was so sure of their value that he did not hesitate to urge this method on Henry, and it seemed the only way for a boy with no capital to get silver foxes. To make this route possible he offered to find Henry a pair of outcastes for $450. The offer was intended to make amends for two years of disappointments and to encourage a boy who had become his friend. But nothing else could have made more vivid the contrast between the Company's fortunes and those of other ranchers.

Now in the fall of 1913 — when the Company had barely started, and did not have the money for the purchase of a $450 pair of outcaste foxes — the silver fox industry had reached new and dizzy heights. Pairs of pups were selling at fifteen to thirty-five thousand dollars, with options selling even on the next spring's pups. Ranches on Prince Edward Island were heavily capitalized; one hundred thousand dollars was not unusual, and the two largest were capitalized at more than six hundred thousand. Dividends to stockholders were astounding. One ranch had announced a dividend of 500 per cent, another of 300 per cent, several had paid more than 200 per cent, and investors could be assured a profit of from 10 to more than 100 per cent on their money in a single year. The boom foretold in 1910 was now on in full force, three years later. The industry had spread to the Eastern states and scores of new ranches were being started. Demand for breeding stock was at a peak and had almost ended the sale of ranch pelts, for no breeder would pelt a fox which could be sold to eager customers at a fantastic price. Fox farming, begun as a pioneering effort to domesticate and produce fur-bearing animals, had become a highly speculative, over-capitalized, stock-selling scheme. Blatant promotion, illicit methods, and even misrepresentation had permeated the industry, and were now a far greater hazard to the new investor than the difficulties of raising foxes. Animals — mixtures of every variety that could be imported — were being sold as standard, the term now used to describe the eastern purebred; and a rusty color had cropped up on many ranches which were supposed to have a thoroughbred herd.

For some time eastern ranches had been importing the western fox. Ranchers had become aware of the special quality of Peace River foxes, native to the district lying between the British Columbia border and Edmonton. These foxes had larger size, bone, and sinew, and they were brighter in color, while the eastern standard foxes were being bred smaller and darker. The lustrous dark eastern fox with delicate silver markings still ranked first in desirability, but breeders were hoping to add stamina and virility to their herds with the infusion of Peace River blood. Foxes from this district had become so valuable that a fine female silver, dug from a den by a Peace River trapper, had been bid for by eastern ranches and finally sold in Montreal for ten thousand dollars.

When James Kane proposed to sell Henry a pair of western outcastes for $450, he was offering a bargain. The Company realized this, and now that faith in the double-cross was shattered, they were more eager to try the mating of outcastes. But they were faced by a depleted treasury. Funds had been eaten by expansion. Every year they had had to build something. Wire for pennage, milling for arbor lumber, the purchase of sprayers, hose, and hardware, had kept them on a precarious footing. But they knew if they were to become breeders of silver foxes they must soon make a start, and somehow they must raise $450.

Edward suggested expansion of the Company, the usual method of handling a firm's financial crisis. Their cousins and neighbors, the Niemans, had money and might be persuaded into partnership. The Company paid a call on the cousins and Edward presented the idea, but before he had even finished his carefully prepared arguments he was refused, and with vehemence. Mrs. Nieman, who was planting beans, said she would make more money from the beans than the Fromm boys would ever make from "stinking foxes." She was as violent on the subject as Frederick Fromm.

Henry, even more than the others, resented his aunt's vivid vocabulary. He admitted foxes had a distinctive odor, and one which clung to the clothing of keepers. Being aware of this may have made him more sensitive, but he felt his aunt's description did his foxes an injustice. He was still fretting about the matter several days later as he and John rode their bicycles to Rib Mountain.

The expedition had been planned for a long time. Rib Mountain, or White Hill as it was called locally, was a geological curiosity. Almost eight hundred feet above the plain, and the highest point in the state, it rose abruptly from the surrounding country, a great jumble of white quartzite left by erosion. A few years before a fire had killed the Norway and white pines that grew on the bold shoulders of the hill, and now blanched tree skeletons and quartzite in summer, or shrouding snow in winter, had earned it the name of "White Hill." John and Henry had never visited the mountain, but eight years before, when Walter and Edward were in school in Wausau, they had cut their names on the top and had boasted of the feat. It had required a chisel, hammer, determination, and real labor to cut letters in the stone. Now John and Henry were determined to outdo their brothers and leave their names on an even higher point of rock. They went equipped with tools, food, and blankets, because the job could not be finished in one afternoon. John was prepared to spend the night. But Henry had to return to feed the foxes.

Pedaling a bicycle over twenty miles of soft road was hard work, and their spirits were low. After four years of effort they still did not have a silver fox on the ranch, and they might not have one next spring if they couldn't manage to raise $450. Henry was nineteen, John twenty-one, and four years seemed a lifetime.

Their wealthy, scornful, cousins had not only refused them but had jeered at foxes. Henry recalled his anger, and at that moment the Nieman automobile passed them. The car looked powerful and prosperous, and the tires sent sand and pebbles flying out behind. John and Henry stared after it. The car seemed the final insult. The boys flared into a sudden rage and vowed that some day they *would* have silver foxes, cars, and everything else they wanted. They wished they had said this to the cousins. But saying it to each other made them feel better.

When they dismounted from their bicycles at the foot of the mountain John asked what they should carve at the top. Henry considered the question as they climbed. The inscription was important. It must be as enduring as the mountain itself. Undoubtedly someday roads would be built up the steep hill and people would come to see and marvel at so strange a geological formation. In itself, this idea held a challenge which made mere names seem trifling, but in another way Henry felt that what they carved that day must be an answer to their circumstances. Invincibility was in his thoughts.

They found the high point of the highest rock. It was only a few feet above the one that held the names of their brothers. John unwrapped the chisel and the hammer and prepared to carve. He looked at Henry. And Henry had thought out the answer. He tore a page from his notebook and wrote:

John and Henry Fromm
Pioneer Breeders of Silver Foxes
1913

Chapter Seven

THE NEXT MORNING HENRY WAKENED WITH A SCHEME to raise the money to buy the pair of outcaste foxes. They might be able to sell the double-cross. The male fox had lost in prestige, but Henry did not permit doubt to creep into the advertisement for the October issue of *Hunter-Trader-Trapper*. He considered using the adjective "fine," but decided this might be unwise. The advertisement read only, "For Sale — Silver black male fox with rusty ear or neck, and shoulder flank. Henry Fromm, Hamburg, Wisc."

The fox sold, and almost immediately. Even more astonishing, it sold for the asked price of $650. The Company had been prepared to dicker. Moreover, the purchaser wrote how pleased he was with his bargain. But apparently the career of the double-cross was ill-starred, for after the next breeding season he was offered back to the Company at a reduction. The new owner was equally bewildered by a litter of red pups. No one understood the mystery.

Not until years later was a genetic law formulated

by Karl B. Hansen which might explain the enigma. Hansen carried on experiments in mating Alaskan and eastern silver foxes to discover that both were recessives, but different recessives. And since the behavior of different recessives, even if similar in appearance, is, when mated, the same as that of a straight strain, the recessive is lost and offspring tend to return to the normal. Litters of cross foxes would be the expected result. This outcome had been the more bewildering because no one had known the exact geographical boundaries of the habitant of the Alaskan fox. It comes from the interior of Alaska, and the Peace River District silver foxes are apparently not of the Alaskan variety, since they had always been mated successfully with eastern or standard foxes. The boundary between the two strains, eastern and Alaskan, lies somewhere between Peace River and Alaska, and it is barely possible that the famous double-cross that cost the Fromm boys two breeding seasons might have been a real Alaskan silver.

James Kane, in wishing to befriend Henry, had found for him a black fox with only two rusty tinges for $350. Quite unwittingly he might have selected an Alaskan silver which, when mated to a standard, could never produce silver pups. It had been the Company's ill fortune to be involved in a genetic mystery when geneticists had not yet given their attention to silver fox breeding, and fox ranchers were not even aware that fur farming was a genetic problem.

In the middle of November the pair of outcastes arrived by express. Kane, by now quite as eager for a successful breeding season as the Company, wrote full instructions. Especially he warned Henry against over-feeding. Too fat a fox would not breed. The male was a big fox, greyish red and wolfish, undoubtedly from Peace River, and he had an aggresive bearing that delighted his new owners. The female was finely molded. The pair was installed in its quarters and Henry, with Kane's warning fresh in his mind, took care not to feed a large supper. He was determined to make no mistakes in this breeding season.

The evening was a happy one. It seemed almost too good to be true that at last the Company was prepared for silvers. The double-cross would never again confound them, and as fine a pair of outcastes as anyone could wish were now members of the herd. Even the night guard in Fort Moreland slept the sound sleep of achievement.

Early next morning the Company went to inspect the new foxes. The male appeared to be in even better spirits. A moment later they saw the tail of a fox lying on the ground. It was all that remained of the female. Half of $450 had gone down the male's gullet.

The crime might have resulted from a scanty supper or a quarrel, or the Company might have bought what fox men call a "killer." At the moment, however, the explanation seemed irrelevant, even trivial. It could not change the fact that the Company was again the possessor of a single fox. The boys wrote Kane of this fresh disaster. His dismay matched theirs, and by this time he must have been as determined as the Fromms, for he wrote at once offering a second female, and for only $150. Any female outcaste was worth more, and when the boys saw the fox they realized how generous the dealer had been. She was finely drawn, and had a sharp red dark coat almost the color of the Kamchatka red fox. She arrived with careful instructions for the introduction. Neither the Company nor Kane could continue to feed the male with expensive mates.

The dealer directed that the two foxes should first be sprinkled with alcohol to make them smell alike, and then kept for several days in a wire cage three feet square, with a dividing netting in the center. This would give each fox living quarters of a foot and a half and a constant awareness of the other. When the boys read the instructions they doubted Kane's wisdom for the first time; if their male were a killer, such imprisonment would only aggravate his disposition. But they carried out the directions faithfully. The male seemed somewhat baffled by the barrier and intrigued by his companion, although the boys had no way of knowing whether he was regarding her as a mate or as a meal. After four days the foxes were moved to their pen and Henry, even at the risk of jeopardizing breeding season, pressed large meals upon them. But the foxes were already friends, and by breeding season they were devoted to each other.

Henry knew the pair had bred, and wrote the whelping date in his notebook. That event passed off successfully, for later Henry heard the pups. The weeks ahead would be a period of anxious waiting, but they had worked too hard and through too many years to risk disaster now. Henry stopped beside the pen only long enough to slip in food and water. The litter meant so much that not a member of the Company was even tempted to investigate. They hardly dared think of the outcome. The results were already decided, and only those most concerned did not know the answer.

Henry had caught not even a glimpse of a pup when the litter was a month old and a three-day May snowstorm covered the ground with two inches of fluffy snow. Then the sun came out. It was a lovely morning. Henry gave breakfast cereal to the outcaste pair, and as usual the mother picked up food to carry to her young. Then, as she went toward the house, she called her family. It was a strange little sound, half sigh, half grunt, because her mouth was full of cereal. But the youngsters heard it, and a red pup came to the opening of the funnel and started down the ramp. Henry stood motionless, his heart beating so hard he could feel it thump. A second red pup followed, then a third, then a fourth, and Henry was beginning to fear there were no more when a fifth pup appeared and came down the ramp.

Its blackness against the snow was unforgettable. After five long years of effort at last they had a silver! The puppy fur glistened in the sunlight. Henry knew that never would he forget that moment of delight. Then he thought of the others, started for the house on a run and burst through the kitchen door to shout the news.

And it was the happiest day the farm had ever known.

Chapter Eight

THE COMPANY HAD WORKED FIVE YEARS FOR THIS PUP, had been planning silver foxes more than ten. Henry was twenty, John two years older, Edward twenty-four, and Walter twenty-six. The little progress they had made was frightening.

The Company considered its position. Silvers could be obtained from outcaste reds, but the process was slow. One breeding season, though successful, did not guarantee another. If the partners tried to build a herd by the addition of a single pup each year, they faced at best a long period of sluggish growth, plus the hazard of an annual chance of failure. They did not even know whether outcaste matings were certain.

Genetics was an unknown word to the Fromms, and only a few ranchers, far more experienced, realized the import of the Mendelian law. Geneticists had but recently established the fact that the silver coat character was recessive to the red, and followed Mendel's rule of the recessive's three-to-one ratio, a proportion based on averages. In a thousand matings it would work out with accuracy, but a single mating, or half-a-dozen, always held the possibility of misses or departures from the average. The Fromm boys had been lucky that in a single outcaste mating the hidden or recessive silver characteristics of the parents had bred true in one pup in the litter, and there good fortune ceased. Undoubtedly others of the offspring were half silver, but this did not show, the silver color being recessive to the red. Thus, even had the boys known they had half bloods in the litter, it would have been difficult to differentiate except by breeding, and that would take another year. The fox's annual reproductive season was an inexorable time obstacle. Another year, with its risk and uncertainty, was out of the question in their minds.

This left one way out — the purchase of breeding stock — and now, actually possessing one silver pup, they felt anything less than bold, aggressive action would be a sellout of their dreams. They determined that before the next mating season they would have, not only a mate for their silver, but a second pair of silvers as well. The farm they had envisioned could not be started with less. They had no idea what breeding stock would cost or how they would get the money, but they took the first step and wrote to James Kane. He had adopted all the Fromm boys after learning Henry was the youngest of a firm of four brothers, and if anyone could help them, he was the man.

An answer had not come from Kane when Frederick Fromm departed for his annual visit to his farm in Iowa. A few days later after his departure Kane's letter arrived and offered three silver foxes for $6,800. The boys had hoped the price would be less, but even so it was moderate, and the company knew these foxes would be the three best Peace River silvers it was possible to buy for the money. Kane wrote as a friend. He was delighted they had at last decided to buy breeding stock, the sure and speedy way to a silver herd, and he knew they would not regret it. He would hold the foxes for their answer.

It was now or never for the Company. There was no money and nothing on which to borrow. The first large ginseng crop, the half acre of seed planted so many years before, would mature in 1915, the following year. The neighboring Nieman cousins would never consider a loan against the crop or an investment in silver foxes. That embraced the only possibilities. Then one of the boys said quite suddenly that their mother was the one who owned the farm. The quarter section had always remained in her name.

The Company went to the kitchen to see Alwina. The boys knew the farm had never carried a mortgage and that their parents' ways had been slow and thrifty. They had never spent more than they made, had always waited until they could afford a purchase, and in the early years they had contrived to produce food, shelter, and the family's clothing. Even the boys' suits had been made of homespun because Alwina's fingers could save the cost of woolen yardage. The boys knew of those years of work, knew too of their mother's boundless faith in her sons, but they had never quite taken the measure of her courage nor her spirit, for now Alwina did not hesitate.

"What good is land unless it gives a family a start in life?" she asked.

The Company had intended to be persuasive.

"Fox farms are making money," Walter began, "and—"

Alwina looked at him reproachfully. "What makes you think I wouldn't mortgage my farm to give my sons a chance?" she asked.

Suddenly the Company was sobered. It had not been prepared for the burden of such faith.

"Look at all the things that can happen to foxes!" John burst out. "Ma doesn't know anything about them. We got no right to let her mortgage the farm. She ought to think about this." He had said more words in a few moments than he usually spoke in a day.

Alwina wiped her hands and hung her apron on a peg. "But you boys would have had your chance," she said.

"Next year we can dig a half acre of ginseng." Walter said. "It isn't as though we were depending only on silver foxes."

Henry was troubled. Youngest of the boys, he had been his mother's baby, closer to her than the others, yet no one desired a silver herd more ardently. He had thought about nothing else for years. Now a path which had opened was closing before him.

"But Ma believes we can raise silver foxes," Edward said. "She knows we've got to buy them when we have the chance."

The Company and Alwina drove to town to see the banker. Mr. Gruett had known the Fromm boys since they were youngsters, had admired their perseverance and capacity for work, and he had watched the ginseng gardens grow from the first small bed. But every instinct of a conservative country banker was aroused by the Company's proposal.

"A mortgage on your mother's farm for sixty-eight

hundred dollars to buy silver foxes!" he said. "And your father doesn't even know about it!"

This was only the beginning of his protest. The mortgage was too large even for a legitimate purpose, was poor banking practice, but more important, he had no right to countenance such an action. A banker held the same community responsibility as a doctor. He was a family adviser.

"This is more than business," he said. "It is a moral question."

The Company argued passionately, but failed to convince him that silver fox farming was an established industry with an assured future. Then it fell back on ginseng, the real guarantor of the loan. Even if Mr. Gruett could not believe in silver foxes he must believe in ginseng.

Here the banker was on familiar ground. He had discussed loans with other growers and he knew how seldom the golden dreams of ginseng were realized; as yet no one had succeeded in harvesting a ten thousand dollar half acre. The Company acknowledged it wouldn't, but was sure the crop would run to five thousand dollars. Mr. Gruett conceded this possibility, but spoke of the costs of growing, which the boys knew well. On the firm footing of a practical discussion of ginseng culture it was finally agreed that even if silver foxes proved a failure, ginseng could in the years ahead pay off the mortgage.

Alwina's signature on the mortgage had a new-found boldness. The banker alone was troubled. He must explain this loan to the directors and he knew inner doubts would nag him, but for better or worse he was involved in the hopes and fears for three silver foxes.

Before the boys left town a check was mailed to James Kane. It was wise, the Company felt, for the purchase to be finished business before their father's return. The money passed through their hands so quickly they had no time to get a sense of grandeur. The three foxes arrived ten days later.

The Company would not have admitted it, but the foxes were a disappointment. The magnitude of the investment had given the boys a vision of glorious creatures, and they'd forgotten that it was summer and foxes eight weeks old would still be in puppy fur. The pups should be more impressive, if only to soften the impact of the news to Frederick Fromm. No one had written him of the mortgage, and he was expected home a few days later. If Alwina dreaded the coming interview — for her action had challenged the ways of a wife of her time and among her people — she did not show it. When Frederick arrived it was she who told him that the three big-headed long-legged timorous creatures had put a mortgage on the farm.

Frederick Fromm said almost nothing. Argument was futile with the catastrophe already an established fact, and perhaps he recognized in Alwina that same unalterable determination that years before had marked her refusal to leave the forests of Wisconsin. But he knew that life was altered. From now on tilled fields must be given to fox pens and ginseng arbors, for one or the other of the ventures would have to repay the loan. The mortgage had forced the conflict to a decision.

As the young silver foxes grew and thrived, the Company felt that they demanded names. Eastern silvers bore proud titles befitting aristocracy — Sir Wilfrid, Sir Cecil Frederick, Lady Evelyn, Queen Anne, King

Charles, Count Otto, Pride, Glorious, and Incomparable. The partners chose "Kaiser" for their own pup because of his arrogance and proud bearing. Names of the others were everydayish, almost homely, which was right for creatures who were practically members of the Company. The male was called Tom after James Kane's son, who had brought him. The more quiet of the two females, a large, light fox, was christened Toynette because this seemed a good name for a gentle animal. The smaller female, a wild and excitable creature, was called Alaska despite her Peace River origin, because of the untamed nature of that land. They considered that a name for Kaiser's mother should honor her achievement, but since she had already brought renown to the term of outcaste, they decided not to change it. And in the years ahead, as she became almost a cornerstone of the ranch, producing each season a large litter with one or two or even three silver pups, she was always known as the Outcaste Mother.

Mating the foxes was decided by color. All four were bright, ranging from one-quarter to one-half silver. These terms were used by fox men to describe, not the purity of the strain, but the amount of silver guard hairs in the coat. The wide variation of the silver fox, from black with a white-tipped tail to an all-over silveriness, demanded definite description. The black might have no silver, or a faint suggestion of silvery hairs on the posterior; the extra-dark silver, a faint scattering of silver hairs on the hind quarters, and the dark more silver; the quarter-silver had silver hairs only on the rump and forehead; the half-silver carried the silver toward the middle of the back. The black was rare and had been prized by the Russian nobility, but some fur men argued that the skin could be imitated, in color at least, by dyed red fox, whereas the silver guard hair defied imitation. Its design, unique with the silver fox, consisted of color bands. Close to the body the guard hair was the color of the underfur, followed by a band of sharp black, then by a narrower one of silver with a long black tip. The silver band should be truly metallic, beginning and ending abruptly, since if it were shaded it gave a brownish cast. The long black tip of the guard hairs formed a veiling for the silver.

The Fromms' four Peace River foxes had more silver than the eastern fox. Toynette and Kaiser, brightest of the four, were half-silvers, and so would have the most silvered and, to the Fromms' notion the prettiest, pups. The Company's idea of mating to develop more silver differed radically from the accepted method. In the opinion of the fur world the small dark or extra-dark fox with a limited area of silver was the most beautiful, the most distinctive, and the most becoming to the wearer, hence this pelt brought the highest prices. Eastern ranchers believed that if two light foxes were mated, not only would the silver be too predominant in the offspring, but the black fur would tend to lose clearness and become rusty. But the Fromm boys liked silvered foxes, and the brightness and the life that silver guard hairs imparted to the pelt, and they bred to bring out silver.

This decision was of tremendous importance, both to the Company and to the silver fox industry. At the time it was incredibly presumptuous; it went against beliefs of older ranchers, rulings of fashion, and financial advantage in the face of a heavy mortgage. Farm boys who had never seen a fox scarf on the shoulders of a woman could scarcely judge what would be becoming, and certainly had no reason to believe they could change a trend in fashion. Since the silver fox had first aroused awe and wonder in the courts of Europe, the dark silver had led in favor, and now youths in a Wisconsin wilderness challenged the whole world's opinion. But this fitted with their dream. Years ago they had vowed to raise the most beautiful silver foxes in all the world, and they believed silver was the key to the real beauty of these glamorous creatures. They stubbornly set out to prove it.

Chapter Nine

IN THE WINTER OF 1914-15, GINSENG AND FOXES TOOK
turns in confronting the Company with new problems.
By early autumn it realized that the days were not long
enough to accomplish what must be done. Home supply
of man power could no longer keep up with the demand
of the two enterprises, and the boys who had once
worked for their neighbors now asked neighbors' sons
and daughters to work for them. Committing themselves even to this small pay roll through the rush season was a big decision, but they had already taken a
bigger risk — the mortgage. Ranch output must be
speeded up to meet the obligation.

Girls could rake leaves, transplant ginseng, drop seeds,
and gather ginseng root. Men could bring leaves and
loam from the forest, work the soil, make trenches,
and dig roots. Work could be done in crews of a man and
a girl; team work occurred naturally to the Company,
since for years the boys had instinctively resorted to it
for effectiveness and speed. Now they were ready to
show others, and their neighbors — rural folk who usual-

ly do not take kindly to instruction — were willing to be shown because large production in ginseng culture was new, the assembly-line idea exhilarating, and the Fromm boys worked even harder than their employees. A man moved the soil; a girl dropped seeds. A man dug a trench and drove two stakes at either end; a girl fastened a guide line to the stakes and transplanted ginseng, using knots tied at seven-inch intervals to mark the position for each plant. A man dug ginseng roots with a handfork; a girl picked up the roots, shook off the soil and tossed them to the pile. Two men washed roots beside the stream with the new sprayer and pressure pump; the Fromm car supplied the power. With every task in ginseng calling for speed, with a new job pressing for attention before each one in hand was finished, no one had time or energy to consider whether he was the hired or the hirer; it made little difference when there was so much to be accomplished. Ginseng work took on the communal excitement of a barn-raising, and a crew's pay roll, which might have been the first dividing sign of a new success, brought about instead a fuller sense of neighborliness.

The harvest, the largest yet, was dried in an upstairs bedroom and strained the room's capacity. Racks were needed, and many of them. Then someone remembered the sections of the arbor roofs which, placed one above another like a multiple-decker bed, would increase the drying area. The movable arbors, John's suggestion of so long before, now paid a second dividend.

But while they were succeeding with ginseng the boys heard disturbing rumors about the silver fox industry. Prices of live silver foxes had declined. At first the boys refused to believe this, but as reports of distressed fur farms increased they realized the Company had waited for years only to buy breeding stock at the peak of the market. For a long time men had been saying the silver fox boom could not last, yet it had continued to soar higher. Now values were deflating. They reached bottom with the collapse of the London market. For centuries London had been the center of the fur industry, setting fashions, fixing prices, and establishing values. Since the most remote outpost was attuned to the news of London auctions, this break rocked all fur land. Fox ranchers, really frightened, frantically sold stock; foxes purchased at fabulous prices were offered for whatever they would bring. Over-capitalized companies, with inventories now fictitious, ceased to be, and promoters fled the wreckage. Stockholders tore up paper calculations of a fortune and knew their dream was over. The bubble had burst, as wise fox men had always known it would.

One of the bigger shocks to the Fromm boys was the letter from James Kane telling them that he was ruined. He had returned from a western buying trip with a carload of foxes to discover a market being unloaded in panic. Kane surveyed his losses with equanimity. He'd had the excitement of sharing in the gaudiest era of any fur in all the world, and now had plenty of company in adversity. But he still believed in silver foxes, and he was sure once the industry was rid of speculation and inflated values, real fox men would build ranched foxes into an important business. But the process of getting on a sound footing would be tough for many fox farms.

It would not be tough for the Fromms. The Company had no stockholders to appease, no promotion schemes to justify. Though their breeding stock had shrunk in value — the three silver foxes were now worth only a third of the purchase price — they did not have to sell. Edward was inclined to regret their earlier conviction that it was now or never; patience for a few more months would have repaid them.

But Henry said, "At least we got our foxes. And we like them. Some day they'll be worth every cent we paid for them."

Actually, Alwina Fromm was the one who should have been the most concerned about the collapse of the market, but she only became more than ever a partisan of silver foxes. The three Kane silvers were still worth a mortgage, in her opinion. Frederick Fromm did not say, "I told you so" — he never spent words unnecessarily — but his manner was that of a man whose judgment had been right all along. Mr. Gruett, the banker, was the most troubled. Every Saturday through late summer and fall he had driven to the Fromm farm to make sure the foxes were still alive, and now the collapse in prices renewed his earliest misgivings. The Fromm boys were saddled with a debt that would absorb ginseng profit. Ginseng was their only hope.

In midwinter the ginseng was finally ready to go to market. Weeks had been spent in the tedious job of stripping fiber and prongs from the root and sorting the products — fine fiber, coarse fiber, prongs, second-grade root, and that of the first quality. Each brought different prices. The kegs of ginseng were packed for shipping when the Company learned that this market, too, had suffered. First-grade roots, for which they had expected seven dollars a pound, were now worth only five. Ginseng, as well as silver foxes, had let them down.

But the boys managed to meet the interest on the mortgage, and even to make a token payment on the principal. After this heroic gesture they deposited the remaining five hundred dollars in the bank. Those dollars would have to be spread thin.

Breeding season followed soon afterward, and in late April it was evident that the excitable Alaska had lost her litter — or never had one; it was difficult to reach conclusions about a fox household which was in a constant state of nervous panic. There was no doubt, however, that the Company faced a 50 per cent loss in the year's production of silver foxes. They had not been prepared for a miss. In other seasons they'd always had large litters even though the pups weren't silvers. Apparently fox ranching never lacked a new grief to spring on owners. Henry read everything he could find on the subject of lost litters. He had followed the rules, had not overfed in breeding season, had kept his foxes quiet and secluded through the critical months until whelping time. The bulletin offered no further suggestions. He was on his own, and he brought in a one-man report to the Company.

"There's only one thing to do," he said. "After we've read the bulletin and got the general idea, we'll have to watch our foxes and find out what each one wants. We've got to get along with the nature of each animal."

Asked if he knew what Alaska wanted, he said she was an unusually shy creature. Most of all she needed a sense of security, which might be possible if her pen were made to resemble a forest, with enough brush so that she would never lack for cover. They couldn't eliminate fencing and meals, but they could make her believe she was living the same existence as her wild forebears. Henry's scheme was a radical departure from instructions in the bulletin, which had especially warned against the dangers of brush-cluttered yards. But any scheme was worth trying. A pair of foxes costing $3,400 would be worthless except as pelts unless they could be persuaded to become parents. John and Henry camouflaged the pen so thoroughly that even they could scarcely see the netting, and the tenants could live a practically concealed existence. After a year in this retreat Alaska's fate would be decided. She would be a mother or a scarf.

Toynette presented no psychic problem. She brought out her litter even earlier than seemed wise to the keepers, but she was a natural mother with no hysterical anxieties, and her five silver puppies seemed to thrive the better for her easy ways. The Outcaste Mother, mated to her son, presented the Company with two silvers, and her year-old daugthers added three more silvers to the herd. The outcastes had become an eminent family.

The Company could scarcely believe its good fortune. Fourteen silvers on the farm — vastly different from the year before, when a single silver pup caused a celebration. And the boys prepared to back their luck. All energy, every dollar, must be expended toward one purpose. Though silver foxes were a long-time gamble and the fox farm could not now pay its way, it fortunately did not have to, since there was a second source of revenue. Ginseng must be expanded to carry the foxes, and capital for this expansion had to be dragged out of the ranch and out of themselves. No economy was too small to be practiced. Even personal wants were curtailed. They patched work clothes until patches overlaid the original garment; they knitted socks on the knitting machine and, because time made the hand-turned heels precious, they patched these with cloth to make the heels last longer. Similar rigorous economies were carried out in ginseng and with foxes. There was no choice but to pay money for wire, sawing, netting, nails, new equipment — even outside labor. Extra help had been necessary for the large spring arbor, a crew was needed for the fall season, and occasionally in summer they hired girls to keep down the rampant weeds. But all this outlay was held to the barest minimum. An almost fanatical zeal drove them, bringing the members of the Company very close together.

At long last the first half acre of ginseng was ready for harvest. The boys remembered the autumn of its planting in 1909 when they had talked of a ten thousand dollar crop within five years. It was now 1915, and in those six years, what with plant blight, root rot, slow maturity, production costs, and unstable prices, the crop at the present market value would not bring four thousand dollars.

This year the fall crew was larger, ten men and ten girls. Twenty extra at the table, beds for those who lived too far to go home, heavy cooking, and piles of dishes — the growing business had invaded the small farmhouse. Alwina could be of little help, for she had begun to fail; often the care of her own family was now beyond her. Edward and Henry, both proficient in the house, had learned how to take over, and since a cook for the crew was a job that could be supplied by home labor, they added this to their other responsibilities.

The larger harvests demanded changed methods. Assembly-line systems must be kept flexible so as to adjust to the problems of greater loads. Also increased production could magnify small mistakes into material losses. Last year's crop had run too heavily to second-grade, and they knew that bruises on the tender roots had permitted rot to find a foothold. This fall they built "digging tables" with canvas beds on which diggers threw the forkloads, and girls sorted the root from the soil. Drying, too, was improved through experience. The drying racks were carried to the attic where, with the windows thrown open, there was space and air. The confusion and work involved in carrying a ton and a half of green root up the steep stairs should have reassured them as to its safety. Only a super thief or a phantom could have managed a raid, but robbery was now an accepted danger, and one of the Company always slept within sight of the treasure.

The half acre yielded $3,564.09. The Company had earned it down to the last nine cents.

The check seemed magnificent, but it was not affluence. A payment of fifteen hundred dollars on the mortgage cut the sum almost in half and the remainder had to be put aside for expansion. A stationary engine must relieve the family car, much too clumsy a power plant for washing the larger harvests, and a galvanized wire netting was needed to lay on ginseng beds as anchorage for dry leaves. Leaf mulching had always been a major grief because of tricky timing; if the mulch were spread too early fall winds carried the dry leaves away; if it were delayed plants were in danger of a sudden frost. In the early years of smaller gardens the Company had been able to cover quickly and to patch after each stiff wind, but this was not possible in plantings of three acres. Sufficient netting to anchor leaves on all the beds was a must, no matter how big the investment. Another constant cost from now on would be labor. Arbors were now too large for home manufacture. A supporting structure must be built around three acres, innumerable lath sections for walls and roofs made and set in place, sideboards staked around four sides of 144 beds, each 143 feet in length. In the coming years they must build even bigger arbors. And each year they must build until they had a sufficient inventory of posts or lath sections. Now an enterprise begun ten years before with a few plants brought from the forest was a lusty youngster, taking much and giving little.

Even forest loam, once a free natural resource, had slipped into the cost column. They had scraped their own forest floor and turned to their neighbors. During that summer Edward had beguiled Mother Roehl into selling an acre of forest loam for fifty dollars and the promise not to destroy any growth of young trees. Obviously that was impossible; some young saplings had been uprooted, and the boys had concealed the evidence under piles of brush in a deep ravine. This had seemed more practical than regrets, but unfortunately Mother Roehl's counselor in farm matters must have possessed X-ray eyes, for he went unerringly to the caches. Edward made the firm's apology and promised to do better, and Mother Roehl reluctantly agreed to give them one more chance. The Company had to have that forest loam. But they knew sapling accidents were bound to happen, and if again they were unsuccessful in eluding the snooper, they might have to go farther away and pay even more to some other owner of forest loam.

Walter was already searching for a solution, a man-made substitute for forest soil which contained humus, was light and porous, and had the necessary qualities of decayed forest vegetation. He had planted peas, plowed them under, and set out an experimental garden. But an experiment in ginseng was a long-time process. A year of vigorous growth proved nothing; a healthy maturity was what counted. Even thriving transplanted ginseng could not immediately prove that seeds might be entrusted to anything but natural loam.

In the spring the fox farm had expansion trouble. Now that the herd consisted of fourteen silvers and eighty cross and red foxes, neither John nor Henry had time to hunt nor to set out snares for rabbits. Fox meals, even of ground horse meat, entailed a big job. Where once a kettle from the kitchen had been large enough to carry fox suppers, now a tub was taken to the pens on a hand cart. Henry cut horse meat from the bone, ran the meat through a grinder and baked corn cakes in the oven of the kitchen range. Cereal and horse meat was the unvaried diet. The foxes liked it and seemed to thrive, and Henry believed he'd solved the feeding problem.

Suddenly there was an outbreak of rickets. There was no danger of deaths, but no one wanted to build a herd with broken-down foxes. Henry consulted a druggist, who suggested limewater. This helped the foxes but not Henry; he had to know why healthy animals suddenly had rickets, especially when he knew that horse meat was good food. Then he realized that foxes which had once been fed whole animals now had no bone whatsoever. Wild foxes never lacked for calcium because they ate what they caught, bones and all. The Company bought a hand-operated bone grinder, installed it in the cellar of the farmhouse, and every day Henry ground horse bones into rations. The din of clashing gears and splintering bone, punctuated by loud explosions in particularly heavy going, was frightful and hard on everyone. The man power required to turn the grinder was appalling, but the legs of the foxes stiffened and they walked as foxes should walk, with pride in their bearing.

Chapter Ten

By the spring of 1916 the silver fox industry had purged itself of the evils of its boom time period. Fox farming had paid heavily for its prodigal years, and now the sobering-up process brought about a spirit of reform. Ranchers who thought only in terms of an easy fortune had departed. The real breeders, anxious to see fox farming become a sound enterprise yielding justifiable profits, knew that never again would foxes like the famous Sir Wilfrid and Lady Evelyn make owners wealthy. Sir Wilfrid was reported to have earned almost a hundred thousand dollars, and Lady Evelyn had repaid the five comparatively poor men who had clubbed together in her purchase not only with a sizeable fortune, but had financed a plant of 100 pens, a dwelling house, a barn, and all the necessities of a ranch. Such returns could no longer be expected from silver foxes, but with good foundation stock costing two or three thousand dollars a pair, with wise breeding and good management, a fox farm could be built into a highly successful business.

The ranch bred fox was no longer an experiment; in the estimation of fox ranchers it had earned its place as the equal if not the superior of the product of the wilds. But the fur trade was still prejudiced against the domesticated silver fox. Ranchers realized this was largely their fault. In the speculation era, when prices of breeding stock were at the peak, only the poorest pelts had been sent to market. Poor quality and misrepresentation had done the industry a great disservice, and fox men must now reestablish the reputation of the ranch bred fox by setting a standard for the quality silver fox and uniting to produce only such animals. And, as always, new beginnings went hand in hand with deep convictions. One of these was the belief that the small dark silver should be the goal of all selective breeding. The black must be clear and glossy, the silver truly metallic, never chalky, too extensive, or too conspicuous. This was the idea of silver fox at its perfection. By breeding for and achieving this quality, fox farmers could supply the fur trade with what it wanted and at the same time prove that more and better foxes could be produced on ranches.

The Fromm boys read in bulletins and in the *Silver Black Fox Magazine*, published in Canada, of the vigorous stand taken by the fox industry. But their ideas continued to be as home-grown and individualistic as the Company's entire enterprise had been. They saw their problem as that of any farmer. A successful crop, whether wheat, oats, or silver foxes, depended on both quantity and quality. Quantity in pelts demanded a herd of strong, sturdy prolific foxes, and they knew that a fox with body length and good cavities was bound to be a better producer than a short, stubby animal. Therefore Fromm foxes must not be small. Quality in fur was a matter of texture, gloss, length, and color. And the Company liked silver, hoped to make its foxes even brighter in the future. Peace River foxes had the qualities that the boys admired — size, bone, and sinew — and the coats were strong in silver. So inevitably these foxes conformed to the Company standard as the beginnings of their herd of prolific and lovely foxes.

The breeding season of 1916 was a success. The female Alaska proved the wisdom of a year's retreat by presenting the Company with a litter of four silvers. After this happy event the screening brush was removed, a little at a time, to accustom her gradually to the normal life of a farm fox. Toynette produced her usual five silver pups, an astonishing record in fertility for so young a mother; she promised to be as hard-working as the Fromms themselves. Henry was sure that in time she would be tame enough to eat from his hand. She evinced a passion for dried raisins, and already she had considered proffered tidbits. The outcastes maintained their standing as a distinguished family by producing even more silvers than the Company had expected. Except for one pup they were all fine animals, quite as fine as the offspring of the purebreds.

The one pup was sickly and spent the greater part of the summer in a corner of the pen, practically immobile, but when he lost his puppy fur and grew the coat he would wear in winter, the Company was astonished to discover than an outcaste mother had thrown an extra-dark silver considered particularly rare and desirable. But even ownership of such an animal did not change the Company's opinion about the color. Knowing the pelt had some value, although it was lusterless from ill health and worn by the fox's lying on the ground, the partners sent it when fur was prime to Funsten Brothers, who bought it for $450.

This amazing check aroused curiosity as to the market value of their silvers. St. Louis was now, since the collapse of the London market, an important fur center, and pelts from the entire country would be offered at the midwinter auction. Silver fox was expected to bring good prices. Matched pairs should sell for at least fifteen hundred dollars and fine singles might command a thousand. The Company decided to try out its silvers, and in order to make the investigation conclusive chose three foxes ranging from one-quarter to one-half silver. They were beautifully furred but small animals, and the body structure did not promise prolificness. Henry consented to the pelting only for this reason, and even then the hardest thing he'd ever done was to kill three fine creatures. But when the fur was finally ready for shipping he was as excited as the others. The Company's first crop of silvers was going to market.

Dark silvers sold well at the January auction. A New York furrier paid $1,650 for a pair of matched dark silvers; a single pelt brought $910. But the Fromm pelts sold for $160 each — the three bringing little more than they had received for the damaged skin of one dark fox. If ever a company had a warning it was embarked on a precarious course, this was it.

The most stubborn individualist might have paused and pondered, but the boys did not even reconsider. They knew the silvered pelts were more beautiful; anyone with a sense of beauty must see what the silver did for black, picking it up, giving it life, making it shimmer. If anything, the price of those three pelts only made the Company's faith in silvered foxes the more

111

fanatical. It was sure that bright silvers must some day become the world's preference, once there was a real opportunity to judge.

The effect of the midwinter auction was quite different in the fur world. Ranchers read the prices in *The Black Fox Magazine,* a new American publication for fox farmers, saw that dark foxes topped the list with quarter- and half-silvers trailing at the bottom, and decided that without a doubt the small dark fox was solidly entrenched. Authorities in fox farming began to urge an even more selective breeding to produce such a fox, and gave scientific methods for the procedure. It had been proved in practice that if a dark silver male of 25 per cent or less of silver were mated with a female of 25 per cent or more of silver, a majority of the offspring would be dark silver; and if the ancestors of the pair had been bred with the aim of producing dark or extra-dark silver there was a strong possibility that the offspring would continue to produce dark silver. By this method ranchers might attain a fixity of type.

Although none of these developments altered the Fromms' opinion, they did realize that it was to be a long battle. Their herd was still so small as hardly to deserve the term, and their foxes were far from as bright as they intended to make them. It would take years to achieve the color they desired, and more years to convince the public that the brighter, more silvered, foxes were beautiful. But it had taken years to grow ginseng in order to get a start in foxes; they were accustomed to a long-time gamble.

Since they had formed the habit of keeping their own counsel, they did not write to fox men in the east or argue the merits of accepted beliefs in breeding. With the whole fox industry arrayed against them, they were on the defensive — but a belligerent defensive — and the boys who had carried ginseng in covered baskets, strung a homemade burglar alarm around their first ginseng beds, lived in a lookout tent through a winter, built the militant Fort Moreland, and who still slept where they might watch both ginseng and foxes, now began an equally secretive existence as fox farmers. They were unapproachable to other fur ranchers, did not show their foxes, did not discuss breeding procedure.

They were not at all sure that their highly selective breeding for brighter foxes would be successful. It was the universal belief that mating lighter foxes must inevitably sacrifice the greatest attraction of the pelt — the sharp contrast between clear black and metallic silver. The Company was pursuing a dangerous course when it assumed this was not true, and the experiment demanded a good eye for clear color, sharp contrast, and the first warning tinge of rust. This required, even more than keen observation, an almost instinctive reaction to scarcely discernible gradations.

Fortunately for the Company, John had this gift; it must have been an aesthetic heritage, a feel for color, and it might perhaps have been fostered by days and weeks spent in watching the changing hues of the forest. Some artists claim that an extreme sensitivity for color is developed in the out-of-doors, where tints, shades, and tones change from one moment to another. Perhaps this was true of John Fromm. More and more he became the partner who made the selections in the matings, who knew how far the Company might safely carry its search for silver. Whatever the explanation of his peculiar ability, it has been of enormous value to the Fromms.

Until this day the clear brightness of Fromm pelts has been in great measure due to John's unerring recognition of color gradations.

Gradually, and without discussion, the members of the Company had slipped into their special jobs. They teamed on every project, but each did one thing better than the others. Walter had taken charge of ginseng. Edward handled business matters, was idea-man and coordinator of all their efforts. Henry had a way with foxes that made for healthy animals which would produce large litters. And John fitted in with Henry in breeding a special type of silver. The Company's welfare was the tyrant that drove them all.

To Henry, the keeper, raising foxes had always seemed natural and easy. In the summer of 1917 the Company had sixty-five silver foxes and, counting the reds and crosses, 150 in the herd. They had never lost an animal through sickness. This was an amazing record when other ranchers reported seasons of whelping deaths, seasons of abortions, high mortality in litters, losses from gastric diseases, and whole ranches cleaned out by distemper. None of these things had happened at the Fromms'. So it was the more incredible when their foxes suddenly began to have what Henry could only describe as "fits," because the seizures resembled those he had observed in dogs and cats. He could find no explanation. Food had not been changed or care lessened, nor was there any apparent reason for hysteria or nervousness in the herd.

Henry was appalled the morning he found three dead foxes, two silvers and a red. Since summer pelts were valueless he buried them, and as he dug the hole he hoped there would be no more; the herd could not stand such losses. Next morning four more foxes were stretched lifeless in their yards, and Henry knew this was an epidemic. He was sure it was not distemper, but his inability to guess the identity of the killer only made it the more terrifying. As he cut the animals open he wished he knew how to perform a real autopsy. He was aghast at how little he knew of fox diseases. No special knowledge was necessary, however, to decide what had killed these foxes. The digestive tracts were lined with worms.

Parasites, the great foe of ranched foxes, had caught up with the Company and the infestation had gone unnoticed until the whole herd was infected. Henry called the others. Vermifuge capsules were needed at once, and a lot of them. They were quickly procured and, as the boys dosed their foxes, they hoped that the promising claims of the makers of the medicine were justified. But the remedy had come too late to halt disaster. Each day they found more dead foxes, and it began to look as though they were losing the fur farm. A thoroughly frightened Company, counting up appalling totals, now learned — the hard way — that fox farmers can never afford a sense of security. So long as they own foxes they are vulnerable.

Finally the parasites were defeated. But by the time the seizures stopped and survivors began again to look healthy, the Company had lost half its foxes. This was a fearful setback, but even so the Company had fared better than it had believed possible. Never again would any member of the firm think fox farming was so easy. The fright of what might have happened lasted through the years.

Chapter Eleven

L̲ATER THEY SPOKE OF THAT SUMMER AS "THE BAD year." They had lost thirty foxes but they had not yet discovered how extensive disasters could be, nor had they felt the full prod of a fast-growing business.

The real strain on the Company began the next year, 1918. The spring's increase in silver foxes was larger than in any previous breeding season. Pups of one year are parents in the next, and early efforts to establish a strain of prolific animals began to show results. More foxes required more pens, and this gave the Company an opportunity to try new ideas. It abandoned the woods, originally believed necessary for a natural environment but where construction costs were heavy, and tried blocks of pens in the open. These had alleyways wide enough for a food cart, and Henry no longer had to carry meals from the outer fence.

The new houses differed from early models, for now the Company dared to disagree with the government bulletin. The first departure was in the outside spouts or tunnels. These were an important feature, for they gave

116

foxes the sense of a burrow, but weather was hard on exposed woodwork.

"The foxes don't care whether those tunnels are outside or in," Henry said. "All they want is a chance to make sure it's safe to go out."

"Why don't we put the passageways inside, then?" John said. "The door would be like an opening to a burrow. I bet the foxes will like it better."

"And if we put two nesting barrels in each house, maybe the mothers will stop dragging pups outdoors," Henry said. "Remember how, when we were hunting wild litters, a mother would carry her young from one hollow log to another?"

It was a new idea for nervous mothers. The barrels were identical, but a distraught female could move her family. Fox mothers' unalterable determination to move litters had for years baffled and enraged fox men. Ranchers referred to these stubborn females as "draggers," and had tried all sorts of deterrents. Some ranchers imprisoned mothers with their litters and thus added frustration to hysteria. Others tried distraction. One kept a flock of chickens and threw one into the yard to engage the attention of a mother absorbed in finding a safe place for her young. Now the Company gave its mothers a choice of nests, and freedom to carry out their whims in two homes wholly their own.

Meanwhile the controversy about dark and silvered foxes became thoroughly defined. Fifteen well-known fox men organized the American Fox Breeders' Association. Charter members were from the East, although ranchers in the Middle- and Northwest, unable to attend because of the breeding season, wrote of their enthusiasm and support of measures to encourage the raising of choice breeds, to improve methods, to disseminate and exchange information, to maintain a registry of thorough-bred animals bred in captivity, and to promote and enhance the ranched silver fox.

Requirements for registration were a pedigree of four generations of black silver ancestors, and a rating of at least eighty-five points out of a possible hundred. Color of coat counted heavily in point total and gave dark-silvers a great advantage. Silver foxes were classified by color as black, extra-dark, dark silver, pale silver, and extra-pale silver. Each class was described. The black must be black all over except for a white-tipped tail. The extra-dark must be black except for a small area of silver on the hips. The dark might have a larger silver area on the hips, which could continue to the lumbar region. The silver must be black on the anterior and middle body, shadowing to silver on the posterior, and the forehead might show silver. The pale silver must be black on the top of the neck and sides of shoulders, but the remainder of the body might have a slight sprinkle of silver. The extra-pale silver might have silver all over the body, except that the neck must be black. Point value was graduated down from black to the extra-pale silver, and in this and in size, Fromm foxes would make a poor showing indeed.

New terms crept into common usage among ranchers — "the eighty-five point fox," "proved breeders," "a system of selection and matings," "the elimination of inferiors and culls," "the quality fox." With foxes of approved quality as a weapon, the Association was fighting a necessary battle against a very real prejudice; the previous fall a prominent New York fur house had bought space in a daily paper to tell the public the difference between wild and ranched foxes, and there had been a poetic note in the advertisement: "One is a highly prized animal, upon whose trail an Alaskan or Siberian trapper has spent many weeks. The other is a 'domesticated wild animal,' fur raised on a farm in Canada. There is as great a difference between them as between the genuine and the synthetic ruby or diamond." Fur ranchers, aroused by this threat, had united for defense, and quickly there grew up the belligerent belief that any breeder who failed to make his goal the production of the "quality fox" up to accepted standards was doing a disservice to all fox ranchers.

The Fromm boys did not join the Association nor apply for registration of their herd. Rather, the standard "quality fox" and the point system stiffened their obstinate attitude. They knew that other fox men, even neighboring fox ranchers, said Fromm foxes were no good, and they made no effort to conceal their resentment of chance visitors. But on one point they enjoyed a quiet triumph. Their record of large litters had become known, and a few ranchers who wanted the infusion of so prolific a strain came to buy foxes. The bargaining never had the friendly give-and-take of the usual rural transaction, and although the Company was in desperate need of capital, few fox men were allowed to visit the pens and none were told breeding secrets. Often the member of the Company who conducted the sale carried a gun so casually as to appear that he was never without one, and usually the purchaser was glad to take his foxes and depart. The Company had the satisfaction of knowing that no matter what other ranchers said about Fromm foxes, they were willing to pay more than a thousand dollars to own a pair.

Need characterized the entire summer. The partners needed loam for the larger gardens. Urgency drove them to risk using green mulch from plowed-under peas and rye in the transplanted beds, but they dared not trust seeds to anything except a natural habitat for fear the tender young shoots could not push through; seed plantings were the very lifeline of ginseng culture.

They needed capital. The brothers had received some help when Herbert also abandoned teaching and came home to join them, but now they needed real capital to purchase supplies for an expanding business.

Even more desperate was the need of land. They were fast reaching the end of the cleared fields in Alwina's quarter section. Other growers had experimented with various methods to restore ginseng soil, but not even an elaborate steaming process had killed spores of blight left from the previous harvest. Nevertheless the Company decided to try rested land, and made a transplanted garden in a plot that had been idle for several seasons and might be safe. For a time the boys thought they'd hit on the solution. The plants came up in spring and looked healthy through the early summer, but one morning Edward, who as night guard was using the arbor for a bed, looked down to see red leaves. This meant rotting roots. Later, red splashes appearing all through the green told them the garden would be gone before another season. A whole year's transplantings had been lost, to prove that using land for ginseng a second time was futile.

The most vital need of all was a drying house. In previous years the root crop had crowded the attic. The root's extreme vulnerability to mildew in the final process of drying added a last-minute hazard to ginseng culture. By experimentation the boys had found the safety point in loading racks; the top racks in a tier of ten could carry a larger load than the lower because hot dry air rose; top racks would dry 150 pounds, middle racks 100, and the three lowest no more than 75. But this capacity was already reached and there must be bigger quarters for the fall's larger harvest. A crop that had taken years to grow could not be endangered in the final two weeks.

A drying house with a central heating plant would be costly. Yet the expenditure was necessary, and immediately; this crop of root would buy so many essential things they could not afford to risk its loss. And then Frederick Fromm surprised his sons with a magnificent apology to ginseng. The threat to a harvest had aroused his farming instincts, and he offered an extended loan of fifteen hundred dollars.

The Company began the new two-storied building the next day. The loft would be used for drying ginseng, the first floor for store equipment and stock feed, and the basement, with the heating unit, had room for fox food grinders. No longer would Henry have to thaw out frozen horse meat in the kitchen, and the peace of a household would not be shattered daily by the noise of the bone machine. The heating unit was a hot-air furnace, and an elaborate system of pipes to carry off moisture was designed by a local plumber for the special needs of ginseng drying. It was installed, and the Company began to dig the ginseng harvest with a considerable sense of satisfaction. Drying troubles were now behind them. The crop outran expectations, and at the current high price of eight dollars a pound this was wonderful. But misgivings began to nag as digging teams heaped roots beside the beds and washing crews worked extra hours to keep abreast. Even three-quarters of the crop would push the capacity of the drying house into the danger zone of mildew. The Company was being threatened by success!

Tiers of racks filled the loft and overflowed to the first floor, and still wagons full of washed root drove to the door. All the rules of safety were abandoned; the roots had to be dried. The boys needed the harvest money desperately, but as they heaped the piles of green root they knew they invited trouble. Mildew, final and greatest threat of all, could bring disaster in from thirty-six to forty-eight hours. Only vigilance and the elaborate system of pipes to carry away the moisture could save them now.

After a day they knew the pipes wouldn't save them. Moisture was everywhere. Roots, racks, and even the walls of the drying house were dripping, so now they depended on vigilance alone. They watched the root, brooded over it, turned it, changed racks from bottom to top, did everything they could to give each part of the harvest its chance at warmth and air. John worked hardest of all. He could not give up and each night, long after the others had gone to snatch some sleep, he remained in the drying house moving roots from one rack to another, changing racks from floor to ceiling, trying to find some way to arrest the swift spread of rot.

Before the first five crucial days were over the Company knew it had lost the battle. The boys learned the habits of mildew in a way they could never forget, learned to recognize the cold and clammy feeling of roots in which mildew was about to start, learned mildew's distinctive smell. Its dank odor struck them as they entered the door; it polluted the air, clung to their clothes and skin, and always it was a dreadful reminder of defeat.

They knew they had lost a large part of the harvest, but they did not realize the full extent of the disaster until in sorting they found that half the roots had black spots of rot. Their first major improvement, a drying house equipped with furnace and an elaborate system of ventilating pipes, had cost the Company ten thousand dollars.

And this was to have been their big year!

Chapter Twelve

Edward took nine pelts, good skins ranging from quarter- to half-silver, to the 1919 winter auction in St. Louis. The Company felt it was time the fur trade became aware of the Fromm strain of foxes. Edward was proud of them in the wareroom of Funsten Brothers, where buyers from all over the country gathered to examine offerings, to choose those they intended to bid on, and to decide the limits of their bids.

St. Louis had become the largest fur selling market of the world. It had occupied a unique position in the early days because of its geographical position at the juncture of the Missouri and Mississippi Rivers, where early trappers and buyers had brought their furs by flatboats and barges. Now it had become the big auction center. Its first winter sale in 1916 had totaled less than a million dollars, and three years later the winter sale yielded almost eight million. New York was close behind with a winter sale of six million dollars. Fur was becoming an important industry in America.

Offerings in ranched silver fox commanded general

interest this year, and the number of pelts was larger than in any previous one. The sale opened with the finest pelts, sold singly. Bids were silent as in all fur auctions, which had established their own particular pattern. Since a bid was always for a stipulated amount, a raise could be indicated by the merest gesture, a lifted eyebrow, an almost imperceptible nod of the head, the slight movement of a pencil. The auctioneer knew the gestures, and was able to take quick advantage of competition. The silence was broken only by the auctioneer repeating the latest bids, or by the voices of his "callers," assistants who stood on either side to scan the outer fringes of the crowd and cry "up" when they caught a signal.

The room held a sense of deep excitement. Bidders cloaked eagerness behind blank faces and guarded gestures. Ranchers sat forward tensely when their pelts were offered; for them the profits of a whole year of fur farming would be decided in a few moments. Lucky ranchers who had produced a silver pelt for which the trade competed, were jubilant. Others who sold for only an average price were merely philosophical.

Edward had no reason to be jubilant or philosophical. As he recorded the prices on his fur sheets, he saw that all the first and finest silver pelts which sold well — one for almost eight hundred dollars, several for seven hundred — were skins from ranchers known for their dark silvers. Then the Fromm pelts were offered in pairs, and finally in a trio. The nine pelts totaled only $1,826, an average of $200. Again the fur trade had passed judgment on bright silver foxes.

Edward took the unhappy news home to the Company. The partners had expected it to be better, despite the opinion of the Fox Breeders' Association. It seemed incredible that the easily apparent beauty of the brighter silver fox was not as evident to the trade as it was to the Company, and some day, it was convinced, this beauty must be acknowledged. But its belief in silvered foxes had been costly. The four or five hundred dollars of difference between silvered and darker fox pelts was no loss to be written off lightly. Fur could not be counted on to underwrite the years of expansion. Ginseng must be made to do so.

In October when time came to dig ginseng root, the Company still was not sure it had solved the problem of safe drying. It had not been able to afford an enlargement of the drying house, and this year the ginseng crop would be larger than ever. The safest plan was to dry half the harvest and burn the rest, but no one even suggested this. Too many years had been spent in growing it. The only other possible method was to dry the root in two shifts. This meant an extension of digging time, which was risky. In early October the root was still green and in November a frost might ruin it, but they had to take the gamble; and when the root was ripe the digging and washing crews were started on half the garden. The drying house became a place of tension. The elaborate system of piping out moisture was ignored. Instead the Company installed electric fans, opened windows, and observed the rules of safety for rack loading. As the work progressed it was discovered that even partially dried root could be doubled up, as the long fibers dried most quickly and kept the roots from packing together. This enabled the workers to speed digging, and before the first threat of frost, the drying house was crammed with roots — clean, sweet roots without the slightest taint of mildew.

Unless the ginseng market betrayed them or the process of stripping and sorting developed griefs they had not yet encountered, the early months of 1920 would bring a real ginseng profit. The boys had a sense of triumph as they looked at the great heap of roots in the drying loft. Sixteen years had passed since they had brought those first 150 plants from the forest. It did not seem so long. They had been so busy.

The year had brought many changes in the Fromm family. In June Edward had married. He was twenty-nine and Alice Fredericks was twenty. This marriage was the first break in the almost monastic four who had been too much occupied for girls or romance. Edward had moments of misgiving when he questioned his right to ask Alice to share the confusion and hard work of a life in which farm and industry so overlapped, or even to face the uncertainties of his own future. But Alice had the easy courage of the very young, and had remembered the Fromm boys since a school festival years before when she had looked up to see four youths standing in the doorway. She had known instantly they must be brothers because their bright blue eyes had the same unusual intensity, and she had asked their names. At that time she was a youngster in pigtails and Edward seemed grown-up. Now it was wonderful that she could help him; his was a home that needed a woman. An invalid mother, meals for a crew of twenty, beds for workers, heavy cooking, piles of dishes, an apple orchard, a dairy herd, milk pails, pans, and separator to be cared for, a daily trip to' the creamery, a flock of chickens, water brought from a well a half mile away — it was a case of everyone doing all he could and of long, long days of heroic work. The Company was gambling time, energy, and all its money against a future which still depended on changing the world's opinion of bright silver foxes. But it was a challenge, and Alice was eager to be in the adventure.

That summer Herbert left the home farm. He had not shared the early dreams of his younger brothers, and now his interests were in music and inventions rather than in fur farming. He wanted more time for them than was possible in a Company confronted with such major problems, and he took his share of ginseng and foxes and began his own venture down the road.

That winter Henry also married. He was twenty-six and Mary Jacobs — or Mamie as everyone called her because this name seemed to fit the warm radiance of an outgiving nature — was eighteen. She was aware of the big job she had undertaken. Like Alice she was a neighbor's daughter and knew farm life, but she had been associated with the enterprise and had watched it become something that was neither a simple farm nor yet an established industry. Also, she had a sense of humor to balance the fervor that drove Henry.

The small farmhouse now held three families. With ginseng crew and fox workers, housekeeping might well have appalled young wives, but Alice and Mamie backed the Company's efforts. It was a life, too, in which first things must come first, and company needs were automatic firsts; but if the girls ever thought their lives were harder than those of other farm wives, they remembered that the goals were higher.

The Company itself made the most revolutionary change of all. The four brothers, who from the beginning had carried on a business within a citadel and had avoided outside entanglements, became part of another ginseng and fur enterprise. This grew out of the marriage of their sister Erna and their cousin Edwin, of the Thiensville branch of the Nieman family. The Fromms liked Edwin, and as he shared their passion for silver foxes, Erna was given ten pairs as her dowry. Edwin's father, John F. Nieman, banker and pea canner, gave the young couple land and money to start a ranch.

"I've no faith in fur farming," he said, "but at least this will teach the boy a lesson."

The new ranch prospered and soon John F. Nieman realized it might be as profitable as pea canning. The eventual outcome of his conversion was a new firm with John Nieman and his two sons as partners with Fromm Brothers. This separate venture, The Fromm Brothers-Nieman Company, was established in Thiensville. Double cousinship, Nieman holdings of land, Erna's marriage, and common interests seemed a natural basis for the undertaking. The Fromms invested foxes and ginseng, of which they had plenty, but no money, of which they had none. The Nieman interests contributed land and cash to build up the herd, buying additional breeding stock from the Company.

The Company at Hamburg continued wholly separate from the Thiensville venture and remained so through the ten years in which the enterprise existed. Nothing could have tempted the Fromms to share Hamburg or the original Company with anyone.

On the home ranch the care and feeding of two hundred pairs of foxes had outgrown home labor, and Henry Czech, a lad from the neighborhood, became a full-time employee. This was a real innovation in Fromm fur farm affairs. For eleven years Henry Fromm had fed the foxes. It had been a long, hard grind, and only one of his strength and endurance could have stood it. He had not only strong muscles but an indomitable will to drive them, and his weight-lifting exploits had become a legend in the township. It was time, however, for a full-time assistant. Czech liked the care of foxes and the two Henrys worked well together, but when Czech became an assistant keeper he had no idea that over the years he would prepare more meals for fur bearers than any other man in the world. Czech was not considering world's records. He was looking for a job he liked, and housekeeping for foxes happened to appeal to him.

Housekeeping meant more than meals. Foxes had a genius for digging, and their ability to move earth was astounding. They not only tunneled underground but excavated antechambers along the tunnel, and while depths of four or six feet satisfied the ordinary fox, more enterprising diggers achieved ten and even fifteen feet. These excavations held a menace. Foxes, even those not intent on escape, emerged to find themselves outside the yards. Animals were lost in cave-ins if the ground were loose. Often a whole day had to be spent in digging out a family and filling in the underground retreat. The rocks which the boys had carried to the woods so long before to earn a ginseng garden became invaluable as filler to discourage further digging. The Company exhausted its own pile and carried rocks from the land of neighbors.

The larger herd had brought the problem of identification of many pups. In the early days Henry and John knew each fox, its parents and grandparents. Now that this was no longer possible each pup must be marked when the young were taken from the mothers. Tattooing the ears with a serial number had become the usual method of fur farms. Tattooing, except for a short moment of terror, was painless, and could not be chewed nor shaken off as could a leg band. The right ear carried the year of birth and a mark to distinguish one pup from others of the litter; the left ear had the pen number, which held the key to the history of forebears. It was an ingenious system, but time was required to catch a pup, tattoo each ear with an electric needle, enter the record in a book, and rub vaseline on the tattooing. This, like so many other tasks, was the result of expansion.

Meals for two hundred pairs of foxes provided almost a full day's job. Food was mixed in large flat boxes with a hoe, much as workmen stir cement, then taken to the pens on a stoneboat drawn by oxen. Horses and wheeled vehicles were costly and required roads. The need for roads was already coming over the horizon — roads to the ginseng gardens, roads to the forest for leaf mulch, roads to the pens, and roads in the aisles between the rows of pens. But like land, machinery, equipment, buildings, and wire netting, roads must wait until products paid the way.

When pelting time came in November no one expected the ten-skin crop to bring much revenue. These pelts had even more silver than those of the previous year, but it would have been an admission of defeat not to prepare them for market. Nor would fur houses ever discover the real beauty of silvered foxes unless buyers had a chance to see them.

The Company's was a small voice from a Wisconsin wilderness, hardly a whisper. It owned two hundred pairs of foxes, while in the United States there were between twelve and fifteen thousand silver foxes on four hundred ranches representing an investment of eight million dollars. The position of the American Fox Breeders' Association had grown stronger. Publicizing the ranched "quality fox" of approved standards had raised the value of breeding pairs, and even the price of pelts. In the fall dark silver pelts had sold for fifteen hundred dollars, and ranchers expected these to bring two thousand in the midwinter sale. Now the Association was working for even higher standards than those of eighty-five point foxes. A second classification, advanced registration, had been opened for superior foxes, and these animals scored ninety-three, ninety-four and occasionally even ninety-six.

Points had become the accepted measurement of quality. Originally the point system had been introduced as an educational device in an effort to set a definite and scientific fur evaluation. Points were allotted to various features — general appearance, clearness of color, texture, length and gloss of the king or black guard hair, makeup of silver guard hair, undercoat, and brush. The texture of the fur must be fine and soft, the king hair impart sheen to the pelt, and the undercoat be dense and strong to hold guard hair away from the body. Also the brush must be of good size and the tip a clear white.

This new classification of superior foxes with advanced registration promised a great improvement in ranched fur. Progressive ranchers looked forward to the time when only high-scoring foxes would be produced. Unfortunately, however, the total score gave no indication of the history of the forebears, and a fox that scored in the high nineties might conceivably be the parent of a litter of scrub pups. Obviously the Association was ignoring the whole matter of selective breeding. Another serious defect in the scoring system was that it gave rise to a new profession. Ranchers engaged a professional scorer for a fee, and since such terms as "long," "thin," "dense," "glossy," or "dull" were somewhat undefined, decisions depended entirely on individual opinion. A professional scorer even with the highest motives might be variable in his judgments. Furthermore, since some ranchers were not willing to pay money to learn that no fox on their farms warranted advanced registry, scores were apt to be misleading.

Another unfortunate result of the scoring system was that in the rehabilitated fox farming industry breeding stock had again become the important product. This was inevitable with a fresh impetus behind fox farming, and fox ranches increasing rapidly. Scoring figures, which carried authority, were easy handles for the speculator or dishonest dealer, and the industry which had so recently entered a period of reform was again threatened by the very elements that had once before brought about its ruin. Fox ranching was becoming a game of numbers and the Association, quite unwittingly, was serving the unscrupulous by emphasizing the value of a score. Association members bought pages in fur periodicals to advertise scores and to assure prospective customers that only with such high-scoring foxes could a herd of quality be built. And since a ninety-five point fox was claimed by the Association to be an animal of distinction, men who had never seen a good fox, alive or dead, felt protected in their purchases.

Scores did, however, entrench the position of the dark and extra-dark fox. At the December 1919 Silver Fox Show in Boston, the first to be held in America, the black and extra-dark captured all the prizes. Points justified the fairness of the awards, for in competition with all other foxes these scored the highest. But the triumph of the dark fox worked one advantage for the Fromms. In the Middle West, fast becoming one of the important fox ranching centers, were many new ranches that needed breeding stock. They wanted dark silvers, the very foxes the Fromms wished to get rid of. The Company had now reached a point where herd replacements by younger foxes must be heavy in order to evolve a special type of silver fox. Each year's crop must be an advance, a step further, with offspring carrying the desired traits. In nine generations the color of a silver herd could be changed, but to do this older foxes, which had served their usefulness in establishing the fixity of the strain, must be weeded out to make way for younger pairs that would breed still larger, brighter, better foxes. The quality of a herd depends upon careful mating for the elimination of the inferior, and this procedure is the very heart of fox farming.

No one in the Company called these decisions genetics, and John and Henry would have been astonished to discover they were working along genetic lines. To them it was merely the job of breeders. Foxes must become larger, sturdier, more prolific. Coats must become brighter without sacrifice of texture or clearness of color. Quality must always be the first consideration, for it was future capital. With these ends in view they examined foxes, decided which ones still held value for the Company's aims, and which might better be sold to other ranchers.

In late January Edward took ten pelts to the auction in St. Louis, but he did not intend to sacrifice them as he had the skins of the previous year. He took the precaution of arranging a signal with the auctioneer should the final bid on any pelt be unsatisfactory, so that the Fromms could buy it back. This protection, called "buybacks," is a common practice in fur auctions.

The silver fox sale was lively, despite the drop in price of other furs. This was the auction that did more to establish the value of ranched silver pelts than any so far held in America. Important fur houses competed for the dark silvers, and while a few of the Fromms' pelts were bid higher than in the previous year, they were still far below the prices of others. Each time the bidding drew to a close and Edward saw their pelts being topped by skins he knew to be inferior, he signaled his own bid. At the end of the sale the Company owed the 5 per cent cost of auctioning $3,510 worth of foxes, and still owned the ten silver pelts. When he returned with the news the Company applauded his decision. Thirty-five hundred dollars would have accomplished a great deal on the farm, but nevertheless it was far better invested in the battle for bright silvers. Perhaps next year the tide would begin to turn.

Other fox men read the news of the St. Louis auction and drew their conclusions. Dr. Samuel F. Wadsworth, a pioneer in the industry and one of the first fox men to call attention of other ranchers to the value of the Mendelian law, wrote in an issue of *Black Fox Magazine:*

"If all blacks [black silvers] were destroyed, and all blacks were never used in breeding, we would soon have nothing but pale silvers, and before long we would be getting rusty silvers. The problem is how to keep from getting too much silver and how to produce silver that has the correct blend with black.

"Undoubtedly as time goes on a strain of pure black foxes will be produced which will not become silvered even with age, and when the silver coloration has been eliminated we shall see a wonderful animal from a strain of black ancestors whose value as breeders will be difficult to estimate.

"For this reason I hope to see all fox breeders' associations recognizing the pure black fox as the firm foundation for fox breeding associations."

Dr. Wadsworth had given much thought to the genetics of fox breeding, and if anything could have discouraged the Fromms' dream of a herd of bright and shimmering silvers, that article should have done so. But even the threat of rusty silvers left them untouched.

And then the Company was suddenly confronted by a new and very different hazard and one, moreover, for which nothing had prepared them. The ginseng harvest brought a check for forty thousand dollars, and this was the most dangerous event in its career.

Chapter Thirteen

THIS CHECK CAME TO A GROUP VERY DIFFERENT FROM the four boys who had planted those first ginseng seeds. The close unit had been broken. Two brothers had married. Edward's first child had just been born. Henry was to become a father. The Company had rivals, family ties, and rights of individuals to a life of ease and relaxation from the urgencies that had driven them.

"Forty thousand dollars after years of counting pennies!" Edward said when he told the news to Alice in the hospital where for the second time he had seen his small daughter. "It's frightening."

"What's frightening about forty thousand dollars?" Alice asked.

He hesitated. He was elated, and yet strangely fearful. "It's the first real chance the Company's had," he said.

Edward, at the center of a project spreading out in all directions, was in a position to recognize how critical was the position. That evening when the brothers talked after supper he was still sobered by a sense of danger. It was the first time they had all been together since the check arrived. In the past they had often talked of what the Company could do with money, but would forty thousand dollars, theirs in the bank, bring a change of opinions when so many paths were open? But the other brothers, too, had been thinking.

"The Company's got to have more land," Walter said. "It's got a chance to get into real ginseng production. It ought to buy the Roehl farm."

The boys had always called this the "old homestead" because it was the original farm of their grandfather, Joachim Nieman and, more important, it adjoined Alwina's quarter section. It was cleared, had good land for ginseng, and was the logical first step in expansion.

The others nodded. To have the old homestead had been their secret wish. John asked how much the farm would cost.

"Whatever it costs, the Company ought to have it," Henry said. "But we've got to buy some breeding stock. The eastern strain could improve the texture of our herd. It's a crime that a Company with two hundred silvers hadn't added some standard blood before this. That's what John and I want to do with part of that money. This Company's got a chance to go somewhere with silver foxes."

"And we have to enlarge the house," Edward said. "We need quarters for a bigger crew and a place to feed them. We need a well, and that will cost a thousand dollars. But land and foxes must come first."

The remainder of the evening was spent with pencils and paper and long columns of figures. The Fromms were as poor as ever, still absorbed in devising ways to accomplish the impossible. In the following weeks it developed that the Roehl farm could be purchased for

$18,500. This was the highest price ever asked for land in their vicinity, and the entire countryside was amused that the Fromm boys had so lost their heads over one successful season as even to consider the purchase. The price did not amuse the Fromm boys. They were staggered, but still determined. The deed was signed a year later. Purchases of farms move slowly since a sale must dispossess both crops and family, but the Company was grateful for delay. This permitted digging the well, building pens, and enlarging the farmhouse on money from the Roehl farm fund. All this required management, and meanwhile the Company sold breeding stock and the boys continued to take a mere subsistence wage from the business.

With $18,500 allocated to the Roehl farm, $21,500 was left for the purchase of breeding stock. The boys intended to select the eastern foxes personally, and the buying trip must be postponed until after the fall ginseng rush, but this was an advantage. The purchasing committee could choose from foxes nine months old and in their winter fur.

Not a dollar was spent on ease and comfort. Even the idea had not occurred to one of them. The enterprise in its first comparative success had become even more rapacious of energy and toil than before. The Company and its needs still came first.

This era of even fiercer effort won a convert. Perhaps it was the enlarged dwelling house which Frederick Fromm had always planned to build, or the well, which ended forever the need of hauling water barrels on a go-devil, or possibly an older and more understanding recognition of the drive of youth, but Frederick ceased to frown on silver foxes. Pens and arbors would never have for him the beauty of tilled fields, of grain harvests, or of pastures dotted with cattle, but he finally admitted that ginseng, and even foxes, might some day bring success.

His capitulation did not go so far as an active role in the business, but he proved helpful. If he were at home and not too busy, the boys knew they would not have to take time to guard pens from the curiosity of visiting fox men. Their father had a gracious and quite effective method of shielding company secrets. He had always enjoyed guests, was famous as a wine maker, proud of his cask-filled cellar, and disappointed that his sons cared so little for his wine. But visitors were easily beguiled into an inspection of his stock and a comparative study of the merits of different vintages. Sometimes they departed with no very clear impression of whether they had or had not seen foxes.

The controversy between dark and silvered foxes had come nearer home, for in May the National Fox Breeders' Association had been organized in Muskegon, Michigan. It also had a herdbook, registration of foxes with three generations of silver ancestors, and an advanced registry for superior silver foxes. Its scoring system differed little from that of the American Breeders' Association. Extra-dark silvers were given nine to sixteen points, silvers six to three, and pale silvers three to one. Its first fox show would be held in Muskegon in December. The Fromms had not tried to register their foxes or to join the association. They never had had a joining instinct, and in the face of such general condemnation of silvered foxes the Company made a virtue of remaining aloof from all breeders' associations. Either the Company or the associations were mistaken about the desirable color of a silver fox, and the brothers were sure it was not the Company.

In November came a lull in ranch affairs and Walter, John, and Henry departed for Prince Edward Island. Walter carried fifteen thousand dollars in a money belt, and credit for seven thousand more. The trip was to obtain information as well as foxes, and the three stopped first at Muskegon to visit ranches of National Association breeders. Here for the first time they saw foxes housed on wire netting, an attempt to control the lungworm, which was becoming a menace. None of the boys liked the idea of wire flooring; they thought the animals were being raised more like rabbits than foxes, and had weak legs from lack of exercise. That this experiment was valuable pioneering work in the health of foxes did not occur to them. A defensive isolation in behalf of their crusade for silvered foxes had affected their opinion toward all group findings, and they would continue to learn the hazards of fox raising the hard way, by experience.

They next visited ranchers of the American Association on the eastern seaboard. Here they were entertained by Dr. Samuel F. Wadsworth, but no discussion of the relative merits of black and silvered foxes marred the luncheon. Dr. Wadsworth arranged for them to meet the secretary of the Association and to make a tour of the better-known fox ranches. The Fromms' admiration for the famous fox, Sheffield, a prize-winner and a fine black male, was sincere. His color might in their opinion be unfortunate, but the gloss, sheen, and softness of his fur were revelations. The boys bought six of his descendants, a daughter and five granddaughters. The

141

following day at a nearby ranch they found six more females, not too dark in color, and of the texture they desired.

It was time now to depart on their real mission to Prince Edward Island. Already they had discovered travel to be expensive. They had restricted train journeys to daytime, that they might see the country. They stopped off each night at hotels near the railroad stations, watched the rates with an eagle eye, and ate suppers of fruit and cookies in their room. They could contemplate the purchase of a silver fox for a thousand dollars but still be disturbed, and often incensed, by the high cost of a night's lodging. Personal comfort had no rights over foxes.

They expected to find finer foxes on the famous ranches of Prince Edward Island; perhaps they might even regret not having saved all their funds for the purchase of Canadian stock. But at ranch after ranch they decided against purchases because the foxes were not only dark but small. John and Henry thought the animals were sickly, had no spirit, and showed far too little silver. They had not realized that English markets preferred even darker silvers than did the American fur houses, and had they needed to be further convinced that they could never admire the small dark silver, the visit to Prince Edward Island would have done it. At the end of two weeks' searching they selected their stock. All were light, ranging from one-half to two-thirds silver, and all were large. They had traveled across the country to buy foxes very much like their own. But they had what they went for, stock from a well-established and long line of domesticated breeders, foxes that for years had been bred for softness of texture and gloss of coat.

On Prince Edward Island, still the most important center of the silver fox industry, ranches carried the names of pioneers, and illustrious foxes were still alive. The boys saw Sir Wilfrid, whom some fox men consider the finest fox ever bred, and Walter took his picture.

Henry took their foxes home and John and Walter went to Boston for the fox show. They were delighted to find that Sheffield had again captured the first prize, and they noticed that females from the Sheffield ranch were larger than the others. This promised well for the six females they had bought.

Neither John nor Walter wanted to leave Boston without going to Walden. Thoreau had been a hero to them in school days, and they were delighted and astonished to find that seventy years had left the neighborhood so unchanged. They sat at the edge of the pond, each carried a stone to the heap at the site of Thoreau's cabin, and they visited the graves of Thoreau, Emerson, and Hawthorne. It was very much the sort of literary pilgrimage many American youths have made but they did it more intensively, spending five days in a detailed exploration of the literary shrines. Then they visited Sleepy Hollow cemetery as well as John Burroughs' home on the Hudson and saw "Slabside," his summer retreat. They arrived in New York City at midnight and left before dawn. The Atlantic seaboard held no further interest for them.

At Christmas Edward and Alice spent a belated honeymoon with his brother Arthur in Florida. Arthur, too, had abandoned teaching, and although his rebellion against the white-collar life had not been as stormy as that of his brothers, it was fully as definite. Moreover he had carried the academic career far enough to establish complete proof that it held no appeal for him. After graduation from the University of Wisconsin he taught high school botany for five years, when he decided to use his training in practical horticulture. His escape had not been through ginseng and silver foxes, but through fruit trees on his father's farm in Iowa. Frederick approved of orchards, though not when they meant what he considered the waste of a university degree. But Arthur's wife, Della Plumb, whom he had met when they taught in the same high school, approved of her husband's decision to change his profession, and the two moved to Florida where he could study growing things the year round. For some years Arthur had been the manager of a citrus orchard.

Now by that strange fate which sooner or later involved all Fromms in ginseng and silver foxes, he agreed to become superintendent for his brothers in the new Thiensville unit. The mysteries of ginseng might be even more fascinating than those of oranges.

A short time later Arthur took his wife Della and their young son John to Thiensville, but they did not give up Florida completely. They kept their home there and spent their winters in the south. Unlike the others, Arthur had not been captured by that early dream and could elude its full compulsion now, but the problems of this unusual kind of farming fascinated him. Naturally a student, he examined each job to determine if there were a better method, and although he did not like foxes as he liked ginseng, he evolved a new type of fox house which later was used by practically every rancher in the country and is still known as the Fromm fox house.

The model, worked out after months of study, achieved an economy in material and labor, provided greater safety and comfort for tenants, and eased the life of keepers. A shed roof, hinged so that it could be easily opened for inspection and cleaning, was substituted for the traditional cumbersome peaked affair. But the revolutionary feature of Arthur's model was provision for two entirely separate homes for each fox family. The old type, with two nesting barrels inside one building and floor space for foxes to loll when they should have been outdoors, entailed a serious cleaning problem. In each of Arthur's houses there was room for only nesting barrel and tunnel. The tunnel, leading from the door to the entrance hole in one end of the barrel, had an elbow to shut off light in the nest. The barrel, set on its side in insulating hay, had an opening in the top, the section sawed out serving as a cover, and firmly fastened to prevent foxes from escaping into the hay. This opening permitted keepers to make inspections, keep abreast of fox family affairs, and give the nest a thorough cleaning. The twin houses were connected by a platform which allowed tenants a comfortable nap in the sun and also served as a lookout post, for foxes take a lively interest in neighborhood affairs. Dual houses, each with an identical tunnel and nesting barrel, gave nervous mothers a choice of homes. Litters could be moved, and often were, but no fox matron would be so addlepated as to bury pups in snow and mud if there were a comfortable and vacant home close by. Minor improvements have since been made in these houses; each time a fox discovers a new way to injure itself or its valuable coat, someone has to think up an answer.

Fox farming is a continual struggle between keepers

seeking to make life safe for foxes and fur, and foxes finding fresh ways to make it otherwise for themselves or their companions. Because foxes are wild animals and can never be domesticated as are horses, cows, or other varieties of farm stock, fox farmers must be continually on the alert. Methods that seem sound may at any moment create a hazard. This happened after the first breeding season in the Thiensville unit. In Hamburg a single wall of netting separating adjacent pens had been successful and was an economy in fencing. New pens at Thiensville were built the same way, but the foxes shipped there either developed new personalities in transit or were affected by climatic changes. Of the ninety-two pups born in the spring, sixteen were killed and a large proportion maimed by mothers trying to kidnap a neighbor's young, or mistaking strange pups for their own. A mother would seize a pup on the other side of the netting and try to drag it through. A fox nursery was filled with casualties — pups with broken legs, tails and feet missing, ears and even noses bitten off. The fencing economy was one of the most expensive the company had ever tried.

At Hamburg, too, fox nature was causing trouble. With an increased herd of eight hundred pairs, neglected details were costly. Coat damage was important. Pens had been made safe for fur with lumber planed carefully to avoid rough edges. Tunnels were smooth passages and doorways were sandpapered so that they could not collect valuable hairs from tenants. But foxes still persisted in digging holes, which wore off fur, and in engaging in fights, which tore pelts. Penned foxes became bored, and developed nervous habits. Persistent scratching of an ear, face, or neck made bare spots, and this damage could not be repaired. By August a fox has made its winter coat; in fall and early winter guard hairs grow longer and more lustrous and undercoats thicker, but nature does no patching. Now that the herd was large enough to yield a good crop of pelters, and since these pelters had no other purpose than to grow finer coats, a new way of life was needed for them.

Edward had an idea, and like so many of Edward's it was a good one. Ranched foxes need not be kept in pens when breeding duties are finished. In the wilds a fox took excellent care of the very fine coat he grew, and an open range providing an approximation of a natural existence would give a fox space, a degree of freedom to attend to fox affairs, and relief from the boredom of pen life. To fence in such an area would be costly, but the experiment held tremendous promise. It was also farsighted thinking, as a range would provide the most practical method for handling the enormous crops of fur the company intended to produce in future years. Pelters could be separated from the breeders, and the work of grading, selecting, and sorting could be finished before the ginseng rush. Two or three months of active life in the forest would not only eliminate damages due to pen life, but would add size and value to the pelt. By September a young fox is almost full-grown. From then until late November, when the fur is prime and fully developed, the fox adds weight, some size, and the vigor of maturity. A forest also provides shade for the sensitive color of silver foxes; too much exposure to sunlight will impart a brownish cast to fur.

The Company adopted the idea with enthusiasm. Reproduction of a natural environment had been its only guide in the beginning with both ginseng and silver foxes, and this was a return to early ways of thinking. Almost at once the partners began to discuss the forms of shelter.

"We can't afford to build a house for every fox!" Walter said. "And if we did, how could we make sure the foxes would let each other live in them? They'd be fighting all over the range."

"How about big sheds?" Edward suggested. "They wouldn't cost much, and foxes like to pile up in heaps."

"We could build them in different parts of the range," Walter said, "but what'll we do when all the foxes try to sleep in one shed?"

Henry laughed. "I never thought I'd hear a Fromm boy talk of building sheds for foxes in the woods," he said. "Ever hear of a wild fox that had a house or a shed?"

Edward and Walter looked at each other, shocked to realize how altered their viewpoint had become. Edward's inspired return to boyhood thinking had not quite carried through, and John did not spare him.

"Remember how we used to laugh at those old ginseng growers because they put peaked roofs on arbors?" he asked. "And that wasn't so long ago."

The first furring range embraced forty-five acres of forest and was finished for fall pelters. It was costly in material and labor. Fencing was heavy and high with an overhang, and was extended at an angle eighteen inches into the ground. The Company intended to outsmart the foxes, and then discovered it had overestimated the craftiness of the animal. In later ranges a three-foot carpet of netting laid on the ground proved a sufficient precaution against escape. For some reason known only to foxes, they dig but never tunnel near a range line.

Perhaps they are too busy doing other things; but when the first fox discovers that by starting his digging operations three feet inside the outer barrier he can tunnel to freedom, the lives of rangers will be considerably more harried.

Enclosure of the area was only half the job; the range itself had still to be made safe for fox fur. A furring range is really a compromise. It must combine the advantages of domestication and wild life and at the same time avoid the hazards of both. The wilderness, too, flaws fox coats — one of the arguments in favor of ranched fur. A safe range has to be almost parklike, can contain no berry bushes, hazel brush, logs in which foxes may establish burrows, or even brush piles. All these tear precious fur. Even slanting trees are a menace. A fox loves to climb, and can be injured in a high jump to the ground. All tempting trees have to be equipped with board barriers.

Communal feed pans also presented a problem. These have to be high enough to prevent a fox from soiling the food of others, and they have to be secure. Foxes delight in picking up any loose object and running off to hide it. Large feed pans were set on stakes and firmly fastened. And there were many of them, for range feeding could not be limited. A hungry fox starts trouble, and once a ranged fox has been killed and eaten, foxes are apt to be missing each morning thereafter. No amount of feeding has completely eliminated cannibalism, and it has been accepted as a small but constant drain. It can be kept in check, however, because meals of good ground horse meat require less effort, and foxes are smart enough to know this.

Catching corrals were needed, as it was obvious foxes

could not be chased over the entire range. Wire division fences were so constructed throughout the woods that they could be rolled up on the fence posts during the months of free range and hooked down on the posts when catching crews began work. The Company discovered that a furring range should be oblong, with diagonal driving fences cutting off the driven area and making the triangle smaller as foxes and crew moved toward the catching corral. This should be always in the thickest timber, since it is natural for foxes to run toward cover.

All the problems of a furring range could not be anticipated. Solutions growing out of complications were of great value later when hundred-acre ranges held thousands of foxes. Patrol trails — trees at intervals of seventy-five feet marked by letter and number — must be laid out so that a ranger could report trouble, or a hazard that might lead to trouble. Because foxes killed trees by digging at and exposing roots, more trees died in the furring range than in a forest. Dead trees supplied the farm with fuel, but brush disposal was a problem. If burned, the fire might kill other trees; if piled, no matter how carefully, foxes always managed to contrive a burrow which wore off fur. It could not even be thrown over the high fencing. The only method was to carry it off the range, and entrance gates were far away. Brush became a heavy item in range cost.

Everyone knew there must be an answer — probably a simple one — but no one found it until six years later. One evening Henry limbed a downed tree. It was late. Carrying brush to the entrance gate would take him until dark, and yet he couldn't leave it. He had an axe, and the logical way to destroy brush was by chopping.

This was only a few minutes' work. Then he scattered the pieces over the forest floor in such a manner that the most ambitious fox couldn't contrive a burrow. The forest would absorb the debris, and once again nature had been made to serve the company. Henry's method for brush disposal has been used ever since.

Chapter Fourteen

IN THE FALL OF 1921 THE FIRST FOX PELTERS WERE turned into the furring range and the first bed of transplanted ginseng was made on the Roehl farm. Both fur range and the ginseng garden were important symbols; they were the beginning of the big expansion era.

The Fromms had now outdistanced other growers. With new land permitting even greater acreage their problems would be different from those of smaller gardens, and problems of magnitude. Experiences of other ginseng farmers could not help them. The Company must find its own ways to overcome the limitations that had kept ginseng culture a small business.

Spraying must be done differently and Walter, after considerable work, finally evolved a sprayer to meet their own peculiar problem. It was horse-drawn, and a hose unrolled from its reel as a man carried it down the aisles of the 143-foot beds. Another man rolled it up as the sprayer returned, treating the opposite bed on his return trip. To make this convenient manipulation possible, some means had to be found of maintaining a constant pressure despite the rolling and unrolling of the hose, and this required a flexible revolving union on the pressure pump. No such piece of hardware was on the market, but Walter improvised such a union from sprayer nozzle heads. He was proud of the invention. The gadget was proof that special tools and equipment could carry ginseng culture from a restricted to a large-scale business — how large depended on the Company's ingenuity.

The boys had conquered one big limitation, forest loam, by substituting pre-planted rye for forest vegetation, even in seedbeds. When they discoverd that rye was not ideal because it left disease spores in the soil, they changed to oats.

Walter believed he and Arthur had beaten another limitation, the necessity of a fall covering of dry leaves. Every year for eighteen years autumn had meant anxiety to the Company lest nature would not arrange her affairs for their welfare. The acid from dry forest leaves had been considered essential, since no wild plant ever had any other winter covering, but Arthur had analyzed both leaves and straw and was inclined to doubt it. He and Walter decided to try the innovation of straw to protect the plants from frost, and a year later he was able to report that instead of weeks of worry, with large crews combing the forest for the last odd leaf, a bale of straw would serve each bed. Like so many answers, it was ridiculously simple.

Thus four problems — land, loam, spraying, and finally, dry leaves — were solved. Walter was even confident that he had eliminated another trouble, weeds that sprang from seeds carried from the forest; but he had merely exchanged one source of trouble for another and a bigger one. Field weeds grew even more luxuriantly than those from the forest, and chickweed, which abounded in baled straw, grew most luxuriantly of all.

The silver fox pelters released on the first furring range did not hold the immediate and rich prospects of ginseng culture. Postwar depression had brought a slump in all fur prices, and the ten silver pelts bought back for $3,510 at the 1920 St. Louis auction were sold later for $1,900. The market forecast held no promise of improvement, but the Company still planned to send their few pelters to market. The trade must be kept aware of silvered foxes, especially now that Fromm pelts were becoming known in the East. In November, 1921, the *Black Fox Magazine* acknowledged existence of the Fromm fur farm: "Fromm stock is equal to any other strain in regard to length and density of hair, and hardier and more prolific. The original stock came from the wilds of Wisconsin, Peace River, Yukon territory, and the interior of Alaska. It has been recently crossed with standard. The Fromms are pioneers and have been at it ten or twelve years. Their animals are hard to beat for prolificness. And their stock is found on every fur farm in Wisconsin."

The belief that Wisconsin native stock was part of the original strain of the Fromm herd persists to this day, and the hardiness of Fromm foxes was attributed to this factor. Henry Fromm says this is absolutely untrue, that native stock was never mixed with their silvers, that their special type of extremely hardy and prolific foxes was achieved by persistent breeding for these very qualities. The original strain was from the large and sturdy Peace River foxes, and the eastern standard Prince Edward Island strain was introduced in 1920 to improve texture.

The *Black Fox Magazine* item was received by the Company with mixed emotions. It was gratifying to be mentioned at a time when the two periodicals for fur farmers, this and the *American Fox and Fur Farmer*, both published in the East, usually carried only news of Association members, of fox shows, of awards and points scored by foxes that conformed to accepted standards. But the Company did not miss the challenge in the comment. No reference had been made to color or to pedigree. The Company was sensitive on both matters. When it had tried to register breeding stock sold to other ranchers the request had been refused, not because the foxes lacked the requisite four known generations, but wholly on the grounds that the Fromms "did not have pedigreed foxes." Size and color had ruled them out of the true blue blood aristocracy.

Unqualified approval of the black and dark silver as the only quality fox was now general. Arguments in its behalf were vehement and backers found any amount of evidence. Small dark silvers commanded the highest prices, even winning over the black fox, once considered so rare and glamorous. A dark silver raised on the ranch of the Central New York Fur Company had topped the C. M. Lampson and Company's great winter sale in London; at an auction where 2,375 silver pelts from all over the world were gathered, this skin had brought $662. High scores in the advanced registration and awards of the Boston Fox Show also proved the dark silver's superiority. Even after the point ratings of the American Fox Breeders' Association had been changed because some ranchers had complained that lighter foxes did not have a fair chance in the competition, "the black fox won hands down," as Robert T. Moore, owner of the Borestone Mountain ranch, said in an article in the *Black Fox Magazine*. Mr. Moore had an enviable record as a breeder and a deep conviction on the desirability of dark foxes. A college graduate and a member of Phi Beta Kappa, he had returned from two years' postgraduate work in the University of Munich to be editor of the Ornithological Magazine for the Academy of Natural Sciences of Philadelphia. Becoming interested in silver foxes, he had raised a strain that was beautiful and famous. He had worked zealously to improve the quality of ranched foxes through the use of fine blooded stock.

But the Fromms continued to prefer silvered foxes, and the breeding season of '22 increased their herd to two thousand animals. The paper dreams of early fox ranching were beginning to come true, but rosy calculations of natural increase never take account of what that increase will entail. Where ten new pens had once been an extended venture, now the Company must build pens by the hundreds. Other needs had become insistent — more roads, adequate equipment for the preparation of fox meals, proper refrigeration, and an outer barrier of paddock fencing, which was considered a basic requirement on fur farms in the East. The Company still used the old log stable built by Frederick Fromm in early farm days. Its permanent crew was a mere skeleton of what the farm really required. It had taken on a few workers — and these men had to be able to do anything; ginseng, foxes, building, or general farmwork — and in rush seasons others from the neighborhood joined the organization.

Farm work became a vital part of the company's operations. With ginseng and foxes it was actually necessary to run a large farm, and fields released from ginseng could be turned over to other crops that would serve the enterprise: straw for mulching, milk for crew and foxes, vegetables and meat for the table, hay and oats and corn for stock. All these were merely ordinary operating necessities, and every year there must be permanent improvement. A bunkhouse for the men was built this summer as Emma Thiel's crew of girl weeders had filled the farmhouse. The carpenter, Bill Cole, finished the bunkhouse in time for the big fall crew, and extra rooms and the attic dormitory in the farmhouse could be turned over to the women. But these were only stopgaps. Major improvements such as outer fencing, refrigerator plant, and barn must wait on future ginseng harvests.

Toynette was sold this summer. Breeding stock was bringing good prices, and she was still an excellent fox. But Toynette was eight years old, her litters had become smaller, and she had outlived her usefulness in selective breeding as the Fromm herd became better than its forebears. If ever a fox was entitled to free horse meat for the remainder of her life, it was Toynette; she was a cornerstone of the herd, she had been tame in the years when foxes were even wilder than now, and she was always a dependable and wise mother. Henry hated to see her go, but he made the sale, and had no one to blame for the decision; it was a summer when money was tremendously important. As he put her in a crate he wondered if men who did such things could ever expect to prosper, but he did not weaken. They had denied themselves for so many years that sentiment now would have seemed a folly. He found some comfort in remembering that other ranchers had been forced to make similar decisions. On his trip to Prince Edward Island when he had paid homage to the great fox Sir Wilfrid, a keeper had said that Sir Wilfrid was to be pelted; he was twelve years old and had failed as a sire. The fox that had earned more than most men earn in a lifetime was destined to be a scarf.

In January of 1923 Edward took the Company's first real shipment of pelts to New York. Since the failure of the great St. Louis firm of Funsten Brothers, which had been caught in the depression with large holdings of furs, commitments to fur shippers, and a sudden slump in price, New York had become the acknowledged capital of the trade. Manufacturers, fur dyers, and fur dressers were concentrated in the city and now it had captured the auction field. Its warehouses were filled with raw fur shipped from every part of the world.

The midwinter sale promised excitement. Ninety per cent of the silver pelts were ranch raised, and while the prejudice of the trade had not entirely abated, it was evident at the pre-showing that the buyers liked silvers. At the auction Edward found the bidding the most spirited he had ever known. Prices were 20 per cent above those of the previous fall, but again Fromm foxes failed to win. They were topped by a heartbreaking margin and derisive buyers advised Edward "to take home those western wolves." After the sale the auctioneer, J. Gordon Noakes, a man of long experience in the fur trade, invited Edward to luncheon. Mr. Noakes liked Edward, liked what he knew of the brothers, and liked the quality of their foxes, even though he couldn't admire the color. He wanted to help. If the Fromm boys had not been so obstinate about silvered foxes they might have made a good profit in a market where ranched silvers were selling well.

"Why don't you go home and kill those damned foxes?" he said. "You ought to know by this time that the public will never have any truck with those all-over silvers. All you boys are doing is losing money. What's the sense in being stubborn?"

The advice was based on sound logic. Comparative auction prices are signposts for fur ranchers, and eastern fox men were culling animals that showed a tendency to too much silver.

But the Fromms went on breeding foxes still more silvered.

Fortunately the Chinese agreed with the Fromms on ginseng — even a Fromm did not attempt to change the preferences and tastes of an ancient people. Ginseng had permitted the purchase of the first silvers, and now it must support two thousand foxes and supply capital for improvements. For several years after the first $40,000 harvest, ginseng at from seven to ten dollars a pound brought from $45,000 to $115,000 annually. In '23 and '24 when the Company was digging four- and five-acre gardens, the production from each acre was higher than in any year in the entire history of the enterprise. Never before or since has it achieved such a record. Each acre produced two thousand pounds of first-grade root and there were in addition the by-products of prongs and fiber. All this money went into expansion.

As on any farm, the barn came first; the small log stable could no longer shelter horses, oxen, mules, milch cows, hay, and feed. The new barn that was built in 1923 was not a barn for that year or the next, but for the years ahead, and it was a big investment. It was also material evidence of the accomplishments of ginseng and silver foxes, and a final proof to Frederick Fromm. He had always planned to replace the old stable, and had guarded building timber from the covetous reach of the young ginseng growers. Now ginseng had built the barn.

But being a root of wild and wayward nature, ginseng complicated the summer with a major disaster. For no reason that could be discovered, the entire harvest of seed rotted. The method of stratifying was the same as always, and for years it had been successful. Changes in the procedure could be only fumbling in the dark, but the obvious way to avoid underground rotting was to place the stratifying boxes above ground. Air currents would supply ventilation, and they did, but too much. Air currents froze the granite sand and dried out seeds, and a second harvest was ruined. Hamburg borrowed seeds from Thiensville and the next year tried stratification of seeds in barrels placed in the basement of the drying house. This was so warm the seeds fermented. Seed loss was becoming serious, for if the Thiensville unit should suddenly lose its seed, ginseng culture would be ended.

The following year Walter tried barrel storage in a cooler room, and once again the seeds rotted. The situation was now acute. They had lost four heavy crops, but at least the last experiment had proved that the unsoundness of the barrel scheme lay in the receptacles themselves.

"I'm going back to stratifying boxes," Walter said.

"We lost two crops in boxes," Edward answered, "and the Company can't stand another year's loss."

"I know it can't," said Walter. He was the most worried of them all. "But when we first started to grow ginseng we used forest loam. I'm going to mix that with granite sand."

Arthur thought of other refinements. The loam must be the fine black variety found only in isolated pockets, and below the surface covering of the forest. It required weeks of searching and scraping — an inch here, three inches there—but at last they had enough. They screened it through fine mesh and combined it with granite sand, one part of loam to two of sand.

They didn't know whether it would work, but were counting on a duplication of the most ideal forest conditions. The screened bottom of the stratifying box would permit some ventilation and the mixture of sand and loam would give more. Three inches of the mixture separated each half-inch layer of seed.

"I'm trying still another scheme," Arthur said. "I'll put the boxes half way above the surface and we'll board the sides to allow some ventilation, but no heavy air currents."

"Do you think it will work?" Edward asked.

"It's *got* to work," Arthur said. "But I'm only guessing."

It was a desperate compromise of all previous methods and it worked. The seeds went through the winter in safety.

"We stumbled on the answer," Walter said.

"I wouldn't call that stumbling." Edward laughed.

After four years of disastrous losses, the Company had finally saved a seed crop, but by that time ginseng had developed other troubles.

Chapter Fifteen

THE COMPANY HAD NOT EVEN BEGUN TO APPROACH THE elaborate equipment of long-established and highly capitalized fur farms in the East. Only gradually did it build roads, enlarge crews, set up great blocks of fox pens, add furring ranges, and begin to enclose the farm itself. Finally it achieved a refrigerator plant and a feed-room, which like the barn, was designed to meet not only present needs but those of the years ahead.

In the early days meat for a few foxes could be kept through the summer with natural ice; many fur farms used this method. As the herd increased, Henry Fromm and his assistant, Czech, had prepared each winter enough horse meat for the year, ground it, then had frozen it quickly in outside subzero temperature, and placed it in the storage space of the icehouse. The hollow square, walled with ice, had been adequate. But stored meat for a big herd of foxes made heavy demands on the ice-caked enclosure, and meat spoiled. Each summer as Henry crawled through the ice tunnel to get tubs of meat he vowed that in another year this primitive arrangement must be changed. A warehouse with a refrigerating plant was one of the things the Company could not get along without. But always another need had proved more imperative.

When at last a wing of what was to become a large warehouse was begun, Henry and Czech knew exactly what the refrigeration and feedrooms required. An overhead track carried quarters of meat to the refrigerators for storing and from there to the big grinder in the feedroom. Dollies and hooks made child's play of handling two-hundred-pound tubs of ground meat. A fox chef had only to look at the day's orders, as definite as those of a hospital diet kitchen. So many breeders demanded so many pounds of meat, cereal, water, and cod liver oil, and because fox fathers shared the family pens, they received the same hearty meals as nursing mothers. Pairs that had not produced did not fare so well and drew "blank meals," a term used for feeding a fox and not a nursing family. The food mixer, a double-sized bakery model, tilted to fill the food tubs, and cereal and water were piped to it from the floor above. Every corner of the feedroom could be hosed and even steam-cleaned. In a nearby room feeding pans were sterilized, and two sets of pans made cleaning a task that could be cared for at the crew's convenience. Fox meals, once a full day's work, could now be prepared and sent to foxes in a few hours.

The opening of this long-awaited addition to the fur farm demanded a celebration, and Henry knew what the ceremony should be. He telephoned the rendering plant to come for the stored tubs of meat, opened the door of the icehouse for the last time, then walked back to the new refrigerating room and turned the switch.

As the years passed fox meals were not always quite so simple. Fox dieticians had brainstorms, and carrots, raisins, apples, cabbages, eggs, oranges, and even bananas were tried. The carrot regime came first. The farm raised fields of carrots and bought every available carrot in the vicinity, only to discover that vegetables made the food spoil more quickly and did not improve the foxes' coats. Henry Czech still shudders when he recalls the banana era. "The food was certainly a mess when we tried that out," he said. Eggs delighted the foxes but did not transform fur. The orange experiment, when every fox received his vitamins from fresh citrus fruit, was abandoned because oranges, too, failed to register in either more or better fur.

The 1923 crop of pelters brought a check in the midwinter sales for more than thirty-five thousand dollars. Once that sum would have seemed large. Now it did not begin to stretch over the pattern the Company had set, and that pattern was only beginning to take form. Things were doubling up. Where once there were a dozen foxes, then a few score, now there were many hundreds. The first tiny bed of 150 ginseng plants had grown to many acres. The problem of spreading many thousands of dollars over a business which needed so many more thousands than the partners could give it was not essentially different from that of the early days when they had juggled a few hundred. First things still came first. Edward gave more time and thought to efficient management, had to be quicker and keener because mistakes were more costly. Walter worked harder adapting ginseng culture to increased acreage. John and Henry spent even longer days in the fur pens dealing with the complexities that constantly arose in the care of bigger herds.

It was still all farming.

In America fox farming had become a robust industry, and represented an investment of about fifteen million dollars. It was still directed by two organizations until June, 1924, when they joined to become The American National Fox Breeders' Association, a union long urged by leaders in both bodies. The absurdity of two herd books and two separate registrations of purebred foxes had been evident; if fox ranchers could not agree on the quality fox they could scarcely expect to convince the fur trade. The time had come to bury old differences and to set out on a constructive program to advance the standing of the ranched silver fox.

The first annual meeting and silver fox show of the united associations was held in Minneapolis in December, 1924. The avowed purpose was to halt the speculation, which had again grown up in this second era of prosperity. With the minor boom that had followed the post-war depression, the silver fox had again become an easy answer for the discouraged. Fox farm advertising in fur periodicals held out dazzling hopes. "Do you want to lift that mortgage? Crestview foxes will do it for you," or "Bayfair foxes will pay your bills." Other advertisements, if less practical, were even more arousing. "Make Our Foxes Your Path of Fortune." "The Super-Fox Will Guide You on the Road to Wealth." Foxes with cups and ribbons and high scores were waiting, eager to take charge of the destitute.

The most important decision of the National Association meeting was to abandon the scoring system, an emergency measure in the early days of registration when pedigrees were necessarily vague. The real value of an animal could now be judged best by breeding histories. To continue a wholly fictitious valuation, which could be used for profit in promotion and speculation, was to defeat the purpose of the Association.

Other basic problems were considered. Need of herd improvement, production of fur as fur, and not as foxes with cups and ribbons, and the importance of medical research were emphasized. Dr. W. A. Young of the New York Central Fur Company of Booneville, New York, which had topped the London market in the sale of a dark silver pelt, spoke of the necessity of trained scientists in the study of fox disease. Distemper alone had cost ranchers untold thousands, and whole fur farms had been wiped out in epidemics. Market conditions were discussed. Robert W. Fraser, American representative of C. M. Lampson and Company of London, assured ranchers that their bugaboo, fear of a saturation point in silver fox pelts, was unfounded. The supply of good silver pelts had not begun to meet demand. Also in fur, as in the history of the automobile, a plentiful supply would undoubtedly open up fresh markets. Once few women had ever hoped to possess a silver fox. Now the number that might hope to do so had increased enormously, and the number of future wearers was incalculable.

That the National Association had chosen a city in the Middle West for its annual meeting and fox show indicated the spread of the fox farming industry, and in the same month the *American Fox and Fur Farmer,* previously published in the East, moved to Minnesota. As the new editor, Harry La Due, explained, this "places us in the geographical center of that area of North America best suited to fur ranching." Mr. La Due's interest in fur ranching had grown out of his passionate conviction of the need of conservation of the dwindling fur resources of the country, and the magazine began to reflect his vision of what fur farming might become. Mr. La Due was a crusader both for medical research in fox diseases and for a thorough understanding of genetics for herd improvement.

Preferences in silver foxes had undergone a change. The dark fox with only a faint scattering of silver guard hairs on the hips, was no longer the most popular. There was a definite swing toward more extensive silver, and pelts with 15 and even 35 per cent of silver were finding a ready sale. This was a hopeful straw in the wind for the Fromms, but it was a very frail one. The Company and the fur trade were still a long way from seeing eye to eye, and the Company and the fox breeding association were even farther apart. Dealers and judges continued to insist that the silver fox must be small, or at most medium, in size, the silver must be confined to the posterior of the body and, most important of all, the silver must be veiled. Veiling was achieved through the pattern of the guard hair. Each individual hair must have a long black tip, the silver band in the middle must be fairly short, and from there to the body it must be slate color, which was the color of the undercoat. The Fromms were already breeding for a much wider bar of silver, and this characteristic was always accompanied by two others, lighter underfur and an over-all silvering. All three were a radical departure from accepted standards and, while the Company believed that it was working toward more beautiful and becoming pelts, it was alone in this opinion. Though the market price of silver fox was steadily strengthening and the fur was gaining in popularity, Fromm pelts were still topped by others at the auctions.

In the fall of 1924 the Company's furring range held not a few hundred pelters but 1,335. Herds at Hamburg had increased. Range life had improved them and the Company figured it would do even more for the southern Thiensville foxes, so the Thiensville foxes traveled north for their coats. Hamburg was in a different weather belt from Thiensville; two hundred miles north it was fifteen to twenty degrees colder, and had fewer light-hours, which was an even greater factor than cold in achieving density of fur. Traveling foxes required new equipment. The foxes were put in crates, one fox to a crate, and loaded on big trucks. Each trip brought four hundred foxes, and truck drivers prayed they might have no traffic accidents with their precious loads.

Range life added dollars to each pelt. Skins became deeper furred, undercoats more dense, holding the guard hairs well away from the body; the guard hairs, which were really the animal's winter overcoat, grew longer and more lustrous. The activity of the range — the foxes had acres to explore — helped to preserve color, for in a pen a fox may spend so much time sitting down that the silver on his rump turns yellow. But, most important, the northern range was enough colder to make the fur prime earlier; that last period of suspense when a crop is almost but not quite ready for the market was shortened by weeks. Fur crops have their own peculiar hazards, for while harvests of grain, fruit, or any other agricultural product may be ruined at the last moment by drought, hail, or searing winds, these are Acts of God and not inherent in the situation. Pelts, however, are in constant jeopardy, since they must be entrusted to the foxes until pelting time and foxes are subject to unpredictable calamities. Accidents, battles, even some cannabilism were inevitable when foxes ran together, and now the Company was discovering that the larger the herd the greater the suspense. Every day nearer to a successful harvest meant just so much more peace of mind for anxious owners.

The year-round routine of feeding and housing bigger herds had been evolved gradually. Each crisis had been met as it arose. Now each block of fox pens had its own horse-drawn cart and two keepers. Two men could care for four hundred pens. The horses, like old milk wagon steeds, learned to stop and start without orders. Foxes knew their horses and became upset and nervous if a new horse took the route. The Company agreed with other fox men, and possibly with the foxes themselves, that foxes did not like to be served by gray horses. This was assumed to be because of racial memories, although no one had ever explored the question of color blindness on the part of foxes. However, the Company's horses were always bay and keepers did not wear bright colors but only subdued gray or tan.

Fox food carts were elaborate, carrying food, two men, two pairs of scales and a huge pile of sterilized pans for each day's feeding. Fox food was weighed. The daily ration was a pound, of which two thirds was meat. The feeding hour gave keepers an opportunity to check on the health and general welfare of their charges. This was important in fox units where pens, forty by fifty feet, spread over a great area and the supper hour might be the keeper's only visit. Keepers noted foxes' appetites and demeanor. If uneaten food remained, the fox might be sick or desiring a change of diet. The fox's address, his pen number, was recorded for an early morning visit. Too many addresses in the same neighborhood was alarming. The entire Company shared John's and Henry's passion for thrifty animals.

Matings too were a vital problem. At Hamburg foxes lived in pairs. Henry and John had never changed their first opinion that foxes were more content in family life, although in the early days of the industry ranchers discovered that the fox, known for its devotion to one mate, could in some instances be persuaded to be less faithful. Such a change in fox ways had obvious advantages. The blood strain of a superior male could be spread more quickly through a herd, and a valuable sire need not devote an entire year to paternal interest in one family. But the fox was not a natural roamer, and schemes had to be evolved to break down his fidelity. Some ranchers kept pairs together until the actual time of ovulation and then quickly changed the males. Describing this method in a fur trade magazine, the writer warned: "Care must be observed to remove the mate not only out of sight, but as far away as possible, so that the female will not be distressed by any awareness of him, and the polygamous male must be removed immediately after mating for fear the two animals will become accustomed to each other and the male thereafter refuse to be polygamous."

Later it was discovered that certain males accepted a polygamous existence without protest. Some fox men have argued that the fox might not have been originally monogamous, since male survivors of pairs in which the female had died or been pelted often became dependable polygamous breeders. But other males, accustomed to a regular home life, insist on one mate, and the large number that do so makes the proven polygamous fox a definite asset in a herd.

Polygamous fox mating is costly in labor. The period of ovulation is short, only three days, and a female must be examined daily as this period approaches. Then mating plans may miscarry at the last minute. A male may kill a female. Or even worse, an intractable female may so intimidate a valuable polygamous male as to make him useless as a sire. The silver fox is sensitive and, if repulsed or hurt in a fight with a belligerent female, especially if he is young and inexperienced, he loses all interest in that female or any other for the remainder of the breeding season. The males, too, are seasonal breeders, and their season is short. There is always the possibility that they will be unavailable before all the females have reached the period of ovulation, thus rendering potential fox mothers non-producers for a year.

In either system infertile matings are a constant and unavoidable loss. In young foxes, "misses" run anywhere from 15 to 35 per cent, and in older foxes at the peak of productiveness they are 6 per cent. Any number of factors will increase this. Excitement during the breeding or whelping seasons registers in census figures. Diet is of great importance. Overfed foxes will not breed, nor will the undernourished. Vitamin deficiency lowers productiveness, as the Fromms discovered in the early thirties when 40 per cent infertile matings cut herd increase. After this crisis every company fox was made to eat his vitamins.

Bright With Silver

At Hamburg John and Henry backed their convictions on monogamous pairing with the argument that a year's food and shelter for a faithful sire cost less than the extra labor and uncertainty of polygamous breeding. But the Thiensville unit believed the advantages of the latter repaid for its trouble. Their keepers had success with polygamous sires. However, the unpredictable nature of the male silver fox defeated them in one instance. A superior and proven polygamous male with an excellent record was bought at great expense. To foster his tractability and self-assurance, keepers made a pet of him. He was given raw eggs and oranges when other foxes ate only cereal and horse meat, and his house was in the center of a private estate. Because he was a beautiful fox and a valuable animal he received a great deal of attention, learned to take eggs from the hands of keepers and to expect each visitor to arrive bearing gifts. He began to like people better than he liked foxes, and, perhaps, by some queer fox reasoning, decided to be the only fox in the world. For no matter how glamorous or how eager was the female, he disdained all advances, and this complete lack of interest continued through the years. Not only did he give up his polygamous habits, but he refused to be even monogamous. A thousand dollars' worth of fox lived in comfort, ate fruit and eggs and carried on his neurotic ambition. He was content, and so beautiful no one could bear to pelt him.

Now with the furring range a proven success, each Fromm fox had three homes in his short lifetime. He was whelped in his parents' pen. When weaned he was placed with seven other pups in a kennel where he lived until fur was graded. Then, if a pelter, he was turned into one of the furring ranges to make his winter coat. If he was selected for breeding stock, he was put in a breeding pen with his new mate. Occasionally a fox might not instantly approve of John's choice for his companion, but John and Henry were as adamant about unbroken homes as about monogamy. The only way those foxes could get a divorce was to escape from the pen, and new construction discouraged tunneling.

"The pair might bicker a bit at first," Henry admitted. "But one good fight would clear the air."

It was pragmatic reasoning, but it worked. However, incompatibility was never fostered by the pangs of hunger. Keepers saw to it that the meals were hearty. The Company had learned its lesson when that first fine male outcaste had devoured his mate in lieu of supper.

Larger herds had already made the Company aware that it was beginning to have real trouble in the increase of Sampson foxes. Several Sampsons had appeared in the Company's herd a few years before, but had aroused no real misgivings. Every ranch had its Sampsons; they were skeletons in the closet, for the admission of their existence would affect the price of breeding stock. But now, where once there had been only the odd Sampson in an otherwise good litter, whole families of the horrors were being born. Naturally the Company culled them, but as the pelt of a Sampson brought only a few dollars the culling of these undesirables had begun to mount into a real loss, and this loss must now be added to the low but unavoidable mortality of the furring range.

Then the Company forgot all these lesser losses in their panic when an epidemic suddenly broke out in the furring ranges. It was like no disease known to fox men. Foxes apparently well and in good condition were stricken suddenly, sometimes died in a few hours. A fox would stagger or run wildly, then fall to the ground in a convulsion. It seemed like a form of apoplexy. This should not be infectious, yet the epidemic stalked through all the furring ranges. Henry suspected food poisoning, watched meals from raw ingredients to range feeding pans, and even tasted some of it, but could find no support for his contention. Also, penned foxes ate the same food and showed no evidence of the symptoms.

Edward sent carcasses of foxes to the University of Wisconsin for autopsy. Laboratory reports were worse than useless. Technicians suggested that paint or some other highly poisonous substance had been left within the reach of ranged foxes. The absurdity of such a theory only proved that science held slight hope in the present crisis. No child was ever more zealously guarded against possible poisoning than were the Fromms' precious silver foxes.

Toward the end of the furring season the epidemic abated. Mortalities had been heavy. The deaths of 250 foxes, almost ready for the market, when pelts were bringing $200, was devastating. The Company had lost $50,000. This was shocking, but the mystery of the strange new disease was far more frightening. That year, despite the plague, the Company sent a major portion of the harvest to the market, $200,000 worth of pelts. But the Fromms wondered what would be their defense the next year should the epidemic strike again.

Expansion had added to their vulnerability.

Chapter Sixteen

THE NEXT YEAR'S CROP OF 3700 PELTERS WAS MORE than double that of 1924, and the foxes were moved to the furring range in the middle of September. The Company now had four ranges of from thirty-five to fifty acres each, separated by wire fencing, and the entire area enclosed by a double fence. Roads led from one range to another, and feeding stations were set along the roads. Catching fences were installed, rangers' quarters built, and the entire wooded area made safe for fur and foxes. It was a large and costly project and had used a good share of the previous year's fur check. The benefits of range life had registered in pelt prices in the winter auctions and warranted the gamble of holding a large population of foxes in one area even at the cost of daring an epidemic.

For several weeks everything went so well the Company began to relax. It seemed possible that the previous year's disaster had been an isolated instance. Then trouble started. The epidemic broke out on all four ranges and struck with fury. Dead foxes were picked up each morning. The Company took every possible precaution to halt the spread of the infection but so little could be done. Range foxes lived in close contact. They ate from the same dishes at the feeding stations, stole food from one another and in a quarrel stood face to face with forefeet braced, mouths almost touching, as they threatened each other with deep-throated snarls. They were cannibalistic and ate the dead and dying although the rangers patrolled continuously throughout the day to secure the bodies before they could be devoured by range mates.

As the epidemic spread and deaths mounted, the Company feared a wipe-out of the entire fur crop, perhaps even the end of the fur farm. Then, as suddenly as the scourge had come, it reached its peak, leveled off and subsided as it had the previous fall. But a heavy toll of foxes mounted into big figures. The Company took accounting. The percentage of mortality was about the same as the year before, but with a herd almost doubled, this meant a loss of 555 silver foxes. To have discovered nothing more about the identity of the killer made this the more appalling.

Pelting was in progress when Dr. Robert G. Green, an associate professor of bacteriology in the University of Minnesota, came to see the Fromms. Edward knew of him, had read his articles on fox distemper in the magazine, *American Fox and Fur Farmer*. The doctor's entrance into this field had been accidental. He had started mouse colonies for a study of virus disease when he'd been detoured by an appeal from the Fox Breeders' Association, and now his interest was stirred by the strange epidemic on the Fromm farm.

The Fromms and Dr. Green needed each other, although neither may have recognized this. The Company was desperate for a scientist's help in the diagnosis of their trouble while a laboratory of four thousand foxes made mouse colonies unnecessary for the doctor. His interest and enthusiasm for doing a real job in original research were the first ray of hope the Company had found. Edward and the doctor planned a campaign. Obviously the first steps must be made in the University's laboratory and classroom. The doctor offered to contribute his time and knowledge if the Company would finance laboratory expense and provide a herd of red foxes for experimental study. If spade work began at once, the doctor and his students would be ready for a constructive attack on the epidemic should it occur on the ranges next fall.

The Company had no doubt but what it would. Their fur crop was in danger until the nature, cause, and cure of the disease were known. A fund of seven thousand dollars for medical research seemed reasonable, even encouraging. It proved that the doctor, like the Fromms, was not a man of halfway measures. Edward wrote the check and Company hopes for the next year's fur crop ran high.

The pelting of an enormous number of foxes was a new experience for the Company. Only five years earlier Edward had taken ten pelts to market, and in 1923 not more than two hundred foxes had been pelted. The bodies had reached the warehouse a half hour after the animals were killed, and each man on the pelting crew could skin a fox in regulation trapper style. The 1924 harvest of fifteen hundred had demanded some team work, but the pelting crew had been able to handle each day's kill. But with 3,700 foxes in 1925 the time from the range to the pelting room was longer, piles grew larger, and trouble started. In three or four hours putrefaction can ruin the skins of foxes piled in heaps, because of body heat. Skins can turn green and valuable pelts suffer damage within an hour.

The harvesting technique had to be entirely changed to fit the new dimensions of the crop. Killing crews were instructed to lay each fox on canvas, never permitting one body to touch another. Trucks equipped with shelves, carried these to the farm. In the pelting room the foxes were hung around the walls on large wooden pegs, and a method was devised by which each man performed only one task in skinning, keeping the animals moving in a continual procession from peg to final pelt. The last station was the table where Walter took the records from the tattooed figures, showing ranch, pen, and number of the fox. Later, when the fur was sold, the price would be entered, and thus the history of the skin would be complete from forebears to market. Actually the bottlenecks in pelting were not ironed out all at once. Ten years of study went into a system that made it possible to pelt two thousand foxes in a single day, day after day, so that the huge harvests could be gathered while fur was prime.

Range methods, too, had to be altered. Larger herds must be driven to the kill, and the arrangement of division fences was important. The final scheme was to divide the range longitudinally and cut these two long strips into smaller sections. Driving started in the largest section, and when this was emptied it was shut off. As more division fences were lowered the territory for driving lessened, and in the final days the depleted herd was concentrated in the section leading to the corral. This prevented missing stragglers. Each day's drive gathered only enough foxes for that day's pelting, and the first days of driving were light, allowing foxes to double back.

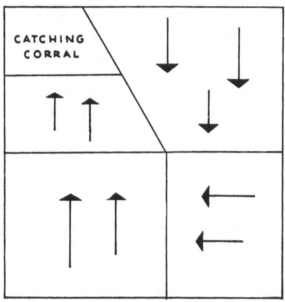

Catching methods were worked out only after several years. At first the driven foxes piled in heaps in the catching corral. Those at the bottom were suffocated and, while a dead fox represented no loss at pelting time, the heaping was hard on fur; the clawing and fighting injured pelts. Either each fox had to be pulled quickly from a heap or must be run down in the open by the crew. Though it is not difficult to catch a fox if a man knows how — with the tail grasped in one hand and the back of the neck in the other, the fox cannot bite — catching a range full of foxes individually took hours.

Edward was sure there must be a better way. The inspiration of the range had come to him through thinking in forest terms, but this approach appeared to hold no solution for the catching problem. Wild foxes are not caught. At this point Edward's subconscious apparently took over, for he awoke one night with the idea of burrows. In the wilds, foxes always run to burrows. A thirty-foot tunnel with a low entrance would appear to the fox as a protective burrow and would hold many animals. A number of these tunnels were built across the end of the catching corral, each one with several top-hatches that could be opened to extract hiding foxes. The scheme worked perfectly. Enough foxes for a day's pelting could be driven to cover in a half hour.

The actual killing was the work of a few moments. For many years the Company used a syringe injection of carbon tetrachloride in the nostrils. Later it changed to electrocution, which was swifter and more merciful. The charge from an automobile battery, stepped up by a transformer, made possible the use of electrodes on needles, and a puncture into the skin at the neck and another over the heart ended life almost instantly.

The 1925 fur crop sold for $489,967, more than double the receipts of the year before. They had not convinced the fur trade that unveiled silver or lighter foxes were desirable, but the permissible line of silver had again moved up. Now the onetime favorite, a quarter or even less of silver, trailed. It began to seem possible that silver might some day be allowed to go unveiled.

Both foxes and ginseng justified the purchase of more land. The ginseng gardens were approaching their limits on the Roehl farm, and the Company bought the eighty-acre Krentz farm across the road. Bigger ginseng acreage, however, demanded greater precautions against root rot, which had begun to threaten the Fromms so seriously that they could not let it creep further. The vast acreage of virgin land in the county had been perfect for growing ginseng, but now that the soil had become contaminated, many growers were in trouble. The Fromms had tried various schemes to check the blight. Machines and equipment were not permitted to go into a fresh planting until every particle of soil which might carry disease spores had been washed away. Roots had been dipped in spray fluid before transplanting. Now the Company decided that transplanting itself was one of the chief causes of blight. Not only did handling injure tender roots and allow rot to start, but moving two-year-old nursery stock from the seedbeds to the gardens was spreading the infection. The stratified seed must be planted in the permanent bed.

But it was impossible to broadcast seed in such large acreage. To sow one acre by dropping seed into a trench and covering it with soil required a week's work of ten men, and the entire planting must be done in a two-week period. There was no machinery for the purpose; the Fromms themselves, the only large-scale ginseng growers, had created a unique need. Surveying the planters devised for other crops, Edward decided something might be done with a hand-pushed garden planter. It was an idea. Walter and Herbert Kleinschmidt, ginseng straw bosses, went to the blacksmith shop and set to work. They mounted the planters on drawbars, six in one row, seven in the other, and by offsetting achieved a single unit that would plant thirteen rows across a bed. The machine required six men to haul it and two attendants to feed the seed, but with it a crew of eight men could seed three acres in a day. It was the Company's new weapon against root rot, and it removed the limitation which, despite new land, would have kept them small.

As always, the summer of 1926 was spent in building. The boys who had first thought in terms of single dollars and then of hundreds were now dealing with many thousands, but their point of view had not altered, nor had the situation. With the business still suffering growing pains, available funds must first be spread over the most pressing needs. They built pens in numbers that would have staggered them in early years. They purchased timbered land for a fifth furring range and enclosed it. Then, having attended to the requirements of foxes, they built a boarding house for their workers. For years the Company had looked forward to the time when crews could be fed and housed in their own quarters. Now this final divorce between home and industry was regarded, at least by the housekeepers, as the greatest single achievement of ginseng or silver foxes.

In September 6,150 pelters were turned into the furring ranges, again almost double the crop of the previous year. The animals were in good condition. Pen deaths had occurred but not in alarming numbers, although Dr. Green was almost certain the real source of the epidemic lay in the pens but had not showed serious consequences because large fox yards and wide alleyways between pens held down infection. It would flare when foxes were thrown together, and then the symptoms could be recognized and valuable data gathered.

The Company accepted this prediction with mixed feelings but took comfort from the presence of a real scientist on the job. Soon afterward the doctor had his first opportunity to observe the epidemic in action. It struck suddenly and with violence. Scores of deaths occurred at the onslaught. Through the fall of 1926 Dr. Green and his assistants spent every week end on the furring range, set up a laboratory in the warehouse, studied carcasses, made slides of diseased tissues, collected blood and specimens of brain, spinal column and vital organs from infected foxes, then drove home with a carload of dead animals for laboratory tests to supplement their field work. Through the furring period, while the epidemic lasted, they spent their days with the dead and dying, with stench and pus; then at pelting time they returned to examine healthy bodies and compare these findings with those of the plague's victims.

To the doctor the research was beginning to take shape. To the Company the outlook was very dark. The Fromms had been hoping for a speedy solution. Now they were aghast at the third year of heavy loss, 12 per cent of the crop. Seven hundred and thirty-eight foxes! The Fromms listened to the doctor's report on his progress. He had proved the source of the infection was in the pens. The violence of the range attack was the result of the quick passage from one fox to another, which added to the virulence of the infection. Those animals unable to rally their forces to combat it quickly died. Others recovered. Since each epidemic had expended itself in a month, it appeared that some of the herd had developed an immunity against the disease. Immunity for all was the only answer.

In the laboratory the doctor had been able to infect healthy red foxes with the blood of diseased silvers and cause deaths in three days. He hadn't discovered how or why it killed them, but he was convinced the infection was a filterable virus that attacked the higher centers of the nervous system.

These findings had not saved foxes of the 1926 crop, but the Company knew the heartbreaking delays of long-time battles. They had waged them, and in fairness now they gave science the benefit of patience. But if science couldn't help, their only chance for survival lay in growing so big even disease couldn't touch them.

Already they were thinking, not of a herd of a few thousand foxes, but of one of forty thousand — even fifty. Fur trade favor had begun to swing in their direction. At the midwinter auction, while the over-all silvers still failed to win approval, full half-silvers had topped the sale. Fromm pelts had not established record prices, but the crop of 1926 had brought the gratifying check of $785,153. Such sums would carry the Company a long way in its fight for brighter foxes, and this battle was the only road to a real success. In New York Edward had examined pelts of other ranchers who took awards at fox shows, were big names in the stud books, but who sent pelts to market which had no size and no excellence. Such men, who saw fur farming only as a chance for the promotion of breeding stock, never thought in terms of fur. To the Company, however, it was the fur that counted, not one record pelt, but a crop in which each pelt was a skin of quality. To achieve this meant a longer gamble, but the winnings might be great. In another year the Fromms would return to the market with more pelts — bigger, brighter, better.

The robust check from the fur crop compensated somewhat for ginseng troubles. In spite of all precautions, root rot was increasing. The blight that had forced so many growers out of the industry was now a real threat to the Fromms. Of the many growers in the country who had once carried on a large and profitable business the Fromms were almost the only survivors, and they must continue to survive. Extensive land holdings, a big inventory in shade arbors, machinery, trained crews, equipment — the whole plant investment, representing years of work, could be liquidated now only at tremendous loss. But they did not intend to be defeated, and backed this determination by buying a third farm, eighty acres across the road. It was good land for ginseng, and a companion piece to the Krentz farm which rounded out the company holdings.

The family in the old homestead had increased. Edward and Alice had two daughters, Henry and Mamie had a son and a daughter, and in January Walter married Mabel Woller, a girl of the neighborhood. They had known each other for years and had met when, as a youngster, Mabel had weeded ginseng. They both loved flowers and growing things, and it promised to be a happy and companionable marriage. But young families, and three generations, overflowed the old farmhouse.

The Company needed homes as badly as it had once needed roads, fences, pens, arbors, barns, drying rooms for fur and ginseng, crews' quarters, and all the equipment of a fur farm. Henry and Mamie saw possibilities in an old log cabin in the center of the homestead furring range. Built of birch logs, it had been the Company's first office and later was used for maple sugar boiling parties. When these woods were converted into a furring range the foxes had spent their days trying to tear the cabin apart, but Henry, who enjoyed creating something out of nothing, chose it for his home.

"I always liked that old cabin," he said, "and we want to live in the woods."

Walter too desired trees around their home, but he and Mabel wished to have a great open space for a flower garden. He found a site in the furring range that provided both. Fromms like to live near their foxes.

John's wants were slight but unalterable; he insisted on privacy. A corner in the upper floor of the warehouse was ideal, because it could be barricaded against intrusion. Footsteps on the stairway could warn him in time to escape to the roof, and the telephone, which the Company insisted was a necessity, could be silenced by taking the receiver off the hook. John's energies were never wasted by the irritations of a telephone, for he made sure it could be used only for outgoing service. When he planned his upper-story citadel the Company feared he had forgotten how necessary the forest had always been to him. "There's miles of woods around me," he said, and the others knew that John's old habit of solitary wandering was not broken.

That the Company should build and furnish these three homes and modernize the old homestead for Edward's family seemed as natural a procedure as in the early days when a boy had needed shoes or Henry must be sent to a sanitarium and the Company had provided. A farm was expected to take care of its people and the Company was still essentially a farm. Nothing had altered the old association of "The Wolves" or the two main drives of the quartet. Four boys who had known only toil and hardship, with human energy and comfort rated as the least important asset, had formed a Company to raise silver foxes, and by so doing effect a better way of living for its founders. The four had given unstintingly to the Company, and now, having become a thing of substance, it repaid them in kind.

This was an unusual method of conducting what was in reality a partnership with large holdings, but the procedure was a natural outgrowth. The Company had become a real entity, something apart, wholly within itself. It had its rights and its obligations. It had no fear of being raided. Its welfare was of common concern to its people. A Fromm never says "I" and seldom "we," but always "the Company," and the words still mean what they meant to the boys who first used them as a symbol for a structure in which four sharply-defined individuals could find a common denominator of achievement.

As the Company's cattle provided butter, cheese, milk, and cream, its forest supplied fuel and its gardens produced vegetables for all its people, now with homes needed, Bill Cole, construction boss, and his crew began to build them. There was no talk of estimates any more than a farmer counts eggs used for his table. To Henry, as inveterate a builder as any beaver, each year's improvements opened new vistas. A great glassed-in room would permit sunlight for growing shrubs in winter; an elaborate system of screens and shades would make it a cool retreat in summer. A fountain, fed from the near-by spring, would add the charm of tinkling water, and since a fountain was so easily achieved, an indoor swimming pool was possible for all the Fromm children to enjoy in the dog days of August. Before Henry ran out of building ideas ten years later, the big house did not contain one stick of the original log cabin.

Walter's approach was more methodical. He knew before the plans were drawn that his conservatory must be high enough to shelter full-grown orange and grapefruit trees. In the winter he had an exotic setting. In summer he could enjoy the forest, and the making of his garden proved to be as long a process as Henry's building. Year after year it continued to expand, down the slope, into the woods, across the road, and over the fields.

While all this building was in progress, range foxes participated in and added to the excitement of construction. Foxes pick up any object — hat, coats, handbags, cameras, lunchboxes, and tools — carry them away and usually manage to conceal their loot so well that it is never found again. For months foxes were seen carrying tools, and they seemed to prefer hammers. Workmen learned never to put down an implement or to hang coats on tree branches. Habits had to be adjusted to fox neighbors. Henry's children guarded playthings. Mamie and Mabel watched the laundry on the line. Cars were never parked outside or garage doors left open. Henry enjoyed all these proofs of fox sagacity and cunning until the day he laid down a hammer and a moment later saw a fox loping with it into the forest. Henry chased the fox for an hour. When the fox decided it had put a safe distance between itself and Henry it would drop the hammer and pause to rest, but always, just before Henry was within arm's length, it would pick up its loot and start off again. It was a grand game for the fox, and Henry never retrieved the hammer.

Foxes always managed to make life diverting for their owners. Occasionally they timed their deviltry. In the period when the price of silver fox was high and scarfs were most popular, foxes suddenly took to biting off the tips of tails. No one knew whether they bit off their own or the tips of others, but how it happened was not nearly so important as the fact that the habit spoiled the value of the pelt as a scarf. The Company decided to stop it by dipping the tails of all pups into a solution of pine oil. This could best be done when the tattooing crew removed the young from the mothers and put them in pens. Already the crew consisted of a half-dozen agile boys to catch the pups, a man to tattoo, another to read the record to the tattooer, and a third to rub vaseline on the tattooing and treat the ears to prevent ear-mites. Now they added a tail dipper, a specialist who wore rubber gloves and a rubber apron. This was the first job on the fur farm for Arthur's twelve-year-old son Johnnie, who was as thrilled by foxes as were his uncles.

In the fall of 1927 almost seven thousand foxes were on the range in September. Even if the Company had not believed forest life was more than justified by results in quality of fur, it was committed to furring ranges by the magnitude of the herd. And in the years ahead, when herds were larger, nothing else would be possible.

Almost at once the epidemic got under way. Deaths occurred early when the pelts of dead foxes, far from prime, were practically valueless. To make this even more depressing, the price of silver fox was advancing and each animal picked up by rangers represented a bigger loss in dollars. It was the fourth year, and Dr. Green had not yet identified the disease nor been able to make a virus which could be transmitted to experimental red foxes. Until he did so he was working in the dark. He and his assistants spent every week end on the furring range. The first day of October they picked up male fox #998. The carcass was still limp, warm, and in good flesh, with no evidence of other complications. A virus culture was made from the brain and spinal cord.

Ten days later in the university laboratory Dr. Green

transmitted this virus to a healthy fox. He made sure it was capable of producing death. After two years of following false clues and dead-end paths, of failure and discouragement, he had run down the killer. Now his road was straight before him. In the flush of what he recognized as only a bare beginning, he named the disease "fox encephalitis" and planned the work ahead. It might take years, but when he finally succeeded in immunizing silver foxes against encephalitis he would have made a significant contribution to fur farming.

He was confident and looked forward to telling the Fromms what he had accomplished. Next morning he received a letter from the Company. Dr. Green read it with amazement. The Fromms had never shown impatience at the slowness of research and Edward's letter now carried no suggestion that they felt defrauded. He wrote only that after posting up range losses the Company had decided to discontinue medical research. The results thus far from the expenditure of seven thousand dollars did not warrant going on with their arrangement or with further exploration.

It was a critical time for fox research, for the Company, and for Dr. Green. A scientist might be expected to have a feeling of outrage at being halted just on the threshold of success, but the doctor's reply was an astute approach to the situation, the more so because it was not written to be astute, only as the statement of a scientist. The Fromms owned the foxes. They had never inquired how he'd spent the seven thousand dollars. Dr. Green didn't protest the Fromms' decision, didn't report his success with the virus, made no promises for the future. He did say he'd spent only two thousand dollars and that if his work was to stop, the Company, not he, was entitled to what remained of the research fund. Then, without waiting for an answer, he departed for Hamburg and his usual week-end study of dead and dying foxes.

To the Fromms, who from boyhood had felt they must defend the Company from all outsiders, this was an entirely new experience. They had added the seven thousand dollars to range losses, accepted it, and had not considered an investigation of how the money had been spent or whether Dr. Green had actually contributed his services. Now they encountered a type of man not too interested in financial gain and as dedicated to his profession as they were to the Company.

No one in the Company spoke to Dr. Green about their letter or his reply. Fromms don't speak of things, especially if there is a difference in opinion. This quite often puzzles others and leaves them ill at ease, for they sense that the old wall once drawn around the tight little circle has never really crumbled. Perhaps the Fromm habit of keeping their own counsel is the result of years of isolation and their long fight against the judgments of the entire fur world.

But after the seven thousand dollar fund was gone the Company poured more thousands into the work. In the next ten years more than a million dollars was spent on research in fox encephalitis and distemper. The mutual faith and understanding between the scientist and the Company was an enriching experience for each, and certainly the knowledge of animal diseases profited immeasurably.

At the end of the season, the range loss was 17 per cent. As long as endemic encephalitis existed in the breeding pens the Company must expect this. A firm must grow big to absorb such drains. But if grief from epidemics and root rot was mounting, as was the need of gearing the assembly line to care for more foxes and ginseng, so was the income.

The January 1928 sale of the New York Auction Company was a triumph for the Fromms. The market news reported that the sale offered 8,841 silver fox pelts, and of this number 6,600 came from Fromm Brothers of Hamburg and Fromm Brothers-Nieman Company of Thiensville, and that "taken as a whole the collection of Fromm pelts was the best ever sent to New York markets. From the moment the sale opened it was apparent that records would be made."

It had been a long time since that first dream, but at last Edward sat at an auction that made fox history and watched company pelts bid to $500, $550, $565, $600, even $685. This brought as great a sense of triumph as the check. It read $1,021,000, the largest check ever written for the fur of a single shipper. The fur trade had approved bright silver.

Again foxes had to pay the way for ginseng. The last ginseng garden had not been worth the digging; at least 90 per cent of the roots had been destroyed by rot. The Company hesitated. Should it go on? Was the market for this exotic root as precarious as the growing of it? To learn at first hand whether ginseng had a real future as an article of trade, Edward went to China. He became convinced that the Chinese were a people of enduring customs, that ginseng was firmly imbedded in common usage, and he reported on his return that there would always be a market. The real threat to a ginseng future lay in blight. Known methods of dealing with it had proved useless, and now the Fromms believed that disease spores were carried by the seed itself, spores that must be killed without destroying the fertility of the seed. It would be a delicate operation, but unless the secret of how it might be done were discovered, ginseng culture was ended for the Fromms. Arthur, a trained horticulturist with a college degree in botany and science, was the only member of the family equipped for the experimental work. And even Arthur was not sure whether it could be done or how many years it would require, but he began.

When more than eight thousand foxes were turned into the furring range in the fall of 1928 there was some hope that an epidemic of encephalitis could be avoided. Dr. Green's work had gone far enough to make an attempt at immunization. Before the pelters left the pens, every fox was injected with a preventive vaccine, using attenuated virus. Later when the disease appeared, the mortality rate was lowered. Dr. Green considered this an early sign post pointing the way to ultimate success. The keepers, who had watched the hypodermic treatment with misgiving, muttered that it was probably the needle and not this new disease which had killed their foxes. John reported that more than the usual number had failed to fur out properly and were culled as Sampsons. He added that until they knew what vaccination did to fur, it was dangerous.

No one, scientist, ranger, or member of the Company, could overlook the fact that the herd of pelters had suffered a dreadful last-minute loss, and in a year when company foxes brought record prices. The 1928 fur crop was again a triumph at the midwinter auction, even greater than the previous season. This year the New York Auction Company's check was for $1,331,679. Fromm foxes had a new name in the East. The fur trade, which only five years before had advised Edward to go home and kill those "western wolves," now called them "the million-dollar foxes." Company pelts had topped the sale.

But Edward and the others knew that this sudden turn in favor was only a halfway victory. The fur trade had accepted a brighter pelt, shimmering silver unveiled by black, but the ultimate wearers were not even aware of its existence. Until the public knew how glorious the silver fox might be and demanded Fromm foxes, the Company's future product could not be sure of a market. In the years ahead the Company would raise thousands of foxes, and each fox must find a wearer. To make certain of this goal, Edward proposed that the Company declare a large appropriation for an advertising campaign which would make the Company's name familiar to every woman in America who might buy a scarf.

There was still so much to do. Foxes without a sure public! Ginseng threatened with blight! Herds menaced by encephalitis! Foxes themselves not as bright and beautiful as they might become! It would be years before the Company could achieve a silver fox as lovely as they'd dreamed of but now the tide was with them.

This Eastern triumph could mean no more to anyone than to Alwina. She had lived to see those first three silvers grow into a mighty herd and to know her boys had fulfilled her faith in them before death finally released her from a long invalidism.

Though for years illness had shut her off from friends, she was a woman not easily forgotten, and everyone who had known her came to the little Lutheran church where she had worshiped and from which she was buried. Families drove in ancient sleighs from small hamlets, automobiles arrived from the cities, and the little churchyard with blanketed horses and shining modern vehicles was somehow right for Alwina's funeral. A pioneer whose wifehood had begun in a log cabin, she'd had the vision to see new ways coming and the courage to salute them with spirit. The Fromm farm with its ranks of fox pens and ginseng arbors was not the farm she and Frederick had imagined when he felled trees in a virgin wilderness for their first log cabin, but hers was the valor to smooth the pathway of a daring dream.

Chapter Seventeen

M ILLION-DOLLAR FOXES BROUGHT NEW PROBLEMS AND major changes in the Company. The Fromm idea for an extensive advertising campaign did not meet with unanimous approval. John F. Nieman, one of the partners in the Fromm Brothers-Nieman Company, disagreed. He put his faith in quantity production.

"Raise so many that disease can't kill them all," he said. "That's the way to cover losses. And why waste money on advertising? I'd raise foxes if they made us only two dollars a pelt. The answer is just more foxes."

His son Herbert agreed with him, but Edwin, a real fox man, was closer to the Company in his feeling for fur and believed a firm raising thousands of silver foxes must fight disease. To him an advertising appropriation of $100,000 was not out of line with the present price of pelts, and quantity alone was not their goal.

So early in 1929 the Fromms broke with John F. Nieman and his son, Herbert. Holdings in the Thiensville ranches were divided, and the two Niemans formed a company of their own. Edwin remained with the

Fromms under the name of Fromm Brothers-Nieman Company. The Thiensville operation had been scattered over many farms and these were exchanged until each organization could center its possessions. The Fromms' investment in the southern unit was large, with a huge inventory in breeding pens, roads, feed mill, and warehouse, which could not be moved. And undoubtedly the Fromms would not have wished to. The Company was too settled in its ways to make changes or to accept new members at the Home Farm. The two units, Hamburg and Thiensville, continued as separate ventures and still do today.

But the break with John F. Nieman and his son Herbert, and the consequent division of the mighty herd at Thiensville, not only startled the fur world but was of immediate consequences to the Company. What had promised to become a kingdom of silver foxes was split into two separate dukedoms, each resolved to grow big in its own right. This split would result in fewer pelters for the Company in the fall of 1929 as only by reserving every breeder possible could it rebuild the herd for the next year.

To raise more foxes than any other fur farm was the Company's determination, and they added pens, not by scores but by many hundreds. The silver fox market warranted large expansion. America was having a buying boom. The stock market was creating new millionaires, and women who had never dreamed of owning a silver fox were now potential customers. In the past ginseng had financed expansion, but with the present blight in the gardens, a rapidly declining price in root, and a large advertising appropriation ahead of them, the Company turned to banks. For the first time it became a heavy borrower. Banks now regarded fox ranching in a different light than fifteen years earlier when Alwina's quarter section had been mortgaged to buy three silver foxes.

While in the mood for reorganization, the Company incorporated. This did not change their way of thinking. It was still essentially a partnership but now wives shared stock holdings equally with husbands.

"This Company wasn't built with only manpower," Henry said. "The wives saw it through tough times too."

But it was still just the Company, just a farm. The Fromms knew from experience that the million-dollar checks would be plowed back as cash crops always had been. The four brothers drew equal salaries and still do, and in a corporation of like size these would be considered less than nominal. Top staff members receive almost as much. "Million-dollar foxes" had not altered the Company's viewpoint except on the need to raise more foxes.

In June Dr. Green decided his work with virus and with serum from hyperimmune red foxes had gone far enough to warrant an experiment on silvers. A group of twenty-five young foxes in Thiensville was selected for an initial test. The purpose of a combination dose of virus and serum was to give a mild attack of encephalitis, control it with the serum and achieve immunity. A week later when the initial twenty-five showed no signs of disease, fifty were injected, and after another week one hundred were treated. Apparently all three experiments were successful. Even keepers who'd had no faith in hypodermic needles were convinced that practical results could go hand in hand with research. At the end of the third week, when no fox was sick, between two and three thousand of the fall fur crop were vaccinated with the combination dose.

But encephalitis, the scourge of foxes, had a card up its sleeve which no one had suspected. A few days later the first injected group developed encephalitis. It was obviously a delayed infection when the serum in the combination dosage had been so thoroughly eliminated it could not build added defense against the infection.

The import of this was at once apparent. Every fox given the deadly virus was in danger. As deaths occurred the pattern of mortalities could be charted. Anywhere between thirty and thirty-five days after the injection foxes in each group would die. Serum was used promptly, but this crucial period for the final large group of foxes promised a catastrophe. It was not as bad as it might have been without the serum, but the Company lost fifty thousand dollars' worth of silver foxes.

This was a magnificently large experiment, and although its extent was unintentional, findings were definitely conclusive. These however were cheering only to a scientist. Medical research fell even lower in keepers' estimation and Dr. Green and his needle were regarded as a menace. The Company was more understanding about the disaster and Edward even achieved a bit of humor.

"Doc," he said, "we've never quite believed the stuff you had in that little bottle was really what killed foxes. But you've convinced us."

The Thiensville experiment in June proved all hope of immunizing fall pelters was futile, and again the fur crop was treated with a vaccine of only attenuated virus. Range losses fell to slightly over three per cent, the lowest the furring range had shown in years and lower than it would show in years to come. It was unfortunate that this lessening of the attack occurred in the year when a need to rebuild the herd had cut the number of pelters to a minimum. The forest ranges held only 3,786 foxes, all the Company could afford to part with.

In spite of the October market crash, the price of fur had not declined. The Fromm shipment was not so large as it had been in the two previous million-dollar years, but the quality of the pelts was better. This consistent improvement of Fromm foxes aroused Eastern comment, and one fur journal carried a leading article comparing Fromm products with those of others.

"The insistence of Fromm Brothers that their continued success in the production of high quality silver fox pelts was due mainly to skill in handling of animals during the so-called furring season, was met with some skepticism by the fur trade prior to the offering of the latest crop of Fromm pelts. . . . Comparison of the Fromm Brothers' collection with the rest of the world crop has brought a marked change in the attitude. . . . Skepticism gave way to surprise, and many were the skin handlers who sought explanation. The Fromm answer was the Fromm claim advanced before the marketing of the crop; that the handling during the furring season is the determining factor, and that to this handling too little attention has been paid by the breeding trade as a whole."

This confirmation of the Company's belief that the quality of the fur crop held the real answer to success, stiffened its determination to make fur ranges safe for foxes. Soon after the midwinter sale the scope of research was enlarged by the establishment of the Fromm-Green Research Foundation, which was to make a study of both encephalitis and distemper. Range losses from encephalitis had deepened the Company's fear of the possible advent of distemper, for while encephalitis preyed on furring ranges, distemper stalked through pens and whole farms.

The Company realized that the time to prepare against disaster was before it was upon them. Even Edwin Nieman, who might have had misgivings after the fiasco of the serum-virus injections at Thiensville, agreed that a concern which intended to raise large herds must find out how to fight fox diseases. The fox ranchers' association had done almost nothing in research and had no funds for such work. Although the ambitious program of the Fromm-Green Foundation would be costly, it seemed a justifiable gamble on the future. If the Fromms were intrepid long-time gamblers, so was Dr. Green.

He had not yet cleared up the mystery of encephalitis, had only recently surmised that the disease invaded not the nerve cells of the brain itself, as he had first thought, but the cells in the capillary bed of the brain. As yet this was only a vague guess. Thousands of slides must be made and scores of red foxes sacrificed to the scientific mill before he could hope to uncover the hidden pocket of infection. But the man was as unswerving and as determined as the Fromms themselves. Foxes, money, years of work, and the reputation of a scientist were to be wagered on the uncertain odds of ultimate success. The Company opened laboratory quarters in Thiensville. Funds for the work were raised by assessing both the Hamburg and the southern unit at three dollars a fox. Not only were Fromm herds to serve as test cases in the laboratories, but each fox must do its share to make the world safe for all the glamorous foxes which were to come.

The question of protection of the 11,000 pelters of the 1930 fur crop was complicated by John's report of a sudden and mysterious increase in Sampsons. He suspected the vaccine was imparting a brownish cast to pelts and making fox coats hard and dry. Foxes were being protected against encephalitis only to be transformed into Sampsons. It was a well known fact that chemicals, hormone secretions, even malnutrition, had a definite effect on fur, and many fox men still believed Sampsons were made, not born, although the government had carried on a study of Sampson foxes and reported that established facts "tend to prove" Sampsonism an inherited trait. Since then it has been suggested that this characteristic may even be a recessive, following Mendel's law of recessives. Thus any carrier of Sampson blood would be a menace in a herd. Like other fox ranchers, the Fromms had culled recognized Sampsons, but had permitted others with no visible trace of the characteristic to go on breeding. The Sampson strain had been spread through the herd like spatters from a mud puddle, and inevitably half blood Sampsons had passed on the taint.

The Company made two decisions. John was to begin a rigorous extermination. The father, mother, brother, or sister of any Sampson was to be culled from the herd no matter how beautiful the color or how fine the fur. Also the vaccine was to be discontinued. On this John was adamant, for he did not intend to cull handsome foxes only to make more Sampsons. Dr. Green did not believe an acid found in pure castor oil would harm fox coats, but he didn't argue. Not only did the herd belong to the Fromms, but a company which had waged so long and so unyielding a battle for its beliefs would be stubborn in its opinions. This trait had been their strength and might have been their greatest weakness had not each Fromm allowed the other the complete right to his opinion in his particular domain. Color and condition of fox coats was John's responsibility and, since he suspected the vaccine, some other method must be devised to protect the herd of pelters against an attack of encephalitis.

The disastrous Thiensville experiment had proved that serum from hyperimmune red foxes gave temporary immunity of from twenty to thirty days. This was better than nothing, and if the eleven thousand pelters were given serum in the pens, then turned into the furring range and pelted early, the crop could be harvested before an epidemic took too many victims. The Company accepted this idea but was unhappy about the shortened furring season.

Range life was important. Foxes should have forest shade by the middle of September. Adults' coats deteriorated even more quickly in pen life than those of pups, as the guard hair was apt to lose its clearness and impart a rusty cast to pelts. Early pelting was not desirable because two full months were needed to make the undercoat dense and strong and to grow guard hairs.

This year, however, early pelting was a lesser evil. One dosage of serum held off the epidemic for almost a month, and the 11,000 herd was harvested as soon as possible thereafter. Mortality from encephalitis was kept to eight per cent, a heavy toll in so large a herd. Even more depressing to the Company was the loss of those last fur-making weeks. The Fromms were seeking perfection which could be achieved only by turning foxes on the range the last of August and holding them until fur was at its best in the middle of November.

Not until science had eliminated epidemics would the

most glamorous foxes be possible and neither Dr. Green nor the Company suspected how distant that time was. Meanwhile the Company was committed to the scheme of furring ranges, had spent extensive capital on land, roads, and miles of fencing to produce big fur crops of fine quality. Not to make full use of this investment was a loss.

After considerable discussion the Company hit upon a solution for the fur range of the following year. They proposed a procedure which was both unique and ambitious. Since serum gave an immunity for only twenty to thirty days, and at any time after three weeks encephalitis trouble could be expected, the pelters should be given successive injections to be sure of protection. Then the herd might be carried through an entire furring season in safety. As a scientist, the doctor was certain these succeeding shots would maintain immunity, but he had no idea of the practical difficulties involved. The Company was well aware of these, but was still undeterred.

"We should experiment on one range this year," Edward said. "Two range shots would carry the crop through a full furring season."

"It'll be the first time anyone ever caught up fifteen hundred foxes in the thick woods," Henry said. "We can't drive them into the tunnels. They would be sure to suffocate."

It was an entirely new problem. Foxes must be caught, treated, and returned safely to the range. Some mortality was inevitable, since every time foxes are caught and handled losses occur. Accidents, rough treatment, or overexcitement might kill them, and there were bound to be a few broken legs. Considerable thought was given to the catching cages. These were made of netting, and sixty of them were built in a row across the end of the catching corral. The doors were operated by trip wires stretched to men hidden in the woods, who would drop the doors when cages held not more than twenty foxes. The foxes were to be driven in a body past the doors. When the leaders reached the last cage and found themselves cornered in the corral they would run into the open door of the cage, and when this was closed others would fall back to the next, and continue thus until all the cages were filled. The plan seemed perfect. If foxes behaved normally and door attendants acted promptly, the pelters would be confined and ready for an injection with a minimum of loss.

The driving crew ate its usual six o'clock breakfast and was on the range at seven for a day that will never be forgotten by owners, rangers, or keepers. The foxes of the range were started toward the catching corral, and as driving fences were closed to shut off retreat, the herd massed in smaller areas. It was a warm October day. The temperature reached seventy by midmorning and even in the early hours foxes fell exhausted from running in the heat. Others ran so fast that they broke their necks in collision. What was to be a flowing stream of animals turning into open cages became a mass of milling, terrified creatures. Door attendants did not always act promptly, and a moment's hesitation meant forty or fifty foxes piled in a heap so that ten to twenty foxes were apt to be suffocated. Men worked desperately to separate mounds of clawing, snarling animals. Others tried to drive stragglers into the empty cages.

The morning became a nightmare to keepers and owners. The hypodermic dosage of heavy serum was large and given in the abdominal cavity, which made it necessary to hold the fox upside down for the injection. Some foxes, released after treatment, ran a few steps and toppled over dead. Others ran a hundred yards into the woods where John and Walter found their bodies, and returned to report that dead foxes were lying everywhere. This was the final straw for Henry.

"Better let encephalitis kill them!" he stormed. "It's a sin to do this to healthy animals."

Henry was for stopping the experiment at once, and the majority opinion was with him. Those who had lost all faith in science bitterly protested such wanton destruction. Even those who believed in the injections argued that the loss from encephalitis could be no greater, and that loss was only a probability. These foxes were dying or being crippled before their eyes. Keepers angrily demanded why they should run foxes to death or kill them with a hypodermic needle. Suffocated foxes, foxes with broken legs, foxes which had died from the injection, were a terrible indictment of science and of doctors. If the treatments continued no one could guess how many would die. Yet if all the foxes on the range were not treated there would be no way of determining the value of the experiment. Everyone had ideas, arguments, protests, or suggestions.

At such a time Edward, clearinghouse for the ideas of all and the most farsighted gambler of the Company, usually made decisions. The role had been both thrust upon him and was of his choosing.

"What'll we do, Ed?" the boss of the treatment crew asked.

"Finish the injections," Edward said. "These dead foxes have been wasted unless we can judge results."

Research in silver foxes requires stalwart men.

The work went on. When the job was finished, 346 silver foxes lay dead in the corral, but every fox still alive had been given an injection. Eighteen days later they received another, and encephalitis did not take its annual toll from that range. The following year almost twelve thousand fur range foxes received two injections of the serum. In later years this procedure was followed with as many, and even more, range foxes, but never again was another day as bad as the first. Methods improved with experience. A better serum was used and the dosage was cut so that foxes need not die of shock. The driving crew began at earliest daylight so as to finish in the cool morning hours. The Company learned to wait if possible for a cold day, but the timing had to meet that inexorable deadline of three weeks between injections. Driving technique changed. Experienced men handled the needles, assistants filled syringes, and the injection was subcutaneous in the loose skin of the flank.

With this better technique and luck in weather and fox behavior, two thousand foxes were treated in two hours and losses were only about 2 per cent in each treatment. With worse luck seventy-five foxes would be lost in every fifteen hundred. Only one range could be treated in a day, and a crew of one hundred men treating foxes on twelve ranges robbed the fall ginseng rush of needed labor; but the injections held range losses to approximately 8 per cent and at the same time enabled foxes to reach full perfection in winter coats. But whether the Company had good or bad luck in the range shot of serum, the method was quite as hard on owners and keepers as on foxes, and everyone looked forward to the time when permanent immunity could be achieved with one shot given in the pens.

Chapter Eighteen

THE DEPRESSION CAUGHT THE FROMMS IN 1931. FOR the first time the Company had bank trouble. The large expansion, seemingly justified in the summer of 1929, had put them in debt. National advertising, necessary if the Company were to take advantage of hard-won trade favor, had been a heavy drain. So had disease and funds spent on medical research. Fur and ginseng prices had slumped, and still lower prices were indicated. Only strictest economy could prevent banks from becoming the real owners of a herd of silver foxes.

The program of the Fromm-Green Research Foundation was drastically curtailed. Distemper was a potential menace but financial difficulty the immediate danger. Yet research in encephalitis could not be halted. This was as necessary as buying food for foxes. National advertising must go on. Women in America could not be permitted to forget the existence of Fromm foxes.

The Company was worried but not in a panic. For the first time ginseng and fur prices had dipped simultaneously. Always before profits in one crop had balanced losses in the other. Now the price of root did not pay the cost of growing. Floods, revolutions, and political unrest in China had caused hard times. American growers were forced to sell as low as one dollar a pound, and rather than do this, the Company stored its ginseng harvests.

The situation in China was beyond even Fromm control, but the silver fox problem was on home ground. The 1929 fur crop had been small. Foxes which would have brought good prices early in 1930 had been held over as breeders to rebuild a herd depleted by the break with the Niemans. Now the glamour of a silver fox, even for a woman who could afford it, was not in line with the economies the depression had made fashionable. Present low prices could not be lifted, so markets must be widened. This was Edward's province, and he had a brilliant idea. Instead of a single pelt around a woman's neck, why not a two-skin scarf, four or five skins in a garment, or even silver fox as lavish trimming?

Multiple-pelt manufacture would be an innovation. Fur garments had usually been limited to the short-haired variety and silver fox had not been manipulated by a fur process which the trade calls "letting out." This is accomplished by slitting skins in narrow strips and sewing them together to obtain the length required. This piecing gives greater pliability for draping and permits perfect matching. "Letting out" was used in fashioning mink, seal or other short-haired furs, and also long-haired furs which were not too bulky or in which the color was more or less uniform and was the only possible method for garment manufacture. A coat made of an unworked skin, even in so small an animal as a mink, would resemble a badly pieced patchwork quilt.

Fur workers had never used this technique for the precious silver fox. Always sold as a scarf, its beauty was never desecrated by razor or sewing machine. Now it must be, if the fur were to be used for garments or for trimming. In 1932, when the price of silver fox went to forty dollars, a fur once so costly that a single skin was a prized possession could be used in profusion. It appealed to Edward Fromm as an inspired treatment for silver fox.

"What an evening wrap the silver fox would make!" he said. "Think of that richness wrapped around a woman!" He meant it. To Edward the silver fox has always been the most glamorous fur in the world. Naturally he thought of evening wraps, and of wide collars, lavishly trimmed coats, and borders of silver fox around sleeves and skirts.

Edward went to Paris. The Wisconsin farmer visited every famous couturier. He talked to designers and argued with fur workers that the silver fox could be manipulated as a lavish trimming or as a luxurious garment. Edward was very sure and intensely earnest, but the originators of the world's fashions did not catch fire. They took the matter under consideration. Edward left silver fox pelts in his wake with a prodigality which departed from the frugal precepts of his early training, but no new fur styles appeared to be forthcoming. Having failed in his missionary effort, he turned to the second purpose of his European trip, the sale of Fromm foxes. He trudged from one leading furrier to another just as years before he had made the rounds in New York. French and Italian women saw the large bright silvers, and liked them.

On his return Edward continued proselytizing for

multiple-pelt manufacture of silver foxes. Not only would this enlargement of the fur's purpose help to absorb Fromm harvests, but Edward was sure it would reveal the entrancing beauty of the pelt. A few American designers showed interest. The silver fox was a becoming fur and could replace the luxurious sable, which was rapidly disappearing. Almost overnight, as so often happens in fashion history, that trend became a definite style, and the current started in the direction of Edward's thinking.

Silver fox gained countless new wearers, and even at depression prices the Company ceased to worry about banks. Volume, the Fromms' old bulwark against disaster, again served them, but another long-sought Fromm goal fitted into the new picture. The uniformity of their pelts simplified the matching of fur, so necessary in multiple-pelt manufacture.

As markets widened and herds grew larger, new problems in merchandising confronted the Company. Thousands of nondescript silver fox pelts had been going to market from competing breeders, skins that resembled nothing so much as a strange breed of cat in bad condition, and yet because they were silver foxes they had brought good prices. American women had to be informed of the proper qualities of a silver fox pelt. Many had never seen a good one and, oddly enough, while women are the wearers of fur, few have an instinctive feeling for its beauty and enchantment. The Fromms proposed to tell the public about silver foxes, and especially Fromm foxes, but a large appropriation for advertising necessitated some means of identifying the Company's product. This was difficult. A label must not harm the pelt or be lost in manufacture, must be readily seen by the customer, and easily removed before wearing. An ear marker would spoil the appearance. Tattooing would become illegible in dressing. A stamp on the skin side of the pelt would be hidden when the fur was made up. Yet it was essential to the Company that a woman be assured the fur she bought had been raised and pelted on the Fromm ranch.

The ultimate solution was a metal medallion. Several methods of attaching this had to be successively abandoned when the Company discovered how easily it was transferred to other pelts to give aid and comfort to competitors. A Company which had guarded property and secrets as zealously as the Fromms was quick to recognize this practice. Finally the medallion was sealed in the nose of every pelt with a wire ring which permitted it to hang loosely. At the time the Company considered this the perfect answer. No other pelts could masquerade in Fromm medallions.

The medallioned foxes were advertised as pedigreed. The Company, once refused registration in the silver fox studbook, was now the only breeder who could use this term. Not only could the Company supply the pedigree of every medallioned fox, but it did so. Each medallion carried the number of the fox, and when it was returned to the Company the buyer received a certified pedigree giving name, date of birth, and breeding history through four generations.

The fox breeders' association did not challenge the use of the term "pedigreed." The famous studbook, once so important, had been forgotten in the collapse of speculation in the depression, and now breeding stock was important only in terms of the fur it produced. Fur as fur had become the objective of fur farming. In this the

Fromms had led the way and had made a definite contribution to the fox industry as a whole. Nor was this their only service. They had proved the fallacy of the old-style breeding procedure of a dark to a silver, had shown that foxes could be bred for a predominance of silver and yet retain purity of color. They had altered a public's preference. Fromm foxes had never won a cup, a blue ribbon, or a high score in points, yet not only the fur trade but even wearers were beginning to prefer them. The four farm boys, who had never seen a fur around the neck of a woman when they decided silvered foxes would be more becoming, had justified the fantastic notion. Now they were engaged in making foxes still brighter.

A definite decision had to be reached on the advisability of continuing ginseng culture. When the price of dry root fell to one and two dollars, many growers sold all roots large enough to harvest and allowed gardens to deteriorate. Even the spraying of plants was too expensive at such a price. Others decided to ride out the storm, and sold roots for whatever they could get. The Fromms had stored their ginseng since 1931, but in 1933 trouble in China threatened even a worse situation.

The Company's problem was complicated, because ginseng culture was threaded through the fur project. Rush seasons in the two industries dovetailed and made it possible to employ key men throughout the year. Fur alone would not permit this, as men of high caliber would not be attracted by seasonal employment. Nursery stock, too, required years to develop and, if abandoned, might never be rebuilt. Vast holdings in land and an enormous inventory in ginseng arbors and special equipment represented a staggering capital investment.

The gardens still suffered from blight, but Arthur was convinced he could eventually defeat root rot with a seed treatment. Experiments in ginseng were necessarily protracted. Not only did seeds require a year to germinate and another half year to develop green shoots, but root rot often did not appear until the second or third year of growing. Arthur's scientific attitude demanded certainty, and this could not be possible for several years. But the Company had learned to wait on science. Encephalitis was giving them practice in patience, and they were as certain that Arthur would eventually solve root rot as they now were that Dr. Green would defeat encephalitis.

Storage of harvests and the costs of production were different matters. Ginseng culture, which had to be large because of the investment, would cost forty to fifty thousand dollars each year. Nor was it known how long ginseng could be stored with safety. A weevil had destroyed small crops of other growers, and no one knew its origin or what it fed on when it had no ginseng. Farmers reported that boxes and closed barrels of the root were chewed into powder by the pest. The Fromms had stored two harvests in warm rooms above the power plant and, though frequent inspections had not uncovered weevils, they did not know whether such luck would continue.

The Fromms held a company meeting, one of the few in their history. Usually a matter was decided by a chance encounter when two partners involved in a question talked it over and relayed their decision to the others. But continuance of ginseng culture was too important for such informal methods. The four partners met in the office. Walter, as head of ginseng, spoke first.

"We've worked too hard on ginseng to give it up lightly," he said.

"We could put the money in silver foxes," Henry said. "Most fur farms don't have a second business."

John said nothing. He talked only on policies affecting the blood strain or the quality of the herd.

"In ten years or less there will be no overproduction of ginseng," Edward said. "Growers will dig root already planted, sell it, and give up the business."

He went on to speak of conditions in the Orient. Since his visit there he had not believed Japan would be content with a small section of China, and the "incident" might start a war which would last many years. But a market in ginseng would exist so long as there were Chinese people. Of this he was convinced.

The argument went on for an hour. If the Company continued ginseng culture they would have the product to sell when the market was re-established, while other growers would have neither nursery stock nor seed. The Company might become not only the largest grower of ginseng in the world, but perhaps the only grower. Meanwhile they could be building a stock pile for the Chinese nation, and ten years was not too long for a Fromm gamble. They had spent almost thirty years in carrying 150 plants into big acreage.

Walter looked relieved.

"I'll tell the boys we'll seed that eighteen-acre garden," he said. "It's ready for fall planting. And we needn't worry about where we'll store the root this year. The crop won't run over ten thousand pounds."

Save for root rot, they would have had a harvest ten times as large, but no one reopened the question of ginseng culture, nor did anyone suggest Walter make the fall seeding smaller. The Company need not have held an official meeting. Walter and Edward could have talked the matter over and relayed their decision to the others, for no member of the firm had the slightest notion of turning his back on an unfinished project. Ginseng and silver foxes had started out together, and they must continue until the end.

In 1934 the Century of Progress Exposition in Chicago offered the Company space in the General Exhibits building. This would be its first public appearance in the consumer world. Edward thought forty thousand dollars could be well spent in telling the women of America about silver foxes, and obviously Henry was the one to tell them. He took charge of the exhibit, and because creative drive was tied to fervor, he completely ignored the appropriation. The project cost one hundred thousand dollars, but Henry achieved one of the most unusual and talked-of exhibits of the Fair.

Henry's way of telling the story of the silver fox had the drama of contrast. The central feature was a floor show. A large circular revolving platform was divided in two sections; mounted foxes in a winter scene occupied one side, and models wore beautiful fox furs in the other. The platform made a complete revolution every two-and-a-half minutes and the models maintained a constant parade. They appeared from one door of a dressing room, walked across the stage to disappear through another door, and came out wearing a new fur. A dozen models, with scarfs, muffs, capes, and evening wraps were in a constant procession, and the platform revolved from ten in the morning until ten at night.

216

Since Henry, the perfectionist, was determined that the foxes must appear to be in a real forest, the outdoor scene required continuous redressing. A truck made weekly trips with balsam, moss, and shrubbery from Hamburg. The use of artificial snow could not be avoided, but Henry made certain it was heaped and sculptured to look drifted, and the lighting had to give the feeling of the woods on a cold winter morning. Henry badgered workmen, changed installations and light bulbs, and sometimes remained all night to experiment with a new and inspired scheme. In the first weeks of the exhibit he slept as often on the trunk holding the fur garments in the dressing room as in his hotel, but a night's sleep was well lost if he could more nearly capture the illusion of foxes on the range. When Henry was finally satisfied, if he ever was completely satisfied, the scene probably appeared the coldest ever achieved outside of the north woods.

The rest of the exhibit completed the story of the silver fox. Photomurals seven feet high showed the life on the range. A continuous moving picture followed the work of raising and feeding a herd of foxes and grading pelts. It also showed the color development of the silver fox from nature's first experiment in a cross fox to the full silver of man's selective breeding. Mounted foxes were of varying degrees of silver, as were the furs worn by models.

The exhibit caught the public. Henry accomplished what he set out to do, for men liked it as well as women. He dramatized the history of the silver fox, and people without previous interest in, or knowledge of, what man had done with a mutation, learned the difference between the old black silver, three-quarter, half, one-quarter, and full silver. It was showmanship but not conscious showmanship, and therefore more effective. The luxurious garments and the sophisticated black and chrome fittings of the hundred thousand dollar exhibit were only superficial evidences of the compelling passion that had made the presentation possible.

It was more than a story of silver foxes that Henry told. It was a sort of folktale of America; a strange mixture of small beginnings, mistakes, and fortitude; a homely story of hardships and great courage — the age-old story of many boys who have dreamed of accomplishment and who have followed the narrow pathway of that dream. It was not yet a finished story. The herd of silver foxes was still not the great herd they had envisioned. Nor was it a story of security won, or of an impregnable citadel, or of a venture beyond the reach of disaster.

For suddenly disaster struck. Before the exhibit closed Henry received the news that distemper, dreaded scourge of fur farms, had broken out in two Hamburg units. Mortalities were 75 per cent in the infected areas. If the disease spread with the same severity, the farm must surely be wiped out, as had been the farms of other breeders. Even as he talked of silver foxes, Henry knew that in another year there might be no Fromm foxes to be bred into brighter silvers.

Chapter Nineteen

Ｉ N HAMBURG THE COMPANY PREPARED TO AVERT
catastrophe. They realized curtailment of medical research three years earlier might now prove a costly saving. They had fully intended to resume a study of distemper, but the depression had only begun to fade and
ginseng root still remained unsold.

The obvious first step was to take all known precautions to prevent spread of the disease. Crews washed
their hands between tasks and walked through disinfecting solutions as they left each yard. Yet distemper
hit as had no previous epidemic. Farm stock lay dead
and dying. Whole fox families were cleaned out and entire blocks of pens doomed. Only the enormous extent
of the project saved them from a wipe-out.

Dr. Green and the Company held a conference. His
earlier investigation for the breeders' association had
been contemporary with the research of other pioneers in
canine distemper. While the idea of the modification of
a virus in an animal host had its origin in the discovery
of smallpox vaccination by Jenner and had been used

by Pasteur in his work on rabies, it had proved valuable in experiments with dogs. Three families are susceptible to distemper, the weasel, which includes the mink and ferret, the raccoon and the dog family, which includes the fox. The ferret is highly susceptible to distemper, regardless of whether the virus originated from a related species, such as mink, or an unrelated species, such as dog or fox. Obviously the ferret was the animal host to choose for the modification of the virus. The modification was in the nature of an induced change to make the virus extremely virulent for the animal host and at the same time lose its virulence for some other species. This required a serial passage of the virus from one host to another. Dr. Green had no idea how many passages of virus generations (the term used to describe the fatal termination of an infection in an individual animal) would be necessary. He warned the Company he would not undertake the project unless assured of support through a hundred passages.

This undertaking might, and eventually did, cost more than a million dollars. It was a single-handed battle against a scourge which had already bled many million dollars from the fox industry, but it was the kind of battle that appealed both to the Company and to Dr. Green. The work would be extensive. The Company bought a bankrupt fox farm a few miles from the Thiensville ranch and opened the Fromm Laboratories. The main building was converted into a laboratory and the pens provided housing for a herd of experimental foxes. A small permanent staff was installed and the Company prepared for a long and aggressive campaign.

Before these plans were even underway, Thiensville reported a violent distemper outbreak in its pens, and now both farms were engaged in a struggle to save foxes. The only defense lay in the use of antidistemper vaccines and serums already on the market. The Company bought these in vast quantities, used them with abandon, but could not control the infection. But in spite of the epidemic the Company was able to put twelve thousand pelters on the fall range in 1934. Even here distemper continued the attack. Range mortality was 18 per cent, as bad as in the early days of encephalitis, and until a sure method to immunize foxes was discovered there was no hope that losses could be cut. Compared to distemper and its real threat to the Company's future, encephalitis paled as a killer. The only cheering feature was that the best animal host for the modification of the distemper virus was well known. In seeking one for encephalitis, Dr. Green had vainly run the gamut from mice to monkeys.

Laboratory research was well under way in the summer of 1935. Much preliminary work had been done. The particular strain of the virus had been selected and the experimental unit perfected. Every precaution against contamination from other strains was taken. Ranches from which the ferrets were purchased were inspected, laboratory ferrets were kept in quarantine, and inoculations performed in small pens in the center of a large fenced area. The individual cages were covered with fine copper mesh to prevent the entrance of flies. Cages were opened only in a heavy mist of fly spray. When a virus generation was completed by the death of a ferret, the carcass was immersed in lysol and taken to a special room where the spleen was removed and placed in a vial for culture to be used in the next transmission.

Setbacks occurred despite these measures. After one

contamination was discovered, the Company built a special ranch for quarantined ferrets which were brought to the laboratory in sterilized cages. Twice experiments went wrong when experimental red foxes became infected with a natural strain of distemper. Thereafter only wild foxes, dug from dens, were used, a costly procedure. Another contamination, the cause of which was never known, ruined a long sequence of transmissions. An even more tragic interruption happened when the virus had been carried through fifteen generations and promised effectiveness. All cultures were destroyed through a mistake of an employee, making it necessary to begin again.

To further complicate the work of the Fromm laboratories, and to prove how many things could happen to foxes, Chastek paralysis broke out in the Company's pens. This disease was named after a fox rancher on whose farm the symptoms had first been found. The initial spastic paralysis was progressive. A fox first ran with short stiff jumps instead of the usual easy fox gait, then exhibited more bizarre movements as other muscles became affected. After this strange behavior complete paralysis followed, the animal becoming rigid with head drawn back. Coma and death resulted in one to four days. On the Fromm farms the disease began with a few cases. Then fatalities climbed to an average of twenty-eight each day. This was serious.

Dr. Green proved the disease was not a virus infection. Then by clever scientific work he learned it always appeared after a month of heavy fish diet. Yet food poisoning was not the reason because in every case the fish had been of the best quality. In Dr. Green's experiments that summer it was enough to prove that a diet of more than 10 per cent of fresh fish produced a Vitamin B_1 deficiency. This was a definite and immediate contribution to fox farming. Vitamins were indicated for all foxes. Not until several years later was he able to carry research in Chastek paralysis far enough to determine that a constituent in fish, especially if the heads, tails, skins, and intestines were used, inactivated thiamin in the fox's stomach. This was very similar to the disease in man of alcoholic encephalopathy in which alcohol raised the Vitamin B_1 requirement of the tissues, causing extreme vitamin deficiency. The discovery satisfied Dr. Green's curiosity, although ranchers had ceased killing foxes with a diet of raw fish.

Nor could encephalitis be neglected in medical research. Now Dr. Green was certain he was on the path to ultimate success, but it could be only after a long and tedious exploration of the behavior of the virus. He had gone far enough to be sure he could perfect a technique with a combination dosage which would permanently immunize silver foxes against encephalitis. He made no promises, nor was he asked to make them. To the Company distemper was of chief importance.

If fox diseases were driving laboratory work forward with feverish anxiety, the troubles of the scientists were not comparable to those of the fox owners. Hamburg had a second severe outbreak of distemper in which daily pen losses ran from 50 to 150 foxes, while Thiensville went through continual tribulation with the disease. No one understood why the southern unit suffered more, but Thiensville had little respite. The intensity of the disease varied. It died down in winter, only to flare in spring and summer, when the young would die in great numbers. If June were passed in safety, distemper attacked in July. Foxes that had received a dozen treatments of canine serums and vaccines might live through the summer only to die before the pelting season. The dose was increased, new remedies were tried, but nothing held down deaths. The animal loss in pups went as high as 40 per cent, and four thousand and even five thousand annual mortalities occurred in a herd of from twelve to fifteen thousand foxes. Distemper became a nightmare. Every scheme man could devise to control infection was useless, even the most ingenious elaboration of sanitary precautions. The feeding crews wore special overalls, rubber aprons, and gloves, walked through disinfecting fluid at the door of each yard, changed gloves and had aprons sprayed with disinfectant between pens, and never touched a sick or dead fox during feeding routine. Such ·measures doubled the time needed for feeding, and each evening huge vats of the gloves required for the day's feeding went to the sterilizer. Fox carcasses were picked up by a separate collection crew, and each carcass put in a special air-proof bag.

Yet morning after morning foxes sickened, carcasses were carried from the pens, and a pit large enough in which to burn from 150 to 200 animals was dug. Crews were doubled to perform all these extra tasks of a farm which staggered under an epidemic. The horror and hopelessness of it weighed down men's spirits. Even the months of reprieve were months of dread waiting for the inevitable revisitation. The research which was to save them was only a vague report, a mysterious process being carried on in a laboratory. Keepers lost faith in hypodermic shots, microscopes, test tubes, viruses, and serums.

On top of these big summer losses, the fur range mortality in the herd of twelve thousand pelters was 20.8. Pelters reached the range so weakened by disease that in giving the second immunizing shot against encephalitis, as many as 250 foxes might be killed on each drive. Only the magnitude of the herd enabled the project to survive, and it was a question of how long even such mighty herds could do so. But the Company determined some day the furring ranges would be free from enemies. For more than ten years the Fromms had fought fox diseases and hadn't weakened. Long-time battles seemed only natural to a Company which had waited five years to get their first silver pup.

The fine quality of the survivors in the 1935 fur crop gave the Company courage and they decided they were important enough to make a bold departure from tradition and ask the market to come to them on their farm in Hamburg, 1,200 miles from New York's Seventh Avenue. Since the beginning of the fur trade in America, fur auctions had been held only in the great centers of the industry, Leipzig, London, St. Louis, and New York. Pelts went to the market always, never the market to the producer.

A farm auction was a daring gamble. If successful, it would make fur trade history and add immeasurably to company prestige. If it were a failure it would jeopardize that prestige, built in costly national advertising; and not even Edward, whose idea it was, had any proof to offer that eastern buyers would make the long journey to Hamburg. The other three, none of whom had ever attended an auction, were in grave doubt, but even more eager.

"I'd like it," Henry said, "if the first time I ever saw a Fromm pelt auctioned it could be on our own farm. But will the buyers come?"

"There's one way to find out," John said, "and that's to ask them. And where else are they going to get a crop like ours of full silvers?"

It was a strong argument in the Company's favor. Not only was theirs the largest single offering of silver foxes in the country but it was the only real collection of bright silvers, and in a year when the public wanted brighter foxes. Popular demand for the rare coloration of full silvers had outrun supply. Style trends had changed in a season, but only generations of breeding could add silver hairs to fox pelts. The dark fox males, formerly prized as breeders, had left an imprint on the other herds of the country which could not be eradicated for many years. Fromm herds had never harbored these darker males and now Fromm pelts, instead of begging for fur trade favor, were competed for by buyers.

Henry's story of the silver fox, told to countless visitors at the Chicago Exposition, had aroused an awareness of bright silvers and of the Company that had pioneered them. That exhibit had completely ended Fromm isolation. The boys who had once carried guns and regarded all visitors with defensive resentment were now accustomed to a flood of tourists, eager to see the silver fox at home. No one had enjoyed this new era more than Frederick Fromm. He became the official guide, and spent his days showing his sons' farm to a curious public. He never failed to point out the first fox house built by John and Henry.

"That's how all this started," he would say. "And what you see around here now, they did in spite of me.

I didn't want them to be fox farmers, and they never got any help from me."

But always he spoke proudly. Frederick died at seventy years of age, and while he had watched the tremendous expansion in the enterprise, he did not live to see the real triumph of the silver fox. In 1936 it had become one of the most talked-of furs in America. It was being used lavishly in trimmings. The two-skin scarf was customary. The silver fox jacket, requiring five skins, had swept the country as a glamour garment, and evening wraps were the height of luxury, utilizing quantities of pelts. The old fear that the silver fox would lose desirability when no longer a rare and precious fur had been proved groundless. The saturation point appeared to be as far away as ever.

Stores throughout the country featured Fromm bright silvers, and the drama of a first farm auction would not only carry on the story of the silver fox, but would enable stores to assure customers that pelts had been personally selected at the source. Edward counted on this argument to induce the buyers of the country to come to Hamburg.

"If we are ever to market our own fur on the farm, this is the year to try it," he said.

Emotionally the farm auction meant a great deal to the Company. For years the Fromms had talked of the time when they could complete the circuit on home grounds. To Edward, who for twenty years had carried pelts to market and knew the bitterness of defeat and the intoxication of fur trade favor, the farm auction would be a milestone. The only fear was a refusal from the buyers.

In early winter the Company issued invitations for February. As the Fromms awaited the reaction of the fur trade they were more worried than they admitted, even to each other. If the audacity of the scheme met with a rebuff there was nothing the Company could do about it. Success or failure lay in a wholly unpredictable decision and even John, who usually considered mail, telephone, and telegraph an invasion of his privacy, formed the habit of dropping into the office of a morning.

The suspense was ended by news that a New York group had arranged to come by special railroad car direct to Wausau. The novelty of a fur farm auction had appealed to the trade, and a majority of the buyers was enthusiastic. Those who were not could not afford to miss a sale where competitors intended to buy silver foxes. Furriers throughout the country announced that they would be represented, and Pacific coast men planned to arrive by plane. Now the success of the auction was up to the Company. The Fromms, swinging into preparations, engaged a wing of a Wausau hotel, arranged for transportation to take visitors between hotel and farm, set up a display room in the warehouse, converted the boardinghouse dormitory of the girl ginseng weeders into an auction room, and provided food, drink, and comfort for nearly a hundred guests.

Two days before the buyers would arrive the worst storm of the winter set in. Snow fell for a day and a half and, as always after a storm, the temperature went down. The Fromms helplessly watched the snow fall and read the thermometer, and the visitors came to find fifteen-foot snowdrifts and a temperature of thirty-eight below zero. To the Fromms' astonishment, their guests liked it. The north woods were exactly what they had imagined, and even the few who had come in a spirit of skepticism were caught by the challenge of environment. Each became a stalwart man who dared rigors and hardships to wrest pelts from the northern wilderness. It was a magnificent beginning.

After the party had been installed in hotel quarters, and stores had been raided for overshoes and women's woolen hose for stocking caps, busses followed the snowplows twenty-two miles to the farm. The guests arrived chilled, and hungry for the big noon dinner in the farm boardinghouse. Long tables, flanked by benches, were set with enamelware plates and cups, and steel knives and forks. Kitchen and dining room were one, and odors from kettles and ovens of the big ranges met them at the door.

Farm atmosphere captivated. The Fromms remained themselves, and had made no changes in farm routine. Their only concession to metropolitan life was a bar which could serve any drink called for. A meal or a lunch was available at any hour, and Mamie Fromm, aided by a staff of girls from the neighborhood, acted as hostess.

The traditional pattern of a fur auction was not changed. A period for preliminary inspection is always provided for buyers to examine pelts and estimate values in order to bid by lot number. This inspection is made with care. A blemish, a faint off-tinge, or a worn spot can make the difference between an unusual pelt and a merely average one. The finest pelts are sold singly or in matched pairs, and the evaluation is a matter of the most painstaking judgment. Before the auction each buyer examines the pelts he intends to bid on and knows those pelts in detail.

Three days were allowed for inspection. Henry was in charge of the display room. A staff of 150 men carried in lots, or bundles, of pelts for the buyers' scrutiny. The long table for inspection was under a row of windows, and the Company provided white coats for the visitors, a practical and thoughtful attention, since fox hairs cling to wool. The buyers examined pelts, made cryptic marks in notebooks, and watched fellow buyers to see who might be bidding in competition. The display room was a paradise for fur lovers. Seventy-five hundred pelts were heaped on tables, hung from racks, or slung from shoulders of hurrying men. New York had held larger sales of silver fox, but never had so many bright silver foxes been collected in a single room.

When visitors wandered about the grounds their identification cards were inspected by uniformed guards wearing stars, cartridge belts, and revolvers. The sidearms were a Fromm touch, an idea borrowed from the policy of insurance companies, which had never considered the north Wisconsin woods, a favorite retreat for Chicago gangsters, a safe district. Although no raid had ever been made on ranched furs, an armed escort had always accompanied the fur crop to the railroad. The boys who had built Fort Moreland had seen nothing fantastic in two armed guards accompanying each loaded sleigh to the railroad, or in extreme vigilance now. And metropolitan visitors enjoyed the aura of suggested danger.

The auction began at noon on the fourth day. This was the real test of a market on home grounds. If the sale dragged or buyers were conscious of pressure methods or seller reluctance, the farm auction would be declared a failure, and one more disastrous because the Fromms had been given their chance to prove the soundness of the scheme. No amount of local color and stage setting would make buyers overlook the fact they had traveled a long way to buy silver fox and then had been denied a fair opportunity to do so.

Fur values fluctuate tremendously, and an auction provides a bargaining ground on which producers' hopes and buyers' valuations may reach a compromise. The auctioneer is a selling agent for the producer, but he is also an intermediary. Edward had assumed a dual role, and it was the first time he had ever held a hammer. His two callers, one an auditor of the Company and the other its New York representative, had never stood behind an auction table. The buyers were veterans in the traditional secretive bidding of the fur trade. Each had his unique method of attracting the attention of the auctioneer without revealing his bid to a competitor. Signals were furtive, a twiddled pencil, a raised eyebrow, a momentary glance, a finger to the ear, a slight movement of a thumb, while no other muscle of the body betrayed alertness or even interest. But if Edward had stage fright as he began to cry his first auction, he did not show it. A quick wit, a quicker intuition, and an instinctive sensing of the temper of the crowd, reassured buyers that they had not made the journey in vain. He kept the auction moving and lots sold quickly. If a sale was concluded and none of the three amateurs behind the auction table knew the identity of the buyer, Edward fell back to farm methods and asked the man to introduce himself. This informality and the makeshift auction room in the girls' dormitory were unique in fur history. The Fromms did not pose as anything but farmers, and the hardened buyers liked them the better for their lack of pretensions. And this friendliness helped the sale.

Silver fox sold 15 per cent higher than it had in the previous month in New York. When one pelt was bid to $450, the highest price paid since the depression, the buyers stood and cheered. The first private fur auction established a second record. It was the first 100 per cent sale in silver fox history. Not one of the 7,500 pelts remained when the auction ended, and the average price was seventy-five dollars. Silver fox had made a recovery and the Fromms had carried their pelts one step nearer to the consumer.

The unique sale had made news. New York trade journals carried stories and important buyers gave interviews to the press commending the beauty of Fromm pelts and the soundness of a scheme which permitted stores to select superior pelts on the farm where the fur was actually produced and thus give customers an indubitable guarantee of quality.

Buyers not only promised to return, they asked to be invited the next year, for already the Company was planning on an even more ambitious auction. Since this sale had proved the market would come to the source of the supply, the Fromms saw an opportunity to make Hamburg the silver fox center of the world. They would auction not only their own pelts but those of other ranchers. But as always, wishing to keep the Company a distinct venture, the Fromms planned to establish a separate organization, Federal Furs, to handle sales.

Chapter Twenty

SINCE AUCTIONS IN A WORLD CENTER OF SILVER FOXES could not be conducted in a boardinghouse dormitory, the new venture of Federal Furs required larger quarters. The Company planned a seventy-five thousand dollar addition to the warehouse, a two-hundred-foot wing of three stories, and at once began construction to make certain the building would be finished before the rush season of fall harvests. Also they engaged as marketing specialist an old fox man, Dr. William A. Young. He was a pioneer in the industry, had been head of the famous Booneville ranch in New York State, one of the farms wiped out by distemper. Dr. Young was both much beloved as a person and respected for his progressive ideas.

In the early summer months distemper broke out again at Thiensville, and now the infection had crawled into every unit. Crews and owners were tensed for another season of futile precaution, useless injections of canine distemper serum, and inevitable deaths. Medical research reached a new low in the keepers' estimation. Despite the Fromm Laboratories, experiments, and scientists, their weapons against distemper were not different from those used by other ranchers, and the outcome of their battle might be fully as disastrous.

Dr. Green's announcement that he had at last, in 1936, perfected a method to immunize permanently against encephalitis did little to reinstate science in ranch opinion. While the new method of permanent immunity put an end to the need of catching foxes on the range, it transferred an even bigger task of fox treatments in the pens. Three injections were required. A first shot of killed virus raised the threshold of immunity, a second of virulent virus and serum gave foxes a mild attack of encephalitis, and a third of serum alone caught these foxes still low in immunity and carried them safely through the critical period until they developed sufficient antibodies to provide protection. The shots were given at three-week intervals, beginning in late May, and now in addition to all the extra tasks caused by distemper a herd of twenty-five thousand foxes must be put through nine weeks of treatments.

The triumph, once so eagerly awaited, of furring ranges freed from encephalitis went almost uncelebrated. Losses from distemper were so disastrous that owners and keepers could think of little else. Nor did the Fromm Laboratories' report raise high hopes. Dr. Green summarized the distemper situation. Canine immunizing remedies had proved unsatisfactory. But the modified virus of ferret origin was progressing. The twenty-seventh generation had been tested on fifty-six silver fox pups with an encouraging low mortality. A still more effective fortieth generation would be available the following year. "It would seem," he concluded, "that a safe method for the use of virus is at hand."

To a company going through the horror of watching an insidious pestilence creep through the fur farms, a year was too long. If science couldn't protect them now, they must defend themselves, or at least protect their choicest breeders against the danger of contagion. This meant a safe distance from the Home Farm. They learned they could buy the quarter section of a farmer named Bohl, three miles away, and immediately did so. On this new unit they built pens to house fifteen hundred foxes. Three miles would guarantee safety and food supplies could be delivered from the headquarters ranch. All this meant extra work in a summer when the building crew was rushing to complete the warehouse.

The wing of the warehouse became more elaborate with each fresh idea that Henry sprouted. He loved to build and threw himself into this new project with real passion. A large, glassed-in sun porch was added to serve John as an office or a retreat in case of guest invasion. The room was thrust into the green of the forest. The Company hoped that now there would be no need for John's solitary night walks in the woods but was never able to discover if the scheme worked.

The first floor of the wing made possible a large and convenient pelting room, with long, sturdy tables and racks and wall space with pegs from which to hang the foxes. Bigger fur crops had cramped the former quarters. Now the Company was prepared not only for the present crops but for a future when forty thousand, not sixteen thousand, pelts must be prepared for market. The second story was given over to big workrooms where all the equipment of a fur farm could be manufactured. The walls were lined with wood and metal working machinery for making many thousands of fox homes.

The top floor of the wing was devoted to display and auction rooms, and lighting was especially designed for inspection. Harry La Due, one of the three men who judge leading fur shows in America, has said this room has the finest light for appraising fur of any in the world. If light contains either red or yellow rays, even from the reflections of buildings across the street, a cast is thrown on the fur; this is a difficulty in appraising the color of fur in a city. At Hamburg the display room has a northern exposure and faces the forest. Above the wall of windows is a skylight the length of the room. A shield of louvered slats on the roof prevents the direct rays of the sun from reaching the glass and insures shadowless light beneath. To avoid shadows and smudges caused by passing clouds there are shades which can be easily manipulated with ropes. Furs can be examined without an unreal tint confusing the valuation.

The enlargement of the warehouse made other changes possible. Rooms were built for storage of the ginseng stock pile, now the harvest of six years and promising to be that of many more. Extensive meat and feedrooms were rebuilt to meet the demands of larger herds, and refrigerating rooms and added trackage were provided to handle greater quantities of frozen meat. A grinder was installed with a seventy-five horsepower motor. It was the hog used in sawmills to tear slabs into sawdust, and it could grind frozen quarters of meat without preliminary sawing, handling fifty carcasses in two hours and crushing bones with no danger of splinters. (Only heavy molars defied the machine.) With these alterations the feedroom reached its final state of adaptation to the peculiar needs of a farm which fed more fur-bearing animals than any in the world.

Including the Thiensville unit, the Fromm farms used 113,000 pounds of food each day.

Other improvements were made. A gatehouse was built, at which auction visitors presented identification cards. The boardinghouse was enlarged, because three hundred employees had now outgrown the quarters built more than ten years before. New York buyers at the next winter auction would find more room, but steel knives and forks, enamelware dishes, and oilcloth would still be on the tables. In the kitchen, however, every electrical contrivance in the form of bread mixers, cake mixers and whipping gadgets would facilitate the work of cooks.

Construction work was finished before the fall ginseng rush when the Company would dig its first big harvest in several years. Root rot had almost closed in on the Fromms. It had been as constant as distemper, and for no reason anyone could discover the intensity of its attack was variable. Losses might run anywhere from 40 to 90 per cent. In the previous year loss had been so great that the harvest had been scarcely worth digging. Arthur had been experimenting with a formaldehyde solution to kill disease spores. This was not a new method in horticulture, but the strength of the solution was tricky. It must be strong enough to kill disease spores in the outer coating of ginseng seed but not strong enough to destroy fertility, and Arthur was not certain that he had perfected the solution. He believed he had the problem solved, but until his experimental garden had safely passed the third year of growing he could not be sure, and he wanted to be so before a large acreage was planted with treated seeds. The Company, however, considered the formula the lesser gamble. If it worked, it meant success. If it did not, they were no worse off than they had been with root rot. So treated seeds were used in the 1935 planting, and the seedlings had gone through the first of the three summers necessary for proof.

Two years of suspense seemed minor compared to other ginseng problems. The Company's assumption that ten years might elapse before a ginseng market would be re-established in China now seemed the wildest optimism. For four years the Japanese had been seizing territory in North China, and open conflict appeared certain. No one dared to guess how long it would be before the price recovered. But neither blight nor a war in China could induce the Company "to abandon ginseng lightly."

Costs, however, must be cut down. Production of a root for which there was, and might be for years, no market, was costing fifty thousand dollars annually, and every year brought new ginseng grief. If blight caught the garden the harvest was scanty. This year's crop, which had miraculously escaped blight, presented a washing problem. Washing root had always been the greatest handicap; it slowed digging, for digging teams must wait on washing. Different ideas had been tried, and finally the splash method was used, since this did not remove all the soil, and the Chinese preferred a light brown root. The root was splashed in a large metal basket which two men lifted and dropped in the stream. It was backbreaking work, and slow. A dozen men could wash only five thousand pounds a day, and washing the coming harvest of more than a hundred thousand pounds might slow digging dangerously close to frost. Also the root must be out of the drying room before this was needed for the crop of sixteen thousand silver fox pelts; ginseng and foxes were dovetailing in an uncomfortably close schedule. Edward said some way must be found to speed washing.

Herbert Kleinschmidt, ginseng straw boss, and Walter Fromm, arrived at the blacksmith shop the next morning with the same idea. A large wire-mesh cylinder, belt driven, should wash root as clothes are washed. The splash method could be achieved by building in shelves the full length of the cylinder and, as the cylinder revolved, the root would fall from a shelf to the water below and eventually be carried up on another shelf for another splash. The number of splashes would be determined by the length of time required for root to travel from the entry hopper to the exit of the cylinder. The forward movement of the root could be effected by the screw method. Cleats, fastened to the shelves and set at an angle, would thrust the root forward, and the pitch could be altered to hasten or delay the process should the preference in color change.

Walter and Herbert worked two weeks to build the washer, and were so sure it would work that they held up digging until the machine was completed. After that the machine *had* to work; if it didn't, there would be no time to dig root and splash-wash in the stream. Suspense and excitement were high the morning the washer was taken from the blacksmith shop. In the trial run the builders found they had succeeded better than they hoped. Three men could wash six thousand pounds of green root in an hour, thus ending the greatest bottleneck in ginseng culture.

In early January preparations were complete for the

1937 winter auction, to be held February 15 after a preliminary week for examination of almost twenty thousand silver fox pelts. Practically every buyer of importance in the country had announced his intention of attending, and more than a million dollars' worth of skins had made Hamburg the leading silver fox market of the country. The offering was made up of Fromm pelts and those of three hundred other ranchers.

The idea of a selling organization already had proved successful. Other breeders had been quick to see its advantages. Federal Furs' sales commission was 2½ per cent, while the cooperative auction held annually in New York by the fox breeders' associations charged 6 per cent. At Hamburg furs would be handled, graded, and valued by experts in silver fox. All commission money would be spent in national advertising to promote the silver fox, and this would benefit other ranchers as well as the Fromms. But the greatest advantage lay in the fact that leading buyers of the country would come to Hamburg prepared to buy their year's requirements. Federal Furs had unified silver fox interests.

The American National Fur Breeders' Association did not approve, for it, too, had become a selling agent. The deflection of three hundred members would reduce the Association's offerings in the New York sale, and other members were threatening to make the change. Now the Fromms' controversy with the Association was no longer on pedigree or color, but on methods of merchandising. And the Company, with a program for national advertising, spectacular auction and display quarters, large refrigerating rooms, an expert staff for grading and appraising, their first farm auction a proved success, a group of eager and important buyers, and an auctioneer who had already won his spurs, appeared to have the best of the argument.

The Fromms' own crop of fur was the largest as yet in their history. Ranges had held sixteen thousand pelters, and Fromm foxes were brighter than ever with a larger percentage of full silvers, though this percentage was not as large as had been anticipated because of a big loss from distemper. The 1936 epidemic had preyed on the full silvers.

In the pelting season the Company had achieved its ambition of pelting two thousand foxes each day. The assembly line system had finally been perfected, and bottlenecks which piled carcasses had been eliminated. Pelting was done in a series of small operations, each man performing only one task. One slit the skin on front legs from foot to elbow, a second slit the hind legs to vent and around. The foxes were then carried to a table four feet wide, and twenty feet long, covered with gunny sacks to absorb blood and moisture and protect the fur. Here hind legs were skinned out to flanks, toes cut out either with pruning shears or knives, and the tail skinned out almost to the end. At the second table noses were cut as far as the eyes, and the fox was hung on a swiveled chain from the ceiling. Next the head and neck were skinned to the shoulders and the fox went to the wrapping crew, because the pelt must not be bloodstained. A cloth was wrapped around the head and fastened with a rubber band and the fox went on to the back skinners, who ripped out the rest of the tail, stripped bodies and front legs, and cut out the front toes. The pelt was then ready for inspection. If there was damage it was easy to know in which operation it had occurred. Then records were taken from tattoo marks in the ears, the medallion carrying the number of the fox attached to the nose and the pelt went to the final dressing. This was done with a hardwood or bone scraper. The pelt was then fitted on a stretcher board and placed on a rack for drying. After drying, pelts were examined, graded, appraised, and put in lots, or bundles. Each lot contained pelts of as nearly the same quality in fur and color as possible. At this time came the excitement of selecting the best pelt in the collection.

Every auction had a best pelt, first selected by graders and talked of by buyers. Its purchase was an honor. The Fromms studied all their finer furs and agreed that fox Number 2989 was the most perfect pelt they had ever produced. In life its name had been Silver Celebrator I, and it had twenty-eight generations of known ancestors, but 2989 became its title as fur experts grew lyrical over its beauty. It was a large pelt without a blemish, silky and deep in fur, a bright silver with a distinctive black cross on the shoulder. Word of it traveled to New York. This was the perfect silver fox, one of those miracles of nature and of breeding. Fox 2989 became the highlight of the coming auction. Men talked of it as people had once talked of the Hope diamond. No one knew what its price would be, but fur men determined to possess it.

Less than a month before the sale the Company's lawyer, Charles F. Smith of Wausau, discovered an 1858 state law that imposed a tax on the gross sales of any auction held outside a city which sold other than a farmer's own property and products. The measure had been justified at the time. The business of early merchants had been hurt by itinerant auctioneers who disposed of distress goods in rural communities. After the law stopped the practice it was forgotten, but it was still applicable to the Company if the Fromms auctioned the fur of others. Since the act would, in effect, kill a project of benefit to fur ranchers, it ought to be changed. The greatest obstacle was lack of time. The inspection of pelts would begin February 8, only two weeks away, and before that many buyers would have already started for Hamburg.

State legislators agreed the matter was important. A statute was introduced and a hearing set for January 28. By speedy enactment and immediate signature by the governor, the law could be repealed in time. Edward planned to go to Madison with the Company's lawyer, and the difficulty seemed as good as settled.

Then the American National Fur Breeders' Association heard of the proposed legislation and prepared to oppose the new measure. Suddenly the correction of an out-dated law had become a fight. The 1937 auction, the establishment of a world center in silver foxes, and company prestige hung in the balance.

Time was the opposition's strongest weapon, but the Company won an initial victory when the senate and assembly agreed to sit as a committee of the whole to hear the arguments. Edward Fromm, Harry La Due, Dr. Green, fur ranchers, lawyers and neighbors hurried to Madison. Charles F. Smith, the first speaker, explained the miscarriage of the true intent of the old act, and Edward arose to make the main plea.

With his deep conviction that the new bill was just, he did not expect stage fright, but as he looked over the assemblage in the cold and formal setting of a legislative hall, his voice failed him. He tried a second time, and when no words came, he was truly frightened. The whole legislative body of the state was gathered to hear him;

he bore the major responsibility — and he could not speak. He poured a glass of water, took a long sip, and pulled himself together. Then the dam broke. Words flowed more and more smoothly as he explained how the Company had found New York auction methods unsatisfactory and how it wished to promote both fur ranching and marketing. Disposal of fur on a Wisconsin farm in the center of their important industry would permit small producers to be present, sense the market trend, and protect their offerings. A rancher unable to attend a sale in New York often found himself "sold out." Market trends and prices could be determined only in an auction, and men who had spent a year producing pelts had a right to dispose of them under the most favorable circumstances. When Edward finished it was evident he had impressed the lawmakers.

Harry La Due, whose life has been devoted to the promotion of better fur and fur ranching, imparted the lyrical touch. "Fur farming, to me, is the most satisfying, interesting, thrilling occupation of man," he said. "I've seen it develop from a secretive, backwoods, private enterprise to a world-wide, very definite part of animal husbandry. I remember the early pioneers, the fabulous prices for breeding stock, the groping for knowledge, the bitter disappointments, the splendid achievements, the trials and tribulations of those pioneers. I've seen the fur trade turn up its nose and then beg for their offerings. A law should not put further obstacles in the way of such men."

Dr. Green argued for the rights of man, contending that a farmer, whether of wheat, corn, or fur, should be permitted to sell his products within his own state if he desired. A fur auction was the traditional method of marketing pelts, and it should not be denied to citizens of the state.

The Association presented claims that the farm auction was aimed at the interests of the Association and would have a disruptive effect on the entire industry; that the bill was being railroaded for the benefit of a large, wealthy producer. They carried the fight from the joint hearing to an assembly committee room. This delay threatened defeat, and the Fromms wired buyers to postpone departure. They did so with reluctance, but a fruitless journey to a non-existent sale was worse than mere cancellation.

The opposition was strong in the committee room but the bill was reported favorably and passed the house by sixty-nine to twelve. It went at once to the senate, which suspended its rules and passed it twenty-two to six. As a legislative correspondent reported to his paper, neither branch "saw much danger in a bill which would bring business to Wisconsin." Governor Philip La Follette signed it, and the ancient act imposing a 20 per cent tax was dead three days before the opening of inspection week in the Fromm display room.

Word was telegraphed to waiting buyers and they flocked to Hamburg, almost as jubilant over the victory as the Fromms. But when they arrived they did not talk of legal complications. They talked only of fox 2989. Everyone wanted to see the pelt, and it was brought many times to the table beneath the long skylight in the new display room. Seasoned buyers would stand in silence, finding no words with which to appreciate a color, so clear and so unbelievably lovely, revealed in its true beauty. The pure light disclosed the illusive shading, the luster, the sparkle, the real magic of the bright silver. "That display room was worth building just to show such a skin," Henry said.

Men talked of nothing else in the week of pre-showing. Who would buy it? What price would it bring? Not until midafternoon of the second day of the auction did "2989" appear on the board above the auctioneer. Buyers looked at the number. Not a man moved a muscle but tension filled the air, tension that had weight and bulk. "I could feel it from the stand," Edward said later.

The bidding started at three hundred dollars and went quickly to a thousand. Now only the serious contenders were in competition and as bids went up by hundred-dollar steps the field thinned. At fifteen hundred only two remained, and the real rivals were in the open. Trencher Furs of New York and Marshall Field and Company of Chicago had prepared special promotion with fox 2989 as a spearhead, and neither firm had known of the plans of the other. Neither could afford to show signs of weakness, and yet eventually one must concede victory. The "ups" came fast. Edward and the callers turned from one bidder to the other. Trencher Furs offered $2,000, as much as anyone had believed the pelt would bring, but George Metheral of Marshall Field and Company signaled $2,100. Now no one knew where the price might go, but the New York bidder did not raise his head. Edward waited a moment, then brought down the hammer. Fox 2989 had been sold.

Only once before had a higher price been paid for any fox. In the early years of the industry a black fox had brought $2,627 in London, but no one had expected to see such a sum approached again. The thrilling climax to the long suspense of 2989 brought spectators to their feet with cheers. In the excitement the auction was adjourned until evening. Buyers made speeches. Men discussed the bidding as a race is re-run.

No other highlight could approach that of 2989, not even the million-dollar mark in sales that was reached at noon of the third day. When the auction ended, more than a million and a half dollars' worth of silver fox had been sold. Fromm furs brought 10 per cent more than New York prices. Federal Furs, the consigned pelts, more ordinary in quality, sold 5 per cent above New York prices.

Pelt 2989 went on to triumph. Its picture stretched from top to bottom in full-page advertising in Chicago newspapers. The drama of its purchase made this arresting advertising copy: "'Have you seen 2989?' they asked each other, up in the north woods of Wisconsin where Fromm Brothers hold their famous sales. Word sped that this number marked a pelt like nothing ever seen before. A skin so large, so deep and bright with silver that experienced buyers grew lyrical as a debutante at sight of it. . . . Last week, in the tense silence of Fromm's auction, Marshall Field and Company bought the miracle pelt — and made fur history. The price, $2,100, was the highest that a full silver was ever known to bring. Bidding adjourned. Excited speeches were made by buyers not easily excited." Elsewhere the advertisement considered the possible purchaser of the pelt: "We don't know who is going to wear 2989, but we know some things about her. We know she is quick to beauty. She'll see at once that this glorious fur with its thick, soft mane, its deeply marked black cross, its brave bright silver, is a king among foxes. She'll know that the quiet joy of its possession will be hyacinths to her soul. She may be blonde against its blue black, or dark in harmony with it, but she'll carry her head like a princess."

2989, most talked of pelt in America, was displayed in a glass case in the same fur salon where, twenty-four years earlier, Henry Fromm had asked a puzzled saleswoman to show him a silver fox, because he had never seen one. Henry, when confronted with this as a coincidence, did not find it startling. "We've always known we were going to raise good silver foxes," he said.

Chapter Twenty-One

AUCTION SUCCESSES OF THE NEXT TWO YEARS, WHEN the Company held three sales annually, autumn, midwinter, and spring, provided some defense against the tremendous losses from distemper. So long as the Fromms had foxes to sell and prices were good, they could survive, even though sale figures made the mortality rate the more deplorable. Federal Furs, too, was successful. At each auction more ranchers consigned their products to the organization.

Visiting buyers enjoyed the Wisconsin auction and spoke of the farm at Hamburg as "Fromm's Resort." In spring and autumn sun tanning was the noon hour occupation, and when the day's inspection work was done, swimming parties went to Rib River. Baseball was played in the horse pasture, buyers teaming up against breeders. Buyers protested the umpires' rulings on fly balls and grounders, claiming unfair discrimination. Being on the heavy side and short-breathed, they were in no condition to compete with men who grew ginseng and raised silver foxes.

Jokes were carried over from one auction to another. At the sales, where Henry always acted as one of the "callers," everyone wanted to sit in his section. Henry's head was bald and in fly season he went armed with a swatter. Every time a fly approached him he raised the swatter, and he also raised the swatter when he caught a bid. Even Henry wasn't always sure whether it was a bid or a fly. Buyers said flies were costing them $2.50, but no one would have been willing to miss watching Henry's intensive warfare against flies.

The auctions were still farm affairs. This was not because the Company recognized the value of an unusual homey atmosphere. It never would have occurred to a Fromm to change the manner of his living. Eastern buyers and visiting fur ranchers were the Company's guests and ate their meals at the long trestle tables in the boarding-house. Company wives still helped the kitchen staff, which both pleased and touched the easterners. "Imagine the wives of men who own millions of dollars worth of silver foxes serving us our dinners!" a buyer said. The wives never thought of it this way. As they would welcome a neighbor in their own homes, they were concerned with the comfort of the Company's eastern guests. The firm's widened circle had come about so logically that visitors from New York seemed only natural.

Establishment of a sales center for silver foxes accomplished several purposes. Fur ranchers not only met fur buyers but discussed their problems with them. Even the Fromms threshed out a merchandising bobble. It was carried off as a joke but had serious intent. The scheme of sealing a medallion to the nose of a pelt had not proved a successful identification of the Company's foxes. When Fromm pelts were used in garments, the medallion was a by-product. The nose could be cut off and sewed on another skin and often was. The proud Fromm insignia adorned scarfs of the sick cat variety. The Company purchased a number of these scarfs from stores throughout the country, selected the worst of the collection, and made a surprise offering at an auction. The rack was brought in with ceremony. Edward's extravagant praise of the quality and his story of the years of painstaking breeding necessary to produce such specimens was almost drowned in laughter, but it was a warning that this shoddy practice must stop.

In the spring of 1937 the fiftieth generation of virus was tested as soon as young red foxes, dug from dens, were available. The virus showed increased virulence. Further tests proved the ferret passage virus had been contaminated by a more virulent virus in the previous fall, while the thirty-sixth generation was being passed through ferrets in the outdoor screened cages. The work of a whole winter had been lost. The serial passage was resumed at the thirty-fifth generation, and the ferrets were moved to a special quarantined room inside the building. The room was sealed and ventilated with filtered air, and doors were opened only after a heavy mist of fly spray had been turned on for at least fifteen minutes.

Fifteen generations must be redone when time was so precious, and it was work that could not be rushed. Ferrets were killed two weeks following inoculations, the spleens tested for ten days to make sure these were sterile, then ground and tested again. Haste could be made only with infinite precaution, but the work of rebuilding generations was advanced as fast as possible to be ready for a large-scale experiment with ranched foxes in the summer.

In July, distemper flared in two blocks of pens at Thiensville. Each block consisted, as usual, of four hundred pens and was cared for by two keepers. The initial mortalities were heavy. Dr. Green suggested to Edwin Nieman that these blocks be chosen for the experiment with live virus. Faith in research was at a low ebb in the southern unit. Keepers, straw bosses, the office force, and even the auditor were opposed to experimental injections, maintaining distemper was bad enough without adding to the losses. In the face of this general distrust, Edwin Nieman hesitated. As part owner of a fox farm, Edwin had gone through eight hard years — reorganization, expansion, depression, bank trouble, encephalitis, distemper, enormous bills for useless remedies, and heavy cost in research. Now the doctor proposed that he embark upon a major experiment with live virus, attenuated and modified to be sure, but the very words "live virus" had carried a threat since the encephalitis disaster in 1929.

To make the decision even more difficult, Dr. Green could not assure Edwin that the injections would end his distemper troubles. "The infection has bored in so long at Thiensville that it can't be choked off suddenly," the doctor said. "Distemper is bad now, but it could be worse. You could have a wipe-out in those two blocks, and such an epidemic would spread to others. But if we go in this summer and clean up the worst of the infection, you can have a farm free from distemper in another year."

A scientist was talking to a man who needed a miracle. An ultimate wipe-out would mean complete defeat, and

Edwin Nieman agreed to try the modified virus. But his decision demanded courage.

When word of it reached the keepers, indignation boiled over. They recalled the fiasco when the live encephalitis virus had killed foxes. Keepers have long memories, and no man becomes a keeper unless he really likes foxes. Now even the owner of the herd had betrayed them and their charges to the ruthlessness of science.

The morning when the injections were to be given Dr. Green reached the farm at daybreak. He was prepared for trouble. Edwin, universally liked by his men, and whose opinion had never been questioned, did not expect a demonstration. He was startled when the group of angry keepers confronted Dr. Green.

"You've killed enough of our foxes," the spokesman said. "This time we're stopping that crazy needle business."

"This injection is the only way to save your foxes," the doctor said.

"Like the way you saved that lot of fine young silvers from encephalitis!" An old employee stepped forward and shook his fist in the doctor's face. "I was a keeper then and I remember how foxes dropped dead all around us. We've had enough of your meddling. Go on back to your college and leave foxes to men who understand them."

The group moved forward in angry protest. It had become a conflict between the keepers and the doctor. It was in no way a scientific argument. The keepers shouted threats and recriminations, and the doctor shouted back with more vehemence and passion. In the end the injections were given by a sullen crew, although no Thiensville man except Edwin Nieman had any faith in the procedure.

As Dr. Green had warned, the injections did not stop the epidemic. In both blocks foxes died through the summer, and keepers charged every death to the needle. Not so many died as Dr. Green believed would have, had there been no effort at immunization, but the mortality — 40 per cent — was higher than anyone cared to think about. This dismaying loss carried even greater import in the fall when, on top of the summer record, 20 per cent of the 19,821 pelters on the furring ranges died of distemper.

The time had come for appraisal. The Company posted up the books and decided it "was spending a lot of money to kill foxes." Canine antidistemper remedies had cost $100,000 to $150,000 each year, and once had mounted to $165,000. Each furring season had brought a heavy loss in pelters, and this year two thousand silver foxes almost ready for the market had died of distemper. Added to this were the high mortalities in the two blocks of pens where the injections had been given. This was the most discouraging figure in the entire appraisal. Edward called the doctor's attention to it as the two men looked over the year's report.

"Did Edwin Nieman tell you how many foxes we lost in those two blocks?" he asked.

"Distemper had gotten a real foothold," the doctor said. "I think a loss of only 40 per cent is good."

Edward stared at him. "I don't see how it could be worse," he said.

There appeared to be no common ground for argument. The Fromms were not convinced that a modified virus would save foxes. Their doubts made them unwilling to depend on it as their only weapon, and since research was being carried on abroad, the Company suggested the doctor go to London and find out what was being done in other countries. In the years when Fromm pelts were topping the market, four fur crops had been decimated by distemper and if there was any help available the Company could not afford to overlook it.

Dr. Green agreed to make a trip of exploration, although his faith in modified virus was still unshaken. Before he left for Europe he arranged for the laboratory to continue to build up generations of ferret passage, intending to be prepared for the next bout with distemper. He was in New York in February 1938 and about to sail for London when he was stopped by a long-distance telephone call from Hamburg.

The Bohl farm, with the choice breeders, was in trouble. At first only a few deaths had been noticed, one fox gone here, another there. Then empty pens appeared. At first keepers had accepted the few losses as the inevitable mortality of any fur farm, but now distemper was suspected. Dr. Green hurried to Wisconsin, made autopsies and knew the suspicion was correct. For the first time he had an opportunity to use the virus at the onset of the infection, and he telephoned the laboratory to prepare fifteen hundred units, now in the fifty-third generation.

But the Company had already determined on its campaign against this threat to their finest breeders. The decision was based on the record of the previous year, a 40 per cent loss in the breeding pens at Thiensville and a 20 per cent mortality on the range. In neither case had modified virus saved their foxes. Now they could not afford to lose 40 per cent of the choice breeding stock on the Bohl farm. Even more important, and John and Henry were adamant on this, wholesale injections would endanger the precious puppy crop.

In the early days of fox farming a female handled even in midwinter would be too nervous to breed in late winter. Now, although foxes were less wild than formerly, injections after the breeding season would end all hope of increase. Females were heavy and must have quiet. The noise of the treatment crew, the barking of foxes, and the excitement of being caught and injected would so stir up mothers they would never settle down for the whelping season. Abortions and litters of dead puppies could be the only result of injections which were not even of proved value.

Other methods must be found. Edward suggested sulfa drugs, which had been used in canine distemper with some success and might be the miracle remedy the Company needed. The sulfa product was not yet available in the market, but Edward hoped Dr. Green could buy a supply in the east on his way to Europe. Sulfa might prove useless, but would be worth trying.

This request was an effective announcement that virus would not be used in the present crisis. Dr. Green accepted this decision without argument and with understanding. The foxes belonged to the Fromms and a company which had sustained such losses could hardly be expected to continue an unproved experiment on the breeders on the Bohl farm. Dr. Green went east, purchased the sulfa for the Company, and then sailed for London. The fifteen hundred units of fifty-third generation virus lay unused in the Fromm-Green laboratory, and the ferret passage was carried no further in the doctor's two months' absence. What the ultimate fate of medical research would be was not discussed, and the Fromm future was, as always, in their own hands.

By March distemper had invaded every corner of the Bohl farm. The sulfa drug proved useless, and canine distemper serum was no more effective than in previous epidemics. The virulence of the strain of distemper was greater than any yet encountered. The precious puppy crop was almost ruined. Almost invariably all the pups in an infected pen died, as well as one or both of the parents. The Company suffered an 80 per cent loss of pups and a 45 per cent loss of breeders. Nor did extraordinary precautions arrest the spread of the infection. Crews were not allowed to enter infected pens even to pick up dead foxes, and these lay rotting in the sun to add to the horror of the plague. The earlier concern for the puppy crop was forgotten, as anxiety now centered on the parent foxes. These deaths were far more serious. For years the herd had been so ravaged by distemper that the Company was in no position to absorb such losses in breeding stock.

Finally efforts were bent only on restricting the infection to the one farm. Nothing from the Bohl farm was taken to the main ranch. Platforms were built at the roadside and feed carts from the home ranch stopped only long enough to drop the load. Workers were not permitted to visit headquarters. They, and even the farm itself, were shunned by everyone who had the care of healthy foxes.

The three miles that were to have safeguarded Bohl farm foxes were now the sole protection of the main herd itself. Then in early May distemper suddenly appeared in two areas of the Home Farm. Apparently the disease was of the same virulent strain, and if it ran through the pens, taking pups and breeding stock, the Company was finished as far as fur breeding was concerned. A herd which had taken more than twenty-five years in building would be gone. The Company's faith in modified virus was no greater than it had been three months before, but it was the only weapon left. The Company decided that Fromm foxes would have "either their first shot of the virus or their last." Come what might, a fur farm lost or saved, it must take the chance. Edward sent for Dr. Green.

When the two men met in the ranch office, the doctor knew this was Edward's lowest moment. For the first time he did not look at the doctor as he talked.

"Distemper has appeared in two spots on the Home Ranch," Edward said. "You say you never had a chance at an epidemic until it was a runaway. This one has barely started. You're in charge."

The doctor nodded. He didn't speak because he couldn't. This was the opportunity he had awaited so long, and it caught him unprepared. The fifteen hundred units of modified virus were all he had. And he needed scores of thousands to fight distemper in so large a herd. He did not admit this to Edward. It seemed unfair to add to Edward's heavy burden, and another man's panic would increase his own. It was his job to get the virus.

He telephoned the laboratory staff to put the fifty-third generation of virus into fifty ferrets without losing a moment, and to bring him the fifteen hundred units. Before they arrived Dr. Green had decided on his campaign. The amount of virus was too small to be used in offensive tactics. Defense alone was open to him. Certain pens had the disease and he must keep it there. With his meager supply of virus he formed rings of inoculated foxes around the infected areas. The Fromms must have wondered why a man who had always thought in terms of vast experiments on hundreds and thousands of foxes began his work so cautiously, but they did not ask, and he did not tell them.

In the laboratory Dr. Green cut every corner to produce more virus with the utmost speed. Where ferrets had been allowed to live two weeks after inoculation, he killed them in a week. Spleens which always had been tested for ten days to make sure of sterile material were ground at once. But despite the need of haste he took every precaution time allowed, mixing only three spleens in a batch. Thus if one spleen happened not to be sterile he would avoid a large batch of spoiled virus.

The first lot of modified virus was mixed, tested, and rushed to Hamburg in eleven days. With this Dr. Green deepened the ring around the infected areas. Each week end thereafter he drove to Hamburg with more virus to widen the protected area. As each batch of virus was used, other batches had more time to be tested and were becoming safer. Fromms and keepers undoubtedly attributed the small batches to a new sense of caution. The Company never learned until much later that on each trip the doctor had brought all the virus to be had.

Three weeks after the first inoculations the epidemic had not spread. The rings had held. At the end of four weeks there was no doubt that the epidemic was declining. At the end of the fifth week Edward stopped into the doctor's little room in the warehouse.

"We have no epidemic," he said.

Medical research, which had cost the Company almost a million dollars, had saved the fur farm. It had been a long haul, but for the first time in many years the Company knew they would be able to send fur crops to market after a season with no disaster.

Success in the distemper battle, however, had not ended medical research but had opened up further possibilities in biologicals. The virus was put through more generations. Distemper and encephalitis vaccines were produced for other fur farms and a large laboratory, staffed with workers and equipped with latest modern facilities, was built on the first experimental unit. This enlarged project was called Fromm Laboratories and was owned jointly by Dr. Green and the Company.

Dr. Green proposed to make the laboratory serve fur farms of the Middle West, and he envisioned an ambulance service which could dash out and bring in sick foxes and new diseases for scientific study. A special truck was built with a separate double garage to serve as a receiving room for patients. The fox which had produced so distinctive and unusual a disease as encephalitis might have others. The same idea occurred to the Company.

"Suppose Doc brings in troubles we've never had," John protested to Edward, "and then our herd gets them before he knows how to control them."

"The sick foxes will be kept in a special isolation ward," Edward said.

"How about the flies and bugs that will come in on this ambulance truck from the infected farms?" Henry asked. "Let them loose and we're in for trouble. Doc can't isolate a fly."

Dr. Green did not propose to do this. A sprayer installed in the ceiling of the garage would destroy all insect life in the returning truck. The ambulance truck, the receiving garage with sprayer equipment, and the isolation ward were prepared. And stood idle. No other farm developed a new and fascinating disease. Edward found the elaborate and unused service an amusing topic.

"Apparently other farmers don't have the troubles of the Fromms," he said. "I hear the isolation ward still hasn't had a patient."

"That garage won't be wasted," the doctor said. "There's still plenty of work to be done in distemper. Dogs have distemper."

"Perhaps those canine antidistemper remedies don't help dogs any more than they helped our foxes," Edward said. "Would your modified virus work on dogs?"

"Why not? They are a related species. If we can produce a permanent immunity for dogs, we've done something."

So hundreds of dogs lived in the laboratory while it was being demonstrated that ferret-passage virus had an extremely low virulence for canines. Lost dogs, unclaimed dogs from city pounds, black dogs, white dogs, big dogs, small dogs — all were added to the experimental groups. They rendered life unbearable for neighbors with the constant barking, but they served in the discovery of a permanent immunizing agent for canine distemper. The ferret-passage virus was carried to the seventy-ninth generation. Field tests were made with the assistance of a number of veterinarians, and finally the Fromm Laboratories could announce that no dog need have distemper. The research was a logical outcome of all the years when antidistemper serums were poured with such futility into the vast herds of Fromm foxes. This canine distemper became known as the

"Green Method" in honor of the man who had developed it, and it is used by veterinarians throughout the country. Unlike the fox vaccine, its value can not be figured in dollars and cents as those who have known the heartache of losing a beloved dog understand so well, but silver foxes have more than repaid their debt for that earlier research in canine distemper from which the foxes profited. Nor was this their only contribution to dogs. In the middle forties it became apparent that infectious canine hepatitis was none other than the old encephalitis virus which attacked the canine liver instead of the capillary bed of the brain as in foxes. The Fromm Laboratories sent their assistant director, Dr. Heinz Siedentoph, across the country to describe the disease and when veterinarians agreed it had become a problem, a hepatitis serum was put on the market. Later a canine hepatitis vaccine which gives lifetime immunity was made. In addition to these original research studies the Laboratories added another. Because of the similarity in symptoms of canine distemper and hepatitis, it produced a bivalent serum which in one dose treats both diseases simultaneously, convinced the Bureau of Animal Industry that the serum was essential in veterinary medicine, and procured a license for its manufacture. Today all large biological companies make this product which silver foxes pioneered.

Nor did foxes ignore their obligation to the ferret family. Research for a permanent immunization against mink distemper was necessarily slow. Foxes, an unrelated species, could serve as hosts for building up the virus generations, but they had one great disadvantage. Ferrets produced three litters a year in their work for foxes but foxes bred only once. A limited number of hosts, and these available only in the spring, retarded the work. In 1941 the fox-passage virus had been attenuated in twenty-five generations and after first promising success, was so ineffectual that the work was temporarily abandoned. The laboratory centered its efforts on developing a killed-tissue vaccine, and in 1942 this was carried far enough to give partial protection. But the danger of flash distemper epidemics in congested mink units was too great a hazard to wait for perfection. Since then two vaccines have been released to fur farmers, both of which are believed to insure lifetime immunity against mink distemper. Thus far this belief has proved correct, and every mink on the Fromm farm is treated. In the same years work was resumed on encephalitis. The necessity for three injections and nine weeks of treatment was a heavy company burden in years of labor shortage, and Dr. Green considered encephalitis prevention an unfinished task for a company endeavoring to raise foxes economically. In the end he was successful, and now every fox has lifetime immunity against encephalitis from one shot, given in the pens.

Perhaps the strangest twist in the fight against distemper was when the fox vaccine of the Fromm Laboratories stopped an epidemic that threatened to wipe out the silver fox industry of Prince Edward Island. The boys who had made a visit to the island long ago and looked with envy on the long established ranches could not have dreamed that some day Fromm foxes would save the herds in the birthplace of the silver fox industry.

In the fall of 1947 Dr. Green died in his sleep, which is the way a man of his driving force would choose to go. He had just returned from Washington where he had been called by Dr. Thomas Parran for a conference on a special polio research Dr. Green was doing in addition to his work as professor of Biology and Immunology in the University of Minnesota. Fromm Laboratories has continued under the direction of Dr. Siedentoph. In addition to protecting the Company's herds of fur bearers, the Laboratories sell annually three quarters of a million dollars worth of animal biologicals, which is something the Fromm brothers could never have imagined when, thirty years earlier, they asked Dr. Green to find out what was killing their range foxes.

Chapter Twenty-Two

Tнe summer of 1938 that brought peace to fox pens was even removing the threat of blight from ginseng gardens. Enough time had elapsed to prove Arthur's formula for seed treatment was saving ginseng culture. Now at his home in Thiensville he was experimenting with soils. Ginseng and its special problems had become far more fascinating to Arthur than orange orchards could ever be. He had plunged into a study of the root's peculiar needs and habits, had taken a postgraduate course in agriculture at the University of Wisconsin, and was sure he was on the verge of even more valuable discoveries. The Company could continue to grow ginseng so long as they had space to store it in the big warehouse. Each year one more room was filled with cases of fibered root, and now a great heap was to be sorted. It was piled from floor to ceiling and from wall to wall. In jewelry shops in China a perfect specimen wrapped in folds of silk was shown reverently to a wealthy client. In Hamburg was a mountain of ginseng.

After thirty years of driving and being driven the

Company deserved a moment of quiet, but they knew peace should never be confused with security in fur farming. Any year silver fox might fall from its high place in public favor, and at any moment some new killer might prey on herds. Also, exciting events were occurring in the fur world. There was much talk of the new mutations cropping up in fox herds. A few of these had been reported in the middle twenties, but fox breeders had called them "freaks," forgetting that originally the silver fox was considered a freak. The fox family had been casting off mutations ever since the earliest days of trapping, and undoubtedly fur farming had saved the rare color phase, the silver, from extinction. Aggressive hunting would have reduced to an improbability the chance of one silver ever meeting another of the same strain.

But ranchers, after rescuing one mutation, had barred all others, and in the first years of fur farming all variations — pearl, platinum and white-marked foxes — were killed. A litter of pearl pups which appeared on a Minnesota ranch was destroyed, and the Canadian National Association did not permit a freak fox to be housed on the same ranch with registered silvers. Obviously no fur farmer could afford a special ranch for a few foxes of a strange new color. One Canadian rancher, A. K. McNeill, had resigned from the association rather than kill a few white-faced foxes which he liked, and it was this insistence on his right to raise variations which founded the very highly prized white-marked color phase.

This controversy between Mr. McNeill and the association reminded Henry of a female the Fromms owned in 1917. She had a white patch on a paw and her pups had white patches, but Henry had noticed that her pups were brighter than those of others, and the black hairs had a greater luster. He was interested in the phenomenon, but the female and her pups were culled. The rigorous selective breeding practiced by the Fromms was hard on oddities. They were as stern with whims of nature as they were with old foxes which had carried the strain as far as possible. Although other ranches considered a 10 per cent replacement adequate for improvement, the Fromms replaced 35 per cent, and have replaced as high as 55 per cent in their determination to produce brighter, larger foxes of uniform quality. A company following so costly a procedure would not temporize with any fox family which showed a tendency to depart from the type they were seeking. This is undoubtedly one of the reasons the country's largest herd of silvers has never produced mutations.

New fox mutations had hard going through the twenties and early thirties. Breeding was largely pragmatic. A few ranchers with little knowledge of genetic laws but a remarkable memory for pedigrees had developed an uncanny ability to select animals which would "nick," as fur men called it, to produce superior offspring. Judgments were instinctive, but somehow such men — and John Fromm was one of them — could recognize animals with blood lines that could be carried to a high state of perfection. A good fur man cannot always state his reasons but he knows intuitively the difference between animals capable of heading an exceptional strain and those with definite limitations.

After the depression, registration in the studbook, formerly so important both in Canada and United States, was ignored, and line breeding was not so general. Off-color foxes were allowed to live. The platinum, the first of these mutations to be marketed, appeared in Norway, and its possibilities were recognized early. Matings between platinum and silver produced litters in which half the pups were platinums. Olmar Brager-Larsen, a Norwegian fox breeder, espoused the cause of this new color phase, and his work in promotion undoubtedly smoothed the way for all the mutations in both foxes and mink which were to follow, just as the Fromms' long crusade for the liveliness of the brighter silver fox had paved the path for this strange new platinum. The publicity campaign of the Fromms had made the public conscious of the attractiveness of lighter fur and pioneered the appeal of color which is so important in furs of today.

America was ready to receive the platinum when Brager-Larsen arrived with 116 skins of this rare fur. The pale and silvery fox caught public favor, and one pelt was sold in a New York auction for $11,000. Even as a promotion project, this sum was staggering. Custom litigation arising from this importation was not settled until February, 1947, when a federal court ruled that duty had been illegally collected by the United States. The decision held "imported platinum skins are from foxes which are mutations of the silver fox" and were not in existence at the time of the passage of the Tariff Act of 1930 but came into being in a litter of silver foxes "by a fortuitous biological change known as a mutation."

The furor over the amazing sum of $11,000 for a single pelt put all fox ranchers in a quandary. The Fromms were as puzzled as others, although they had spent twenty-five years making their silvers brighter. But silver fox had been esteemed ever since the first pelt of the creature was shown in Europe, and these new color phases of platinum and white-marked foxes might prove only a whim of fashion much too ephemeral to warrant a change in the blood stream of a herd.

"We can't chase every will-o'-the-wisp," Edward said. "And how do we know women will like these gaudy foxes?"

Henry knew he liked them and for him conviction had always demanded action. He went west on a buying trip and was captured by the brilliance of twenty white ring-necked foxes on the Black Forest Fox Farm. The ranch was in receivership and Henry could buy the twenty foxes.

"Even in the darkness of night they shone like diamonds," he said. "The color picked up light and you could see the outline of the whole fox."

Entranced by their possibilities, Henry bought the twenty on approval and sent one fox to Hamburg as a sample. This caution was unlike a Fromm, but Henry had misgivings as to the reactions of the others. His apprehensions were justified. John and Edward thought the new fox garish. "Women won't like foxes with white patches," John said. Edward did not care for the white rings around the necks any more than John. To them this was just a silver fox gone wrong.

John recalled this incident later when the breeding value of the white-marked fox was discovered through live fox shows where perfection of fur was the accepted criterion and ribbons were awarded for the pelt of an animal rather than for a long line of illustrious ancestors. Standards, too, had widened. Platinums, pearls, and white-marked foxes were now shown in separate classes, but judges had difficulty in choosing the grand champions. When the white-marked winner was compared with the silver that had captured first prize in its class, the white-marked was always brighter than the best full silver. The fur trade, too, commented on this fact.

Ranchers considered this phenomenon and in experimental breeding discovered that the white-marked fox could be used to brighten a strain and was a sure, quick route to brighter silvers. When the offspring of a mating of silver and white-marked foxes was crossed back to silver, the pups were brighter and the black was sharper. Ranchers who had worked for more than ten years to overcome the handicap of a dark blood line were able in two breeding seasons to bring their herds to the brighter tone demanded by the fur trade. Owners of the darker silvers could catch up with fashion, and one crossing with the white-marked mutation added dollars to each pelt. Silver fox farmers bought white-marked foxes, and the Fromms prepared to make their foxes even brighter. A characteristic of the white-marked fox Henry had noticed in 1917, when the Fromms had a female with a white paw, might have served as a shorter path to their goal.

"We could have made those ring-necks into good foxes, once we got the white patches off them," John said. "I guess we were like those old fellows on Prince Edward Island who were so sold on somber foxes they couldn't see the beauty in the bright contrast of the silver. We'd been chasing down one trail so long we weren't open-minded."

The Company's vision could not have been as narrowed by tradition as John implied, for in the lull following the defeat of distemper the Fromms made two departures from the single trail they had traveled so many years. Their first experiment with another fur-bearing animal was the blue fox. This, a color phase of the white Arctic fox, offered both advantages and problems. Very prolific, with as high as eighteen pups in a litter, it cost less to feed than the silver, could be housed in smaller quarters, and was the only long-haired fur except the platinum that was blue. But it was small and coarse-furred and had a woolly undercoat which matted and looked shabby with wear. It was not a fine aristocratic animal as is the silver. The Alaskan blue fox had always been in disrepute. At auctions Sampsons had sometimes been sold as Alaskan blues because a lack of guard hair was a similar characteristic. The Greenland strain, however, was a better fox, a true blue, and had some silver. The Company believed that by selective breeding this Greenland strain could be given size and a silver sheen, the blue tone could be deepened, and the undercoat improved. Blue foxes respond to selective breeding more quickly than silvers, and a change in color can be effected in a few generations. But unfortunately the blood strain either improves or deteriorates quickly and replacements might be heavy.

The company paid $7,500 for fifty Greenland foxes. The morning they were uncrated each man in the inspection group was bitten. No one escaped — Edward, John, Walter, Henry, Johnnie, Henry junior or the keepers. All had picked up countless foxes, but the two-hand hold effective with silvers was no defense against the cattiness of blues, which were such contortionists they could double back and bite the handler.

Keepers did not like them. Men accustomed to the reserve of silvers found these newcomers brazen. Blues would stand close to the netting and stare back, even at strangers. They yapped at keepers, their summer coats were particularly untidy, they were addicted to worms, the mothers insisted on dragging their young about the pen, and treatment crews dreaded their days in the blue fox unit. No one got through without at least one bite.

Furthermore, blue foxes are polygamous. This was a problem at Hamburg, where foxes had always lived in pairs. Thiensville, experienced in polygamous breeding, did not consider it too great a defect. Hamburg tried to adjust itself to blue fox habits, had only a three-pup average increase, and then decided the blue fox would have to adapt itself to the Fromms. No one had ever attempted to raise blue foxes monogamously but the Fromms did, and succeeded. They increased the pup average to five and a half and had contented foxes. Thiensville's increase with polygamous breeding was six, but Hamburg refused to struggle for that last half-pup. Blue fox mothers became accustomed to the continuous presence of the sire and appeared to enjoy his company. Eventually there was no more bickering in the blue fox pens than among the silvers.

The Company became the country's largest producers of blue foxes, but the significant accomplishment was the startling change in their appearance, achieved in less than eight years. Vitamins and proper food doubled the size so that four instead of six pelts were ample for a jacket. Color and texture were improved by selective breeding. The entire pelt carried a silver sheen, the fur was thicker and softer and the undercoat less woolly. The color became a lovely shade which can be described only as tawny blue because there is no term for a hue that has such life and interest. Harry La Due examined a long rack of blue fox pelts with astonishment.

"What you fellows have done to improve blue foxes is a contribution to fox farming," he said to Henry.

Henry smiled with pleasure. "Our blue fox is a lot different than those we started with," he said. "It goes to show what proper ranching can do for fur."

These improvements were all of practical value, but wholly from an academic viewpoint the Company proved silver and blue foxes could be crossed, although the two have an entirely different chromosome make-up. The blue has fifty-two chromosomes, the silver thirty-four, and the genetic pattern of the mating is similar to that which produces the mule. It had been believed that the two would not reproduce, but silvers and blues kept together from puppyhood paired successfully. Offspring of the crossing have forty-three chromosomes and are as brazen as blues and as sensitive to disease as silvers.

This sudden plunge into genetic theory was unlike the Fromm way and was the result of Johnnie Fromm's work at the University of Wisconsin. He was taking a four-year commerce course as preparation for Harvard's School of Business Administration, but being Arthur's son and a Fromm, he was fascinated by experimental work in the College of Agriculture and spent his free time exploring genetics and endocrinology. The latter led him into another idea which was in greater contrast to Fromm thinking. The Company had never challenged nature after the early fiasco when Alaska, one of their first silver vixens, had temperamently refused to produce young. Since then they had always honored nature in observing the habits of the silver and conceded a female's right to a year's support for a single litter. Nature had arranged it thus.

Johnnie, however, became interested in hormones. He and Loyal Wells, who had grown up in Arthur's home and was now head breeder in Thiensville, talked it over with a professor and worked out a hormone dosage to bring about two normal ovulation periods a year in vixens. The treatment worked. The boys were jubilant. The Fromm farm could double its production! They expected a little trouble in bringing about a simultaneous breeding season in the male but, having conquered one problem, were convinced they could solve the second. But they hadn't allowed for the obdurate nature of the male silver fox from which no hormones could bestir him. Thiensville had hundreds of vixens calling and not a single fox whistle. That experiment was abandoned. Years later the same thing was worked out successfully with sheep, but silver foxes will always be silver foxes.

A major and more important change in the Company's fur farm crept up on the Fromms. When John first saw mink in pens in the early thirties, he was curious about them, and in 1936 he bought several trios, a male and two females, more as pets than as fur-bearing animals. Mink ranching had been carried on many years but had suffered several ups and downs. Profits, always problematical, had ended abruptly in the depression following World War I. Fox men regarded mink farming as more or less of a rabbit hutch proposition. But John liked mink.

"You can get close to them," he said. "It takes two men to catch a fox, and that scares him. Mink — you can catch them, turn them loose, and they'll come back and peek around the corner at you."

Henry now had time to think about mink. At last his house was completed. It sprawled through three stories, and even he could find no reason to add another suite of separate quarters, another bathroom, kitchen, or recreation room. So Henry and John talked of mink and mink pens, as many years before they had talked of foxes.

Edward did not catch fire. To him the silver fox had always been a breath-taking creature, magnificent in its own right as it surveyed the world from its house top or ran free on the range. The shimmering coat and the bearing of the animal filled Edward with a sense of ecstasy. The pelt was lovely. Untouched, the skin made a glorious garment for any woman. The mink was a small creature with no real nobility, and its skin must be cut, resewn, and become a part of many other pelts before true loveliness was apparent. Since mink held no glamour for Edward, he could look at raising them as a business. The price of mink pelts in the late thirties did not show promise. Walter, immersed in ginseng culture, took no interest in mink ranching. Silver foxes were a common heritage of their boyhood dreams, but if foxes failed them Walter would cheerfully go on raising ginseng.

Henry's arguments were based on logic. Mink would permit diversified farming, which he felt was an advantage. The fur was more durable than that of the delicate silver fox, so durable even mink couldn't wear it out. It was a versatile fur too, could be used in many ways, and so survive a fall in favor. The mink would drape and was not bulky, while silver fox with its variety in color and length of fur was difficult to handle. Even more important, mink farming promised a new interest, and Henry, being impatient as he had been with ginseng weeding when the gardens were the route to foxes, insisted the Company should have mink, and good ones. The Company could afford to gratify its people's wishes, and Henry returned from his first buying trip with twenty dark mink, each costing seventy dollars. As soon as these were housed he made more trips, always looking for better mink or better color. Buying breeding stock and building pens were Henry's passions.

Thus began a repetition of the old boyhood pattern when Henry had read trappers' catalogues and written to fox brokers. But now Henry had a big car and could buy a hundred mink instead of trudging through the dark with a fox in a bag on his shoulder. He clung to his old habit of late returns, and John never knew how many mink he might have to bed down at midnight or later. The general lack of interest in this new venture did not disturb Henry.

"That's the way the Company works," he said, astonished this should be questioned. "Two of us wanted mink. Two didn't. But if four men agreed on everything there'd be no sense in having more than one man in the Company. A bit of conflict never hurt a concern if everyone is agreed on the main job. A scheme is worked out better when everyone doesn't see alike."

Henry didn't mean ideas were threshed out in conflict. The Company believed in the rights of individuals. If a member is convinced a new project will forward Company welfare, in some odd way which even a Fromm finds difficult to explain, the Company goes along. Thus all through the spring and summer of 1938 the Company received bills for mink and for wire fencing. John and Henry found a space in the forest on the outskirts of Walter's garden for a new mink unit but instead of claiming just enough to pen a small herd, they paced off a large area. Walter, who didn't mind living in the midst of foxes, complained a bit about the new smell, and Edward said, "Those are just some mink Hank and John want around the place." Neither realized this was the beginning of a mink ranch.

Henry, as housing expert for fur-bearing animals, took charge of building pens. John attended to details of the mink's domestic life. There could be no thought of duplicating a natural wild existence. Mink are warriors. Ounce for ounce the weasel family excels all others in ferocity. Even battles that do not end in death ruin pelts. Their teeth, sharp as needles, will perforate the skin of an adversary. Ranched mink must be housed individually, but apparently they enjoy this peaceful and separate existence. Mink, unlike foxes, are not monogamous, and matings in the wild are the result of chance encounters, and even a Fromm didn't attempt to change the mink's natural habits. Instead, John explored a wholly new technique in fur farming.

Henry attacked housing problems in an effort to achieve economy in keepers' time. Mink pens are small, made entirely of wire netting, and set on posts. Long aisles of these neat homes stretching through a forest give an inescapable impression of a contented and strangely busy little community. Henry's buying trips to other mink farms had unearthed object lessons in wasted motions due to impractical construction. A nest box in the center made inspection difficult, as the mink had to be driven into the nest and the box lifted from the pen. Or if young were to be examined, the mother had to be shooed out. The Company could not afford a fifteen-minute struggle with a determined mother or spend hours chasing agile animals that escaped when the top gate was open.

Henry placed his nest boxes outside the pen with a circular opening into the pen itself. A metal sheet, fitted in grooves, could be dropped to keep the mink either in or out. The nest box had two hinged covers, the inner of netting for easy inspection of a litter, the outer of wood to serve as roof. The bottom of the nest box was hinged to drop down for ease in cleaning. The floor of the pen was made of netting for sanitation and an extra layer of fine mesh was underslung in whelping season to prevent small kits from falling through. A metal tab on the pen indicated whether the mink was a light or heavy feeder. A rack held a card giving breeding history. Feeding boards and drinking fountains were attached to the netting on the side of the pen.

This general design is still followed on the Fromm farm. Improvements have come as John or a keeper discovered a detail that hindered assembly line methods or was a hazard to fur. When mink chewed the circular openings to the wooden nest boxes, these were capped with metal, for restless mink's countless trips from pen to box would wear even mink fur. Whole batteries of pens were built to test one innovation against another. In the big work room of the warehouse, where pens and nest boxes are built, there is still evidence of the great inspirations which went wrong — feeding boards and pans, drinking fountains, special safety catches, top gates, and catching boxes. To Henry mink housing proved almost as long a building project as had his own home.

The 1938 furring range held more than thirty thousand silver foxes. This was approaching the magnitude of early dreams. In one year the crop had increased by ten thousand pelters. These were brighter than ever, and no epidemic would stalk the ranges. To be sure, the furring season would have its problems. Perfection in fox coats would never adapt itself completely to assembly line technique, and there would always be weather losses. Rain at the last moment would discolor fur and make it rough or curly. Even the range had not settled the menace of sunlight on the fragile color because, after leaves fall, foxes loll in the sunshine of the last warm days.

Priming fox coats is a tricky problem. Pelts left too long on the backs of foxes go off in color or fur becomes overgrown. Priming must be a simultaneous process with fur and leather because only when leather is gray or almost white is the undercoat at its best. Older foxes must not be given too much meat early in the range season as they already have body size and the extra nourishment would go into fur growth. Thus the peak in color and sheen of the long guard hairs might be reached before the leather and undercoat was ready. Pups were still building body in priming season and could be rushed with heavy meals to develop muscle and bone structure. All these questions were natural problems of a company which was the only fox producer to use forest ranges for priming fur and which must operate on an assembly line technique to be able to pelt so many animals in so short a time.

Forty thousand silver fox pelts were offered in the January auction at Hamburg. Not only was the Company's herd larger, but membership in Federal Furs had increased, and in a year when both producers and buyers were disturbed and unsure. The price of silvers was not stable. Despite the tariff, Norway had flooded the market with silver foxes and no one knew whether the price would be further weakened by so large an importation. Uncertainty compelled fur houses, which formerly had purchased a stock pile for a year's manufacturing, to buy only for temporary needs.

Sales resistance was further complicated by an inherent defect in the idea of a farm auction so distant from the center of the fur world. Buyers had begun to act as a unit. One could purchase for many, and share costs of the long journey. At Hamburg, too, there was no possibility of the surprise bidder who might change the whole trend of an auction. In New York he is the silent man whom no one knows, who has inspected offerings, attends the auction, sits in a corner, and suddenly gives competition to buyers who had expected to purchase for much less. His presence has the same potentiality for drama as the man who has filled a straight flush in a poker game and lies low. But at Hamburg in the ten days of pre-showing, buyers knew which lots competitors would bid on. Treaties were made over evening card games at the hotel. Had silver fox been in keen demand, competition would have been sharpened in a group of purchasers, but the Fromms could easily be the victims of a falling market.

Tension was high as the auction opened. Federal Furs were offered first and brought prices as high as could be expected. No rancher felt the need to protect his furs with a buy-back. Producers and purchasers had found a middle ground for trading. But with the first offering of Fromm pelts, which always had sold at a premium, prices dropped. After a few lots had been disposed of, Edward began "to take bids off the chandelier," as fur men say when an auctioneer looks over the heads of buyers and accepts a mythical offer. It was an announcement that the Fromms did not propose to sacrifice their pelts. This procedure continued through several pages of the catalogue, each of which listed a dozen lots. At the end of the sixth page Edward stopped.

"The situation in silver fox is not good," he said. "But is not as bad as your bids indicate."

He explained that while there might be some justification for doubts as to the future of the market, the over-all picture did not bear this out. Good silver fox was in demand and would continue to be. The price must strengthen soon. "If you have not come here to buy," he said, "we will have to discontinue the sale."

It had the force of the wholly unexpected. Auctions had been canceled but never in fur history had one been stopped after it began. Buyers insisted the sale must go on. They had come to buy silver fox and should be given the opportunity. Edward agreed to offer the listings of six more pages. The auction was resumed but prices were no higher. Edward continued to buy back Fromm furs. The buyers waited, certain that the Company's faith in their silver foxes would be shaken. At the end of the sixth page Edward closed the book.

"Gentlemen," he said, "the sale is ended."

The announcement took the buyers by surprise. No one had thought Edward would dare to take so unprecedented an action. The Fromms waited behind the auctioneer's table. The buyers gathered in angry groups below and then asked for a place in which to discuss the matter. Henry led them to a large room used for cereal storage. The staff carried in chairs and the buyers retired behind closed doors.

The Fromms held a conference. They were determined, though they knew the situation might mean disaster. Then they heard men stomping down the stairs of the warehouse. The Fromms looked out a window. The buyers were crowding into busses bound for town.

Chapter Twenty-Three

ASECOND COMPANY AUCTION HAD MADE HISTORY, BUT not the kind of history the Company desired. Buyers returned to New York vowing they would never again go to Hamburg. Ten days later, when the price of silvers stiffened in the Montreal auction, they were not so vehement.

Edward wrote a letter to the trade, pointing out that the low bids at Hamburg were not justified by market conditions and that already facts had proved him right. The letter was followed by an announcement of an early spring Fromm auction. The same pelts were offered, the same buyers arrived. The bids were acceptable, the auction was a success. The trade wanted Fromm silvers. "The decision to stop the midwinter auction, which might have resulted in a major disaster for us, proved to have been wise," Edward said.

Although the early spring auction had provided a successful market for silver foxes, the Company had discovered the vulnerability of farm sales. Four years earlier they had served a purpose, had stimulated an interest in silver fox and carried the Company one step further along the way of pelt to wearer. Now this single step was not enough. With the price of silver fox declining and the use of the fur decreasing, a continued downward trend would make an isolated farm auction perilous. The Company had invested a million dollars in advertising, with the device of the Fromm medallion as an integral part of the cam aign, but what had been intended as a guarantee of Fromm production was still appearing on skins easily recognized as inferior. In the previous season more medallioned pelts had been sold throughout the country than the Company raised. If this continued, the medallion would soon be worthless and the Company's reputation jeopardized. To John and Henry, in charge of the herds, this was more distressing than the decline in price, but marketing was Edward's problem. He proposed a solution one evening when the four brothers and their families met for supper at Walter's. No one thought of it as a company meeting, but the affairs of the Company were a natural topic when the Fromms ate potato pancakes and syrup. It was like the early days when the boys had made cakes over a campfire while they talked of silver foxes.

"We've come to the time when the Company must complete the circuit from pen to wearer," Edward said.

He meant manufacture. It was a new idea to the others, but they had learned to take new ideas in their stride. Since four farm boys had decided they preferred silver foxes, they had been embarking upon uncharted courses. All had been logical assaults on barriers across their paths, and now Edward felt they faced a new one. Silver fox must be kept alive in the market. As only fur farmers the Fromms must depend on others to develop styles and push the product by opening fresh possibilities for silver fox. But as manufacturers they could do all this and at the same time protect the medallion, even profit from the former pirating. At least the pirates had made the public conscious of this unique identification.

The Company was particularly well situated to become a manufacturer. An enormous fur crop was a subsidy. A large inventory permitted mass production and a year-round operation. Fur workers could handle one type of fur instead of having to work on many. Silver fox garments would be not only better but produced for less money. And the control of the product would enable the Company to intermesh all the processes of carrying a crop to the ultimate consumers. One process could be made to serve another.

"We'll have to open an eastern office," Edward said. "We can begin with an auction and follow up with a factory."

A headquarters in New York was the most startling idea of all. No one liked it, not even Edward who'd proposed it, but the Company could take this big step forward only in the east. Fur workers, highly specialized craftsmen, were centered in New York and would not consider an untried venture on a Wisconsin farm. The enterprise must in the beginning be near the markets. Thus for the first time the needs of the Company were in conflict with the desires of the brothers.

"I couldn't leave the ginseng," Walter said.

Henry was even more direct. "And I wouldn't live in New York even for the Company. There are some things no man should have to do."

John did not bother to state his views. So thoroughly

had he established his right to a detached existence he knew no one expected him to live otherwise.

Edward agreed to stay in New York until the showrooms and factory were operating, but made reservations in even this promise. "It's a temporary detour," he said. "Once we're established, we can bring the factory to the farm."

Thus the last step in the circuit from pen to wearer was begun. The introductory eastern auction was held in the fall of 1940 in the new Fromm headquarters chosen and arranged for manufacture. The auction was a great success. Silver fox sold readily and for almost as much as it had brought the previous year. The factory was opened in January, 1941. Edward commuted between Hamburg and New York. Johnnie Fromm, who had completed his two-year course of business administration at Harvard, brought his family east and learned factory methods as, when a boy, he had learned to raise foxes.

The four farm boys had come a long way in the twenty-five years since they sent those first three pelts to the St. Louis auction. Now they were not only the largest fox ranchers in the world but Fromm-grown and manufactured garments could be purchased in New York. The great fur center regarded the Company as permanent invaders, but already the Fromms were looking forward to the time when their temporary exile from Wisconsin would end and the Company could be again a close-knit unit. They saw no reason why ranch and fur workroom could not go hand in hand.

New ventures never seemed to come singly to the Fromms. As Edward's project had carried the Company into one radical departure, a conviction of Henry's plunged them into still another. Two years earlier he had bought $70,000 worth of mink. "Hank just brought them in," Edward said. Company opinion of this purchase was dubious. The average price of pelts was eleven dollars and threatening to go lower. The Company now had a herd of fifteen thousand and in spite of themselves were committed to mink farming. Thus they were prepared for the exciting era of mutation mink.

Mutations were not news to mink, although they were to mink ranchers. In 1892 Henry Poland, a biologist, in his book *Fur Bearing Animals,* described the varieties existing today. Undoubtedly many trappers caught a silverblu, a pastel, an albino, or a blufrost, and had to sell the pelt for almost nothing because it differed from the accepted color. These freak wild mink were not as beautiful as present day mutations which are improved by selective mating and have an added color interest achieved by crossing two and even three mutations. But abrupt variations had been the history of wild mink as well as foxes.

Why these didn't pop up in the early days of mink ranching has baffled fur men. One has suggested that in the first years when farms of each district held only the strain of that particular locality, genetic departures could not be expected. Only later, when eastern and Yukon mink were imported to improve the middle western strain, cross-mating gave rise to mutations.

The possibility of mutant mink was unknown in the early thirties when a female mink of a strange new color was whelped on the Wisconsin ranch of William Whittingham. This kit, an elusive shade of bluish platinum, was the result of mating a native Wisconsin female and a male from the Yukon River district. Mr. Whittingham liked the color and hoped to produce others but in two breeding seasons the platinum female's kits were standard brown. Fearing her color phase was not heritable, he asked advice from Harry La Due, who had printed several stories of the sporadic appearance of freak fur bearers in his magazine. Mr. La Due consulted W. E. Castle, Harvard geneticist, who thought the workings of the Mendelian law on the recessive might apply to mink. To a fur farmer who had thought of heritage only in fractions of an animal — a half, a quarter, an eighth, and so on — the Mendelian law was only bewildering, although today any high school student in biology is familiar with it.

The greatest difficulty in handling recessive breeding was the need to forget all fractions such as half, quarter, or one-eighth blood. A dominant trait would have been easy to manage because it has the capacity to reproduce itself and a similar offspring would be instantly recognized. But like all recessives, the platinum mated to a standard mink would produce only hybrids which resembled the standard parent but carried the platinum blood line. These hybrids were a vital avenue to the final establishment of the platinum strain, which could be done by mating hybrids or by breeding back to the pure blood platinum. It was, however, this one-generation lag in attaining the platinum color which confused many early experimenters in breeding recessives.

Mr. Whittingham, still struggling with his problem of a single platinum female, one breeding season a year, and a strange genetic formula, was not too happy with results. Then Guy Ingham became interested, and eventually they established the platinum strain and succeeded in producing entire litters of this color. Meanwhile the Wisconsin ranch of Charles Whittaker had been blessed with a platinum mink and he was working to produce more. Mink ranching began to take on all the thrill and suspense of prospecting for gold. A new mink called silver sable and later blufrost, two-toned with light bluish underfur and dark guard hairs enlivened with silver, was reported on several ranches. Pastel mink, a recessive, was whelped in southern Wisconsin and on several far western ranches. This was a delicate shade of taupe and varied from light to soft chocolate brown. A white mink with black markings appeared on another ranch and was christened black cross and later Royal Kohinur. Apparently the time and place for an exciting color variation was as unpredictable as that of lightning. Mink breeders became mutation conscious.

These intriguing color phases made a revolutionary change in the Fromm's opinion of mink farming. The livelier colors were in the pattern of company thinking. Just as four farm boys had not liked somber black silver foxes, they had not warmed to the uniformity of the dark mink then in public favor. But brighter, livelier fur with interesting contrast was an oldtime creed of the Company, and now John and Henry were no longer mink's only advocates. All four brothers were caught by the possibilities of this new and exciting era.

Mutation mink could never lead to the kind of stirring crusade they had waged when the Company had first defied the powerful fox farming industry. Nothing would ever quite take the place of that early dream of raising better, brighter silver foxes. But they had made that dream come true and had succeeded in convincing the fashion world. So mutation mink provided a new horizon that beckoned them to fresh adventure. It would be a gamble and the first project the Fromms had ever shared with others. Until now their long-time guesses had been unique with the Company, but farm auctions and the Federal Furs enterprise had broken down their instinct for isolation.

None of the pioneers had any certainty these new shades in mink would prove of value, that the fur trade would buy them or the public like them. Nor had the new mutations been bred long enough to become fur of fine quality. Ranchers who had spent years producing natural mink with deeply furred coats of soft velvety texture could not afford to sacrifice these qualities in changing the blood line of a herd. Now, before these elusive shades would be marketable, they must carry the quality of fine ranch mink — texture, pile, sheen, and soft leather for the draping of luxurious garments.

Breeding stock in the mutations was scarce and costly. In some variations only a few pairs existed and owners refused to sell. Ranchers reported, too, that platinums were hard to raise, had a capricious appetite, were frail and poor producers with a litter average of two and a half kits. Whether this new mink would be worth the extra trouble could not be determined since it was impossible to evaluate a fur which had never been sent to market. Nevertheless, the Company determined to try to develop this fur of lighter, livelier color and bought both platinums and silver sable. The initial purchase in 1941 was $30,000. This seemed a good gamble, but in the same year the Company invested heavily in Kobuk breeding stock. This, though standard, had a bluish undercoat in definite contrast to dark guard hairs. Almost black mink was still in favor, but the Company's growing conviction was that the greater beauty in lighter, brighter mink must eventually win the fashion world.

The Company's keepers found platinums even harder to raise than had been reported. Valuable mink, apparently in good health one day, would be found dead the next morning. Henry Czech was at his wit's end trying to produce meals they would like, not to defend his reputation as chef for fur bearers, but because a mink which refused to eat couldn't build size or become a thrifty animal. The technique of their breeding still puzzled ranchers. Men accustomed to dividing an animal by halves and quarters could find no conviction in a theory that heritage depended on whether a mink did or did not carry the genes of a mutation. Mink farmers who had only finished grade school began to pore over textbooks and struggle with such unfamiliar terms as genes, chromosomes, homozygous and heterozygous. Even the Fromm boys' early success with the famous outcaste mother fox didn't clear up the matter for them.

"I don't know why," John said later. "We'd been working with a recessive mutation for twenty-five years, but we'd never thought of it that way."

To Johnnie Fromm, who had been fascinated by genetics when in the university, genes were no mystery. He read an article in the *American Fur Breeder* written by Herman Bock, a rancher who'd had success with platinums. Diagrams showed mink men the result of various matings.

Thus, Bock pointed out, a rancher might breed to produce all platinums, pursue a slower course by mating half blood with platinum to produce a split litter, or an even slower course of mating half bloods with half bloods. But most ranchers choose the speediest course in their eagerness to break into the new game of mutation breeding. Trios of pure platinum were at a premium, the price fixed by the association of mutation breeders and every member pledged to observe it. Half bloods had no price rating. Even as pelts they were considered undesirable since they were somewhat lighter than very dark mink then in fashion favor.

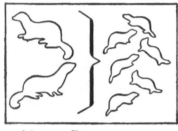

MATING PLATINUM WITH
PLATINUM

MATING PURE DARK WITH
PLATINUM

MATING HALF BLOOD WITH
PLATINUM

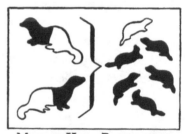

MATING HALF BLOOD WITH
HALF BLOOD

"If we could pick up a few dozen half blood females and buy enough pure blood males to cover them, we'd get half litters of platinum," Johnnie said to Edward. "That's the way it works genetically."

"But how do we know the public is going to like them?" Edward asked.

"We can't know until the mutation is on the market. But after the color catches on we'll have to pay real money for half bloods."

Edward and Johnnie went shopping. The Company bought 106 half blood females for forty dollars each and a dozen pure blood males to cover.

"Johnnie thinks he can do something with those half bloods," Edward explained to the astonished rancher.

In the following breeding season the half blood females produced four hundred kits. Half of these were platinum, and in a year when trios of this color were selling for twelve hundred dollars. The remainder of the litters were half bloods, their breeding value now established. Thus the Fromm platinum herd, one of the country's largest, was begun.

In 1942 the Company spent more than $30,000 on mutations. They bought platinums both pure bred and half bloods, and pastels for which they paid $1,000 a trio, thus adding another recessive to the breeding problem. They paid $2,000 for their first pair of Black Cross, which Loyal Wells found on a southern ranch. The Company was definitely in the mutation game. No one knew which of the new colors, if any, would be accepted. Not all the color phases would win fashion favor, but a Company which had converted the women of America to brighter silver foxes believed these same women would see the beauty in the glamorous new shades of mink.

Even before America entered World War II, ginseng developed a new trouble, manpower shortage. In 1940 factories supplying war materials robbed the farms. The draft added to the shortage and declaration of war made it complete. Where husky youths could once be had for ginseng crews, grandfathers and girls must do the work. Digging root requires muscle, and with additional manpower unobtainable, harvesting twenty-two acres before frost was impossible. Mature roots left in the ground until spring might rot and be worthless. Fall approached and there was still no solution. A machine to serve the purpose had never been built.

The ginseng boss, Herbert Kleinschmidt, saw an obsolete double potato digger in a dealer's warehouse. It had proved unsatisfactory for potatoes, but its width would exactly span a four and one-half foot ginseng bed. Herbert was sure he and Walter could install a central plow to channel roots and soil. Edward bought the digger by telephone, sight unseen. Power would be the greatest problem. The digger must travel slowly through a bed, displacing four and one-half feet of soil and shaking earth from roots on a vibrating apron.

Walter and Herbert took it to the blacksmith shop. Ten days later they produced a machine that worked.

A center plow channeled roots. Sideboards held roots within the bed. The vibrating apron spewed roots onto the ground at the rear. One tractor drew the equipment and a second furnished power. The two-tractor plan had been the solving inspiration, and neither man knew to whom belonged the credit for the idea.

"All we cared was that we'd saved the crop," Herbert said. "We had to find a way to do that."

Having to find a way, and the sense of satisfaction when the way was found, probably accounted for the great number of homemade tools invented for a special purpose on the Fromm farm. This spirit began at the top in the early years. As workers were added they shared it, until the attitude of "having to find a way to do it" sprawled as widely as the farm itself. Demands on ingenuity have always been a part of the adventure of the pioneer, and the Company has never ceased to be one, nor has it ever become anything but a farm.

"You can't run a farm the way you run a business," Edward said. "Every man on a farm is too important."

This sense of an individual's importance has aroused great crew pride in the machines devised to meet any special need or situation. The crews refer to these as "patents," and the greater the crisis the more acclaim the inventor is accorded. Walter and Herbert met a real crisis when skeleton crews and the weather combined against ginseng. The raised beds with sideboards had always been made by hand, and a crew of ten could put in beds on four acres in two weeks. But this fall continuous rain made early preparation of beds impossible, and in the scanty season left, planting a crop of ginseng seed apparently was hopeless. Moreover, the new power digger had made wooden sideboards a problem. Not only were they costly and a source of trouble when frost heaved out supporting stakes, but now all sideboards must be removed before the new digging machine could enter. Again Walter and Herbert went to the blacksmith shop.

Their patent, finished, looked like the work of a pair of demented magpies, but, tractor drawn, it moved across the land, laying beds behind it with the ease of a hen dropping eggs. Two men could do four acres in a day, which reduced the cost of each bed from ten dollars to four cents. The machine was headed with a heavy metal dragger to level the ground. This was followed with a steel pan weighted with rocks to act as crusher. The bed shaper was a fixed frame of two high planks four feet six inches apart and narrowing at the rear to leave a well shaped bed. Two metal rollers on top of the planks rounded the upper edges of the bed and packed the soil firmly. Harrows were mounted between the planks, and at the rear was a heavy steel plate manually operated by a crew member who made sure the proper pressure left the bed smooth. Devising a piece of equipment to perform these multiple duties had afforded a lot of fun for Walter and Herbert. It was a true collaboration as each tried to outdo the other in inspired gadgets.

In one week the Company put in its fall planting on schedule, and ginseng had been carried into another mechanized process. Now only treading out the seeds from the berries, weeding the plants, picking up the harvested roots, and defibering and sorting them need be done by hand.

Ingenuity devised many short cuts as war drained young men from fur and ginseng. The labor shortage threatened Henry's reforesting project begun in the middle thirties. He had always planted trees, just as he had always carried tools in his car to repair a culvert or to remove an obstruction on company roads. The company forest held a special significance for Henry. To him, trees, unlike ginseng, were a physical assurance of perpetuity. He was grateful to ginseng for feeding foxes, but trees could always stand on the vast holdings. Reforestation had caught his imagination, and he had plunged into it with all the fervor he had given to silver foxes.

Henry kept a tally. He considered years in which he planted only a half-million trees as merely keeping abreast of possibilities, but when a million trees were set in the ground he'd made a big step forward. Sometimes when his planting crew was sorely needed elsewhere, the others spoke of it as "Henry's project," but he never called it anything but "company trees." He guarded them with all the zeal he would have given to any other property of the Company. When the first selection, white pine, fell victim to blister, Henry's anger drove crews through the forest to remove wild current, gooseberry, and other shrubs which spread the infection, but at last he admitted he could not make the forest safe for white pine and accepted spruce and Norway. To offset labor shortage, he devised techniques and machinery which would enable the project to continue. A million trees would plant a section, but in the war years he must be contented with half this acreage.

"We'll never live to see those trees mature," he said, "and perhaps our children won't. But their children will have at least twelve thousand acres of forest for sustained yield logging, and that's the way logging will be done in their time."

Young Henry and his sister, Ardene, were still in college, but Henry never doubted that sometime they would return and that a third generation would live in Hamburg to serve and be served by the Company. In company trees he found expression of this conviction.

After farm auctions ceased and Federal Furs no longer existed, Dr. Young, the marketing specialist, took over farm health problems. Veterinarian and a pioneer in fox ranching, he had a real enthusiasm for the physical welfare of fur bearers, and these problems were at hand. The lull following control of distemper was short. Pen mortalities were increasing. Dr. Young set up a laboratory in a corner of the warehouse, made autopsies and then sent for Edward.

"You've lost plenty of foxes with distemper, but do you know how many you've lost from hookworm, lungworm, and just ordinary roundworms?" he demanded. "Know what hookworms do to foxes? Just what they do to people."

The fiery little doctor had become an impassioned crusader. "Look at this lung!" he exclaimed. "Not enough good tissue left for an active fox to breathe with. As for roundworms, chances are your pups get a dose of them with their first milk from an infected mother."

The Company, after thirteen long years of epidemics, now faced a fresh threat to foxes. Keepers and owners had been aware of parasites but hadn't realized they had made so big an invasion. While Dr. Green and the Company had been gunning for the big killer, lesser killers had moved in on them. John, Henry, and the keepers refused to believe the situation was as serious as Dr. Young insisted. Because all foxes are vulnerable to parasites, from time to time vermifuges had been administered. But ordinary vermifuges do not eradicate the hookworm.

This is a tenacious parasite. It has a cup-shaped mouth with cutting plates and can fasten to walls of the intestine and live on the blood of its host. The warning symptom is the poor condition of the herd. Dr. Young continued to weigh foxes, perform autopsies on those that had died of edema, and showed the evidence of pinhead hemorrhages. Men who had the custody of foxes tried to avoid him, but the doctor was as tenacious as the hookworm itself, and at last everyone admitted a wholesale attack on hookworm must begin.

The early method, use of carbon tetrachloride given in hard capsules, was thoroughly in disrepute. Ranchers who had tried it had lost as high as 75 percent of their herds. The drug caused a slow destruction of the tissue of liver and spleen and if, in administration, the capsule were broken and the fox inhaled the drug he was asphyxiated. Later, carbon tetrachloroethylene in a soft capsule was used. This drug had no bad aftereffects and soft capsules were safer, but the treatment still held danger. The capsule must be placed well down the throat and past the larynx.

Tools had been devised for giving medicine to foxes, but Lawrence Schult, boss of the treatment crew, had refused to use the metal speculum to hold the mouth open because it was inserted in front, forced the jaws apart, and was apt to break the teeth. Also its manipulation was almost impossible while holding a fox. The forceps for inserting a capsule was equally unsatisfactory. It was of poor workmanship, did not control the capsule securely, and injured throats. Lawrence used the earliest method, a round notched stick of wood inserted at the side of the jaw and turned to keep the throat open, with a small rubber hose for insertion in the throat. It was slow, but it did not injure foxes.

This technique held little hope for wholesale pilling. In a ten-hour day the treatment crew could pill only four hundred foxes, and control of hookworm demanded that pelter pups be given five pills at monthly intervals, breeder pups six or more, and adult foxes one pill, two if possible. The men needed tools that could be used with speed and safety, as even with the greatest care the loss from asphyxiation was at least one per cent.

When the first fox died in Lawrence's arms he could not understand what had happened. Apparently science had discovered another way to kill foxes. Dr. Young showed by autopsy what had occurred. Lawrence did not grasp the idea at the first autopsy, or in half-a-dozen, but at last light broke. He saw what he had to do to pill with safety.

"That's how I learned," he said, "and how I came to believe that Doc was right on this pilling business. But we had to find a way to do it."

Lawrence went to the blacksmith shop with a set of fine German surgical instruments and an idea.

He developed a new speculum built on the plier principle. It was inserted in the side of the mouth and held the jaws open without causing struggle. This could be locked in position, leaving the fox's head in complete control of the handler. He designed forceps in three sizes, for young pups, medium pups, and adults, for inserting the capsule in the throat. These were curved to conform with the shape of the throat, with capsule grips at the end.

With the new tools and a trained crew, two thousand foxes could be pilled in a ten-hour day. With men not available, the Company employed boys and girls just out of high school and in so doing achieved a super-assembly line plus a sporting instinct. Youth had pep and none of the caution that causes an adult to hesitate before grasping a fox. A treatment crew consisted of ten boys and four girls. They could catch a kennel of pups, vaccinate for distemper, pill, and return the foxes to the kennel in five minutes. The animals had no time to become nervous and scarcely knew what had happened to them before the crew had moved on.

Teamwork was of a high order. Each boy selected a pup, ran it down, caught it by the tail, slid a hand down the back, grasped the neck, and brought it to a girl who

stood at the door to swab with disinfectant and make
sure every pup had been caught. The "grabbers" walked
in a procession around a circle to a second girl who administered the injection. A third girl "folded" the fox
for pilling so that the grabber could hold all four legs
and the tail with the same hand and have the pup in
complete control to be offered to the girl who operated
the speculum. Then, with the pup's neck curved in exactly the correct position, Lawrence inserted the forceps
down the throat and released the capsule.

This system made it possible for the crew in one season to give six pills to each of 35,000 pups and one to
19,600 breeders.

"That's 229,600 pills in one season," Dr. Young said.
"We couldn't have done it without those tools Lawrence
Schult made in the blacksmith shop."

This extensive pilling process was achieved within a
year. It had become a race between the Company and
the worm. In one unit a thousand pups were lost in a
crop of 3,200 before the treatment crew could reach
them. Dr. Young had been proved right, and he was
given a real laboratory. The little building which had
served as gatehouse was enlarged and equipped to
handle diseases of fur bearers. He was barely established
when pen deaths began to rise alarmingly, and autopsies
showed the lungworm was presenting as great a hazard.

This parasite could not be controlled by pilling. The
life cycle of the lungworm that attacks foxes is still not
definitely known, but its eventual destination is the
lungs and air passages. The source of the infection is
contaminated ground where eggs of the worm will lie
dormant for years and then hatch. No drug can eradicate them. The only defense is to remove the fox from

the infested soil, and pups are especially vulnerable. The parasite is treacherous because it can be widespread before a rancher is aware of it, and at Hamburg lungworms were as serious a menace as encephalitis had been. If deaths continued at the same rate, in another year the Company might lose half the puppy crops.

The only preventative was to build new kennels with wire mesh floors set high above infected ground. In past years of ceaseless construction the Company had purchased more than a million and a half posts and wire netting which if rolled out would reach across the continent. Now they needed more. Wire-floored kennels were a must when it was almost impossible to buy either lumber or netting. But the future of the herd depended on the kennels, and this enormous project was begun.

Mink do not have worms, a fact that endears them to keepers, but they have other and distinctive troubles. One is stones in bladder and kidneys. No one knows why mink should have calculus deposits, but it is so common a cause of death, especially in whelping season, that it is assumed to be the answer until autopsy reveals otherwise. Dr. Young turned to medical reports of research among humans and found a suggestion that it might be due to an overdose of vitamins, with D the chief offender. This opened an avenue for experiment. Cod liver oil fed to mink was fortified with vitamin D, and the daily ration was cut in half. Bladder stones continued, but autopsies showed the calculi were now grains of sand instead of stones the size of a man's thumb. Later the Company stopped feeding oil and deaths from stones became infrequent. In 1950 and 1951 the mink were given cod liver oil twice a week and keepers reported an increase in deaths from calculi in the 1952 whelping season. At the present time no cod liver oil is being given and keepers are certain the 1953 whelping season will prove them right in their contention. The Company does not entirely agree with this.

"The experiment hasn't been carried on with enough scientific accuracy to eliminate all other possible causes of this trouble," Edward said. "Until this is done, no conclusions can be drawn."

There will always be frontiers for exploration. No one knows when a virus may accommodate itself to a new and comfortable haven, make an adaptation and flare up. Other mink diseases, nephritis and fatty degeneration of liver tissues, have yet to be conquered. Oddly enough, a creature which in the wilds fishes in creeks, swims in icy water, and is often chilled by cold winds when drenched, is extremely susceptible to pneumonia in pen life and must be protected from wet and cold. Perhaps pneumonia deaths in the wilderness are greater than have been realized, and this may be true of other diseases. Dr. Green's study of the ten-year cycle of the depletion of the varying hare proved it to be the result of shock disease. Parasites and viruses attack animals in wild life, and perhaps fur farmers are dealing with natural hazards that account in some measure for the reduction of wild fur.

Left to herself, nature has always achieved a balance, even though she has been forced to drastic measures on occasion. Mink, foxes, beavers, buffaloes, wolves, or bears might have overrun this continent had it not been for diseases, birth rates, and carnivorous foes. The defenseless rabbit survived through fecundity, and buffaloes had enough grass because cows dropped only one calf a year. As late as 1947 crowded marshes were relieved by an epidemic among muskrats. Predatory fur bearers were limited by food supply. Their numbers were kept down by a periodic disease which in great part destroyed the varying hare. Even the Indian fitted into nature's scheme. He only nibbled at the herds of deer, buffalo, caribou, and antelope.

When a white man stepped ashore in America he began to upset nature's balance. Fur was the land's first product. Fur led explorers across the continent and north to the Arctic. Fur opened the western United States, and the trade was so devastating that it eliminated itself in two decades. In this century the airplane and outboard motor have carried skillful and aggressive white trappers into the most remote districts of America, and the Russians have adopted similar tactics in Siberia. The last sources of wild fur have been tapped.

Man prepared to meet this depletion. Without knowledge of his project, he began with crude cages in farmyards. He met reverses, but he kept on. New animals were domesticated and made to serve. Ten years ago fur breeding had been carried past the experimental stage. The industry had proved it could supply a product which is so necessary that the world no longer ranks fur as a luxury for the few. The industry has also proved it could supply better fur than is caught in the wilds. Selective breeding, proper housing, correct feeding, disease prevention, and a controlled pelting period have improved the natural product.

Mature and established, the fur industry was ready for its most exciting period when mutations, once isolated genetic accidents, were produced in numbers. In early 1942 men who had pioneered the platinum mink met to consider its presentation to the public. They did not have enough skins to sell through retail channels. A mink coat required at least sixty well matched pelts which must be selected from several hundred. So limited an offering might make the platinum only an oddity, yet the way must be paved for the sizable crop of 1943.

The pioneers decided to present the only platinum mink coat in the world to the American Theater Wing to be auctioned for the benefit of the Stage Door Canteen. No single rancher had enough pelts but more than a dozen joined in the venture. The selection of the individual mink to be given was made by Herbert Mezger and was probably the most spectacular feat of grading ever accomplished in the fur industry. Mr. Mezger is one of the three judges at important fur shows of the country. Of necessity, the mink were selected while alive and Mr. Mezger traveled from ranch to ranch, carrying the color in his eye and selecting only animals of the desired tint. Even grading mutation pelts is difficult as the delicate color has many shades, and these shades can be determined only by comparison. Grading on the hoof had never been attempted, but Mr. Mezger did it, and successfully.

"We need three of your herd," he would say at one ranch and, taking four at the next, ten at another, he kept on until the requisite sixty had been selected. Men parted with precious breeding stock which they would have pelted for no other cause. A photograph, the story of the coat's making, and an announcement of the auction in the Waldorf-Astoria on New Year's Eve, appeared in *Vogue*. The coat was displayed to fashion editors in the New York showroom of Fromm Brothers, where one of the pioneer breeders told the history of the color phase and showed live platinum mink. The press took

pictures of the lecturer and the mink, and in its zeal
to get a perfect picture called, "Closer! Closer!" until
the rancher held the mink so close it bit his nose. This
ended mink modeling but made the headlines.

The New Year's night auction in the grand ballroom
of the Waldorf-Astoria was an important event both to
fur trade and to the Company. It was the presentation
of the first and only platinum mink coat in the world,
and Fromm Brothers were sponsoring the introduction
in behalf of the Mink Mutation Breeders' Association
and the Stage Door Canteen. The Company handled the
promotion and donated the cost of manufacturing the
coat, which was made by De Leo. With Brock Pember-
ton they staged the charity sale. It was a formal affair,
and the white ties and tails of the company group were
vastly different from the homey atmosphere of farm
auctions. Many stage and screen celebrities attended the
party, and it was gay.

Edward was auctioneer. Everyone confidently expected the coat would bring at least $25,000. Myrna Loy
set the ball rolling with an offer of $9,000, and bidding
was at first somewhat lethargic. Perhaps so spectacular
a purchase seemed untimely with a war on. Then bids
started to climb, first by five hundred, then a thousand.
At $18,000 Edward brought down the hammer.

Acceptance of that final bid, many times more than
a mink coat had ever brought, was a decisive event for
the Company and for all mutation breeders. Had the
auction gone flat and the new color been repudiated,
there might have been no story of mink mutations today.
This triumph, and it was a triumph, settled doubts in
ranchers' minds, and for the Company it became only a
question of how big their mutation herd could be.

Chapter Twenty-Four

T HE LAST FLING OF THE SILVER FOX BEGAN IN THE FALL
of 1942 and lasted for two years. Almost from the first
the Fromms' New York factory was the nation's largest
manufacturer of silver fox garments and well up in the
middle group of mink furriers. Silver fox and mink were
running together, with fox in the lead both in demand
and in price. Fromm-made silver fox jackets could well
pay the way of other needs which faced the Company.
These were several. Fox puppies must be put on wire,
and the Company spent more than half a million dollars
building over 4,000 netting pens before every silver pup
old enough to leave its mother was on a wire floor. Also
the mink herd must be built up, and the price of mutation stock was fast becoming almost prohibitive. Ginseng too was in difficulties, confronted with a labor
shortage, and the root crop must still be stored as it had
been for eleven years. The Company now was carrying
an enormous inventory in dried root.

Immediately after the New Year's night auction the
Mink Mutation Breeders' Association rechristened the

new mink "silverblu" and began a national publicity campaign. The fur trade and the public were talking of the silverblu before the first crop was offered in January, 1944, and furriers had an opportunity to gauge the interest of their retail customers.

From the moment the sound of the auctioneer's hammer marked the purchase of the first lot, it was evident that the new and glamorous mink would be accepted. The "ups" of the callers came so fast that one sounded like the echo of another. The first coat bundle was sold for $185 a pelt and later bids went higher. One bundle of sixty-five pelts soared to $265 and the prices averaged $147.25. The faith of men in a new-found beauty had been justified.

The Company's interest in these prices was only a natural gratification that a pelt auction had confirmed their opinion of the value of mutations, although the Company had had no doubt since the $18,000 sale of the first platinum coat. The Company had sent no skins to market, and for two reasons. Unlike other mink ranchers who had invested heavily in mutations and must finance the operation, the Company's silver foxes could underwrite the project. Also the Fromms were fur farmers and not in any way promoters of breeding stock. There is a great difference. Although many ranchers believe the greater profit lies in promotion, the Company never saw it this way. In mutation promotion the rancher pelts his finest animals for the introductory auction, thus commanding top prices while the color is new and rare, and topping the auction establishes a good price for his breeding stock which may or may not be of equal quality. There is an occasional suspicion that sometimes a rancher has made sure of a spectacular auction bid with a kick-back to the furrier who made the astounding offer, although this suspicion may have arisen from envy of less fortunate ranchers. But the fur promoter is not trying to build a herd, may not intend to go on working with that particular mutation. The real fur farmer, however, must build for the future. He is counting on the magnitude of coming fur crops of uniform quality in the popular new shade, and he can't afford to harvest his best animals, so necessary for breeding, or cut down the mutation herd with heavy pelting.

In 1944 the Company's crop was 11,500 and 15,000 the next year. In 1946 the Company pelted 24,000 mink and owned 11,500 breeders. The second largest ranch pelted 16,000. In seven years the Fromms had built the largest mink herd in the world, of which a great proportion were mutations.

Tens of thousands of mink pens for a proving ground, endless vigilance and attention to the smallest detail had resulted in a system which provides maximum welfare with the minimum of labor. Mink require more housekeeping than foxes. This did not reduce their rating among keepers, who found themselves attracted by the alertness of the little creatures.

"If they had rubber teeth they'd be great little pets," a keeper said. "But you can't help liking 'em. They're so busy and so curious."

Foxes had to be fed only once a day, but small mink kits must have both breakfast and supper, and meals must be on time. Breakfast is never later than six-thirty lest hungry kits will begin to eat each other. Mink food carts have a jaunty air, and mink, unlike foxes, have no convictions on the color of the horses that serve them. Two feeders can care for four hundred pens, but a separate crew must precede to make sure the flat, fixed feeding boards are scraped clean of the previous meal. Foxes are natural carrion eaters, but mink won't eat stale food or clean up their plates if there is a sour layer on the bottom. Feeders have to be agile when they open the top gate to ladle in the daily ration. A mink is quick and doesn't hesitate to bite the hand that feeds him.

Watering is a real task in a mink unit. A fox needs his pan filled only twice a week but fresh water is a must with a mink. A watering cart with two girl attendants makes the rounds twice daily, filling drinking fountains from hoses equipped with faucets. Drinking fountains must be washed often. Every rancher seeks drinking utensils which will not permit a mink to soil his supply or to wet himself, but mink usually circumvent this. Some carry their droppings to the water pan, and keepers claim they do this on purpose. Many mink manage a shower bath by scooping water up with their forepaws. Watching this performance, one has an almost irresistible impulse to hand the mink a wash cloth.

Fox nest boxes need be cleaned only semi-annually as a fox is usually very neat in his home life, but a large percentage of mink are not. Weekly cleaning of the nest is necessary, which increases housekeeping hours and is a nuisance. An extremely slovenly mink may be pelted out for no other reason. Mink have another habit that annoys keepers — their passion for carrying straw bedding from the nest box and strewing it around the pen floor. This tendency became especially rampant when the Company, desiring to economize on lumber, reduced the size of the nest box. But fortunately the Fromms can always take a hint from their fur bearers.

"They were telling us they wanted room." John chuckled. "What we'd saved on lumber we more than lost on labor. Now we build bigger boxes and they're pretty good about their bedding."

In mink breeding season extra help is needed as a keeper can manage only one hundred females. Males and females announce the arrival of the breeding period by making clucking sounds but the warlike nature of mink presents a hazard. A pair must be introduced with caution, watched constantly, and must be separated immediately after mating. Vicious fights occur between the sexes, and a successful mating is not always possible. A hostile female can destroy all mating instinct in a young male for the remainder of his life, and this is a real disaster in mutation breeding when strains have been scientifically crossed and recrossed in a long experiment to produce a new shade of coat. Usually young males will not bite back unless forced to in defense, although older males may kill a female.

Each female is bred several times during the season as misses are costly. Four kits should be the average production for mink but a lesser average for mutation mink is acceptable since color as well as fertility is so important. Even in strains which are well established, infertile matings cut totals of fine stock and keepers are jealous of their records of increase. No man likes to see too many zeros on the charts when the first rough census is taken a week after whelping. The exact census is recorded later when the kits are a month old, and if the increase averages more than four, the keeper is a happy man.

A card on the pen gives the genetic make-up and the mating history of each mink. Sires' records differ greatly. This is another source of anxiety, especially if the blood strain of the male is needed in a breeding experiment.

Hormone secretions have been used by some of the Company's keepers with success. A dormant male can often be changed into a successful breeder with one shot of hormones. The effect may last throughout the season or the breeding instinct may fade after a few days. But even one or two successful matings is vitally important in the case of a valuable blood strain.

One male defeated all efforts to bestir him. He was a double mutation and the result of accident. Supposedly pure blood Kohinurs, unknown to the Company or the rancher who had bred them, were half blood silverblus and these unintentionally were mated with half blood silverblus in the Fromm herd. Even genetic cards are not always a protection in the confusion of new strains. Kits of these litters were a soft pearl shade with black cross markings and were so interesting and attractive that a breeding program was planned to produce more of this new pearl mink. Meanwhile the mink ranchers held a live stock show and each rancher gave a prize animal to be auctioned for the benefit of the association. The Company sent a male pearl mink, intending to buy it back since it was so valuable in their breeding program. Apparently other ranchers had the same opinion of its desirability for Edward had to bid $2,300 to get back his male. Then, so unpredictable is the behavior of fur bearers — or perhaps the excitement of becoming a traveled and admired mink altered his point of view — this male, a proven and dependable breeder, sired only one more litter and then stubbornly retired to a life of leisure. This fascinated the keepers. They loved to show him to visitors, quote his purchase price and add, "But it's no use trying to make him go to work."

Mink are good mothers. And busy mothers. One wonders how the wild mink manages to care for a family. The ranch mother, with food delivered twice daily, is completely occupied with nursing the litter, carrying supplementary meals to youngsters in the nest box, dragging babies to the pen for naps in the sun or, on a warm day, moving them to the shade under the ramp, whisking them to the safety of the nest box at first sight of a stranger, and bringing them forth again when the danger is past. Transportation is by the nape-of-the-neck method, and nature grows a patch of heavier skin to stand this wear and tear. A half-grown kit, almost as large as the mother, will go limp and let itself be dragged. The speed with which a mother can remove three to ten babies from sight is startling. When the youngsters are safely hidden she comes out to scold the intruder, and a long aisle of pens will be filled with indignant females chattering about the ill-manners of anyone who thus disturbs a community nursery.

Adoptions are attempted when litters are too large for one mother to nurse properly, but distribution of the excess among smaller families must be done with caution. Mink have minds of their own and special rules. Adoptions are not made after kits are three weeks old. Even before then the keeper can only lay the kit on the ramp at the elected foster mother's door and wait to see what happens. If she looks it over and retires that kit must find another home. If she drags the kit in, the adoption is not necessarily settled. She may regret her charitable impulse and a few mornings later the keeper will find the kit lying on the floor of the pen. There can be no argument with a mink, and keepers must have a weather eye out for signs of discord. The record for a delayed repudiation is the mother who took excellent care of the valuable kit of a new and very precious mutation, then six weeks later laid it on the pen floor, bitten to death. Apparently she found the new color much too foreign.

Keepers differ on the sociability of mink. A keeper may have a few pets among his charges which he can handle with bare hands. Another wouldn't consider such intimacy or may have tried it to his regret. One keeper insists he can examine the day-old kits of all but his really nervous mothers, but adds he wouldn't try to do this in a strange unit and that no other keeper could do this in his unit. He admits too that if one of his mink pets is changed to a strange pen, although the new housing differs in no way from the old, the mink will become wild. And no keeper will agree that a mink mother may destroy and eat her offspring because of an evil disposition. They are all sure this tragedy occurs only because an extremely nervous mother gets into a panic.

Tractability apparently depends on the handling of the mink from birth. Last year a few mink were whelped of a new blending of mutations. They are breath-taking in the delicacy of their color, but because of genetic make-up are infertile and so cannot reproduce themselves. The water girls in this unit made pets of them from birth, fondled them, even used baby talk and before the summer was over whenever one was picked up he yawned like a tired and contented infant and snuggled down in a warm lap. Young mink can be housed together if food is plentiful enough so that hunger fights don't start. But they will wrestle like young kittens, and even if they don't bite each other, their needle-like claws leave red marks on the leather.

Mink ranching brought new employees to the farm. Each unit has a pair of dogs to catch escapees from the pens. These co-workers are on twenty-four hour duty and remain in the unit after their owners, the keepers, have quit work. Keepers boast of the ability of these assistants and, following good company tradition, make each pair of canine guards feel that the jobs are important and worthy of real ingenuity. No pair is schooled for the task, so each works out its own technique, and each is different. One pair may believe in surrounding a mink and both barking until a keeper comes. Another believes in specializing, and one dog catches while the other barks. Champion of all the dog police is an old fellow who has learned to catch an escaped mink by the tail and then walk slowly rearwards, maintaining a steady pull so the mink can not double back and bite him.

Another sort of voluntary worker is not so popular. Coons move into the forests near mink units and at night work from pen to pen, panhandling the food of honest mink. They too have a special technique and have discovered they can reach in and grasp a handful from the feeding pan, carry this to the top of the nest box and eat at leisure. Sometimes in a sportive mood, having eaten all they can, they continue down the aisle stacking food on nest boxes and detaching water fountains. Apparently the tricky catches of the water dishes fascinate coons, or perhaps they regard them only as a challenge.

Health precautions are attended to by Lawrence Schult and, unlike the old days of epidemics, are comparatively simple. Each mink receives one immunizing shot against distemper in his lifetime. This is done on an assembly line basis. Each catcher seizes a mink and, holding the head in his right hand and the left foreleg and two hindlegs in his left, bends the body backward. A girl swabs the mink's right armpit with disinfectant.

Another girl places her heavy glove over the mink's mouth, and Lawrence gives the shot in the underarm cavity, the only place a mink can absorb the large dose of vaccine. The mink is returned to his pen in a matter of minutes for the procedure goes like clockwork. Last year Lawrence and a crew of eleven gave 4,200 shots in a ten hour day.

Kits are weaned when eight weeks old, and pelters are sent to the furring pens. This is the final grading time, although checking for pelters and for breeders goes on constantly. Long before this, John Fromm has decided whether a series of matings has served its purpose in the general breeding program and what new matings will further establish the color and quality the Company is seeking. Now the suitability of a mink as a breeder must be finally determined. Its genetic history is significant, but the animal must be carefully examined in a wire catching cage to make sure it has possibilities. Grading live animals is different from grading a pelt when the expert sees the finished job. In live animals the grader must be able to recognize potentialities, and one who can do so is an instinctive fur breeder. This final appraisal is the purpose of John's last round when he moves from pen to pen, studies the card histories, examines mink, and, his decision made, pencils blue crosses on the cards of fall pelters. While this examination is going on, mink families romp happily inside the pens, quite unconscious of the momentousness of the occasion. Someone said there was a certain Jehovah-like omnipotence in John's role.

"I never thought of it that way," John said. "It's a good thing no one has the right to decide in this fashion about us humans."

The appetite of each mink is of deep concern to a keeper. The mink has a shorter intestinal tract than most animals, and food remains in the body only an hour and a half and so must be extremely digestible. July and August are the heaviest feeding months as the Company is building size in the herd. In the spring the food is wet, almost sloppy, as mink prefer it so. But in the fur making months it must be a drier mixture to prevent food sticking to the precious fur.

Nursing mink mothers especially must be watched. It seems incredible such small creatures can supply proper nourishment for such rapacious broods, but they make up in quality for quantity. Mink milk is highly concentrated. At the first sign of a lagging appetite keepers order special meals, such as liver. No one on a fur farm can comfortably conclude that hungry animals will eat anything. They must eat to grow and to make fur, and fussy eaters must be placated. The fur bearers are the real producers.

Henry Czech conducts his department on an assembly line basis, but with the flexibility of a diet kitchen. Reports from keepers list nursing mothers requiring augmented meals, litters weaned, mothers returned to a standard diet, "blank meals" for non-producers, and special foods for fussy or sick animals, as in so large a population there inevitably is some illness. Henry and his crew have tubs of food ready when carts in a long line drive up to the platform, take their loads, and start through the forest to the pens. Twice a day this enormous quantity of food goes through Henry's kitchen. When the last cart has started, the clangor of the huge hog and big mixer is stilled and the feedroom is sterilized. The same routine goes on at Thiensville.

A food strike on the part of even a small number of fur bearers can involve all departments which handle their rations. Once when keepers noticed mink were not finishing meals their complaint was fully as indignant as that of the mink. Unthrifty animals would reflect on them.

"The mink don't like their meals and the keepers don't like them either," the spokesman said.

Refrigerator crew, feedroom staff, John, and Edward held a conference. All knew the food was not spoiled or contaminated, but no one can argue with a mink. Their conclusion was that somehow the meals had changed, and for the worse. Henry Czech suggested a different formula. More water would insure a thorough mixing and greater uniformity. The refrigerator crew reported that meat should be hurried to the freezing room, but too many trips to zero temperatures in the summer when the crew was hot and perspiring caused colds, and an extra man must be added for this service. All of these things were done, the mink sent in a favorable report, and both mink and keepers were happy.

In early fall of 1944 the New York factory completed more than one thousand silver fox jackets. In previous seasons they'd had difficulty keeping abreast of orders, but this year in November, when the peak should have been reached, buyers had not come in. This aroused some misgiving, although silver fox had always shown fluctuations in fashion favor and this might be only a temporary lull. The Company reduced prices, put on a merchandising campaign, and promoted silver fox as trimming. These measures worked, and silver fox moved into retail channels but not with the old-time verve.

317

Mink, however, was becoming increasingly popular. The Company used their entire mink crop in manufacture and were offering garments in the three mutations. Kohinur and blufrost had reached the market. These introductory auctions were successful, although not as spectacular as that of the silverblu, but the variety in colors made mink the news of the fashion world and even stimulated an interest in the standard. In the meantime a new mutation, the aleutian, a bluish tone, was being developed, but the Company decided to sit out this excitement. Aleutians appeared to be not very different from the steel mink; other ranchers were already well advanced in its pioneering, and a new color phase was a big gamble. In mutation breeding a mink farmer must work three or four years ahead of consumer reaction and judge the appeal of a new color seasons before fashion trends are established. There was a question, too, of how large any farm could become and still remain profitable. The Company was raising ginseng, doing a good although not superlative business in silver foxes, and well on the way to being the largest mink ranchers in the world. Also they were experimenting with the blending of various mutations.

In 1944 this was avant-garde mutation breeding, an effort to superimpose a different shading, and it had been suggested that the Kohinur or blufrost, both pattern mutants, might add an interesting differential to the over-all coloring of the silverblu or the pastel. A tantalizing gamble, an intellectual excitement, and a new zest had been imparted to fur farming, and ranchers prepared to surpass even nature in her accidental changes. The dazzling possibilities of shades, not yet glimpsed, sent mink ranchers back to textbooks to learn how to draw genetic charts of inheritance and to figure the blood strains of each square. It was comparatively simple to discover that in mating half bloods of two recessives, pastel and platinum, in sixteen kits there should be nine standards, three platinums, three pastels, and one a blend of the two colors. This one-in-sixteen kit, carrying both factors, might be the start of a new color phase. The more daring mutation breeders even talked of a future when three mutations could be superimposed in a one-to-sixty-four animal from hybrid parents. This, however, would be a real project, requiring three breeding seasons, 34 matings, and 160 animals for the entire experiment. It would be years before the world could see this product since all these fascinating combinations must wait on the immutable fact that mink produce young only once a year.

The Fromms and other breeders were already working on the simplest combination, that of silverblu enlivened and made more delicate and breath-taking by crossing it with blufrost. Eventually this became the Breath of Spring, which reached the market three years later. The breeding routine was tedious. In less than two years a rancher could not hope to produce better than quarter litters of the desired shade and must have luck to do even this well. More important, he must have the courage of his convictions. Eastern fur men were sure the public would prefer darker platinums, but the Company, believing in brighter fur, refused to discard the lighter pelts. This had been a long-time pattern. Henry spoke with real conviction as he watched a famous New York grader sort the Company's crop of mutations, giving the darker fur the preference.

"You're working on the wrong end," he said. Since

Henry had never visited the New York factory or talked to an eastern furrier about mutations, his comment was reminiscent of the time he had studied the silver fox scarf in Marshall Field's fur salon and pronounced it dull.

The eastern factory was managed largely by remote control. This was not the Fromm way of doing things, but the Fromms did not like cities. Even when the Company tried to impress Arthur into assuming eastern management he begged off, protesting he was interested in a research project on ginseng humus. He succeeded in completing the experiment, but only just before his death in the fall of 1945. Some of his formulas had not been recorded, and no other Fromm was equipped to carry on this scientific work.

After Arthur had refused to become interested in making fur garments, his son Johnnie prepared to stand by in the east. Johnnie, too, did not care for cities, and he began to look forward even more eagerly than his uncles to the time when garments could be made at home. The Fromms were convinced this would be possible, but the plan to do so was strangely un-Fromm-like in its leisurely approach. They talked often of a small factory in Wisconsin to supplement the New York venture, but always as something in the vague future. In the early years they would have laughed at such postponement, but even Edward went less often to New York, stayed for shorter periods and depended more on the long-distance telephone.

Johnnie remained in the city through the beginning of the 1945 summer, a victim of heat, humidity, and a yearning for the trout streams of Wisconsin. When Seventh Avenue pavements sizzled, postponement of a home factory seemed a needless waste of years and energy.

Every precept of the fur trade warned him that conversion of raw pelts into garments was a highly specialized craft. Workmen were supposed to be born to it and were centered almost exclusively in New York. In a few previous attempts of other manufacturers to establish factories outside this city, the International Fur and Leather Workers' Union, C.I.O. had quickly won its argument for a centralized industry. Nevertheless Johnnie believed fur skill might be acquired. He had watched garments being made, and it had not appeared too difficult for an intelligent worker.

Soon afterwards several mysterious losses occurred. A fur sewing machine disappeared, as did a jacket bundle of matched silver fox pelts, and a pattern. The shop foreman and workers wondered about this. Johnnie went home for a vacation. Later other sewing machines, sent out for servicing, failed to return. Partly finished garments were taken from the shop to be photographed and never seen again. Bundles of matched pelts and patterns were mislaid. Rumors spread through the union. The Company heard of these disturbing events but Johnnie, vacationing in Thiensville, said nothing. At the end of two weeks he appeared in Hamburg with his finished silver fox jacket.

It was a professional job. Johnnie, a good sportsman, had chosen the most difficult model, with a collar and reset sleeves. The sleeves, made of a single skin, required that a pelt be split and converted into a pair of matching pieces. He did not have a form to work on but his wife, Barbara, served as a model. To lay out, cut, and sew such a jacket in a first venture as a fur worker, and complete it in two weeks, was an astonishing record. Johnnie contended this proved ability in fur work was not necessarily inherited.

"It certainly does," said Edward, suddenly alert as the final piece of the farm unit pattern fell into place. He examined the workmanship. "That's a good jacket. What did Barbara think of it?"

"She thought it was all right," Johnnie said, "and I don't believe it was because her husband made it."

Edward handed the jacket across his desk.

"Tell her the Company wants her to have the first silver fox jacket made in our home factory," he said.

Within a week the missing sewing machines appeared in Hamburg, as did the matched jacket bundles and patterns, as well as a fur worker from the New York shop who could design and cut and, even more important, who preferred small towns to cities. Factory quarters were found in Merrill, eighteen miles from the farm. A fur workers' union in the A. F. of L. was established. Local workers were enrolled, and before suspicions of the New York union were aroused the new shop was started. Never did a factory get under way with less fanfare.

The Company did not expect large production. Workers were inexperienced and could not be trained to produce fur garments in less than six months or a year, but a factory on home ground had emotional value, and many on the pay roll were from families of employees who had worked for the Company twenty years. As in the past when neighbors had come to dig ginseng and harvest and feed foxes, now their sons and daughters were at work getting the fur crop to market. In time this factory might become an important avenue in the scheme of pen to wearer. The Company was very hopeful.

Suddenly it became the only avenue. Officials of the fur workers' union discovered that a shop had been moved out from under them and called a strike on the New York factory. The Company offered a contract in the Merrill factory and assurance that it would not become more important in point of wages or total employees than the New York shop, but this carried a provision that a certain number of employees should be beginners and the wage scale adjusted for apprentices. The union balked. To countenance a Wisconsin factory would open the door for others and weaken the union's insistence on centralization. The Company maintained it was a Wisconsin corporation and entitled to be considered an exception.

The Fromms knew they were in an extremely vulnerable position. The union had won previous arguments with other manufacturers and was sure it could do so again. It had the weapons. A fur factory could not hope to operate with inexperienced labor, and union pressure could not only keep skilled workers out of the Merrill factory, but could affect allied industries and close the door to the sale of raw fur.

"Garments were our only outlet," Edward said, "and the union knew this, and knew that even if we had a thousand willing green hands on our Merrill pay roll we were helpless in manufacture. We needed key men to train the beginners and we didn't pretend we could operate without them. But we didn't intend to close the Merrill factory."

The Company still hoped an exception would be made, but two weeks later it received the union's decision. The Merrill factory must be closed.

Chapter Twenty-Five

THE UNION WAS IN AN UNASSAILABLE POSITION AND need not make terms. The Company was not so fortunate. In addition to a large inventory in ginseng root still being stored after fourteen years, they were carrying between twelve and fifteen thousand mink and thirty thousand fox pelts, with the price of silvers steadily declining. Delayed marketing would bring still lower returns. Moreover, the Company had intended to manufacture only silver fox garments in Merrill. Johnnie was certain local labor could be trained for this, but mink workmen would have to be hired in the east where they'd had years of experience.

The union was aware of this but had overlooked one important circumstance. The New York strike was called in summer, the dullest season. The Fromm factory had operated throughout the year, and its employees had no quarrel with wages or conditions. They were called out without being given a chance to vote, and a dozen older workers offered to move to Merrill.

"With this nucleus and our local employees, we began to manufacture," Edward said. "It was not what we had planned. The local factory was premature, but now we *had* to produce garments in Wisconsin."

Having to do a thing was an old and familiar pattern. The venture started slowly. Only a few garments were finished at the end of several weeks. Production improved, but through the winter the eastern workers found a small town monotonous and gradually drifted back to the city until only three remained. Meanwhile local men and women were proving that the fur craft could be learned. In the New York factory three dozen garments had been produced each day. In Merrill, after a year's operation, 130 employees, all except three of whom had no previous training in fur work, were making thirty a day. A few men who had begun as machine operators were able to cut garments under supervision. The factory was shaking down.

The union in New York and the Fromms remained in deadlock. All attempts at mediation failed. The real issue had come into the open. Until the Merrill factory was closed, the New York workshop would be strikebound. The union was adamant on this.

"They offered to buy the Merrill factory and close it for us," Edward said. "But we wanted to manufacture here at home."

The Fromms maintained that if a man wished to make anything anywhere in the United States he had the right to do so, and with this contention they suddenly found themselves exponents of a theory that was attracting national attention. In seeking to convert raw skins into garments at the source of the fur supply, they had become part of the battle over the decentralization of industry. But success in the home factory did not bring victory. Union pressure closed avenues for the sale of raw pelts and shut off many eastern retail outlets for the Company's garments.

At the end of the first year, when only three eastern workers remained in Merrill, the Company appraised the venture. The expected spoilage had been astonishingly low. Only twenty-five garments showed imperfections, and these were slight. The Company now had a much clearer idea of the costs of production, which in the east had been shrouded in some mystery, and this, with a lowered overhead, had enabled it to use more fur and make a better jacket. Most important, the Company had proved fur could be manufactured outside the national center.

Co-operation between management and labor in Merrill was gratifying. Employees, starting at scratch and knowing their limitations, were eager to learn a new trade, and this spirit made the shop a friendly place. Workers became interested in the product and developed a craftsman's pride. The factory was part of the farm unit, as close as the fox and mink pens and ginseng gardens. For the first time fur coats and jackets hung in the Company's office.

Second-generation Fromms took an active part in manufacture. Johnnie was brought from Thiensville to be Edward's assistant, and the Company built a home for him at Hamburg. Mark Koenig, who had married Henry's daughter Arlene, entered the Merrill plant after his discharge from the army as auditor and eventually opened his own office as certified public accountant with the Fromm farm as a first and important client. The young couple and their four children live on company holdings in a rebuilt farmhouse, one of several dwellings acquired in the purchase of ten quarter sections for ginseng culture. Young Henry too returned from the army with a wife and son and learned fur farming by working as a keeper until he was made assistant to his Uncle John. Thus another Fromm had become a fur rancher, and the Company built a house for him on the home acres. This construction for three young families seemed only a logical extension of the brothers' home-building urge in the late twenties. Henry's vision of a third generation serving and being served by the Company was coming true.

The Company needed its youth as older members became more and more absorbed in what in any other group would have been regarded as avocations. Neither Henry nor Walter, nor perhaps even the Company, considered them as anything but logical projections of early drives. Henry owned thirty-two hundred acres of forest, including two lakes, on the Michigan border. With the need to build guest cabins, make roads and forest trails, construct a patio with rock walls and a huge fireplace, and enlarge the main dwelling, he and Mamie were seldom in their Hamburg house, so seldom that eventually young Henry and his family of three children moved into it. Since all dwellings were company substance and maintenance company responsibility, these shifts need be only by arrangement.

Walter established two outside bases. Ten years earlier he had bought eighty acres in Florida to build a botanical garden. Later he bought a summer home on a Wisconsin lake. Fortunately for the Company's finances, the brothers specialized and built either homes or gardens. The Florida garden near the Bok tower is enjoyed by many winter visitors. Now with one garden in the south, another at the lake house, a third on the home acres in Hamburg, and the need to be on the farm only in the fall rush of pelting, ginseng planting and harvesting, Walter and Mable dashed from one growing season to another. A fine showing of bloom, a harvest of blueberries, or the pruning of the dozens of Colorado spruce in the home garden — all were important to them. That dread word "retirement" will never haunt Walter or his wife. Their sixties are as full and as demanding as were their younger years.

John had steadfastly repulsed the Company's efforts to move him from his corner in the warehouse to what his brothers called a real home. Nor had he given up supervision of the large mink herd wished upon him by Henry's exuberance. A dashing convertible and a magnificent collection of records were his only compromises. He had evenings of music, walks in the forest, and wonderful plans to retire some day and visit remote lands which appealed to his Himalayan spirit. But neither the Company nor John took these threats seriously. He knew as did they that the reality could never approach the vision he had created.

Edward's latter years had been shaped for him. Problems of marketing and the promotion of the Company's interests never ceased. In the first years these were regarded as in his province and still are. He didn't wish it any other way.

"Years ago I went to Florida or Arizona every winter," he said. "Now," and he paused a moment to consider, "now I suppose my real adventure is here."

Perhaps this is why he'd never hungered for a house on a Wisconsin lake or in a vast stretch of virgin forest, but he'd kept the site of the old family homestead, which had burned five years before, empty and waiting for the home he planned to build some day.

Merrill liked the factory. The plant paid the highest wages in town and had a waiting list. Many employees were returned soldiers unwilling to go back to old jobs. "I was a schoolteacher," one said, "but after three years in the army I'd have had to take a refresher course, and anyhow I didn't want to teach. I tried the sash and door factory and got tired of working on one kind of window frame. This fur job gives you a chance to use your head." In a year he had advanced from operator to cutter of silver fox jackets. "Look at this! See how I fitted in this piece from the neck? The fur swirls around as though it had grown there."

A successful cutter of silver fox must have a dash of creative spirit, a feel for color, and an understanding of the anatomy of the animal to fit the pelt into a garment. Markings, texture, and length of fur vary, and since each pelt is slightly different from all others and a jacket bundle has been matched as closely as possible, odd bits from other pelts cannot be used for piecing. This was a challenge to ingenuity.

Mink cutting is far more specialized. A cutter must have a keen eye for the most minute gradations in color and texture, and a good head for arithmetic. Making a mink coat has become an elaborate process since the invention of the fur sewing machine in 1895, which made it possible to sew very narrow strips together firmly. A fine mink coat has nearly five thousand seams yet must look like a single piece of fur, and short furred mink does not supply camouflage for errors. A skin is first split into two pieces down the back and then, with the central character stripe, or "grotzen," as a guide, is cut diagonally into many long thin strips. These pieces are replaced at such an angle that they make a matched fur two or three times the length of the original pelt. This process is called "dropping."

In the Merrill factory sewing machines were run by both men and women, and each cutter, either in fox or mink, had five operators. This group carried on the making of a garment as a unit, and it was the cutter's responsibility to plan, cut, distribute the pieces, and eventually fit them into a final product. Operators watched the garment grow and could share in the sense of achievement.

"When I sewed shoes I saw only one part," a Merrill girl said. "Here I make a sleeve or a back or a front, and when we get a jacket together all of us can see what we have accomplished."

The finishing department, where linings are sewn in, was easily staffed in a community where any number of older women were skillful with a needle. Linings might become monotonous, but a group sewing together found it much like taking one's work and dropping in for a visit with a neighbor.

The Company had counted on the native intelligence of the small town worker who had turned his hand to many jobs. After these people had learned the feel of fur they were able to cut, match, nail, and sew garments. The labor turnover was less than 5 per cent, this mostly in the first weeks when the employees tried a new job to learn whether they liked it.

The Company had not planned to dress its own pelts. This is a secret process, no books have been written on the subject, and even ingredients used are known only to the craft. But this was another trade which had to be mastered, as Edward reported in a fur trade journal:

"In opposition to our Wisconsin operations, the New York fur workers' union induced the dressers' union not to work on our pelts. Hence it became necessary for us to do our own dressing. Fur dressing is a technique dating back to the dark ages and kept dark right up to the present. It is simple in principle but complicated in practice. After many trials and a few costly errors, the pelts began coming through as beautiful as New York's finest. The New York union has done us a favor."

Dressing furs, like good cooking, is done partly by rule and partly "by ear." A man must learn how a pelt should feel and look. The skin is softened, fleshed, then put into the "bite" or pickle, dried, drummed in hard maple sawdust, and oiled. The last process depends more on the "ear" than any other, and only through practice can a worker learn how little or how much oil each skin should have. The skin is then put into the "kicker," which works the oiled pelts, and this, too, must be done with caution. More drumming and stretching follow, and between drummings the pelts are spun in a revolving wire cylinder to "cage out" the sawdust.

Working pelts is done either by electrically driven or bench fleshing knives. Fleshing mink pelts, a delicate process, could be done only with bench tools as extra leather must be shaved off so skillfully the pelt is soft and light as chamois and yet undamaged. This, too, can be learned only by practice. At the end of the year the Company was dressing even the delicately shaded mutation skins.

The Company prepared to produce 175 garments weekly, engaged more employees, and raised wages.

Even after this advance, the scale was less than in New York, but the Merrill factory operated at capacity all the year, and in the east the season was from six to nine months. Workers took this into consideration.

"We know we aren't getting New York wages," an easterner said, "but neither is this New York. I've worked for higher wages and felt a lot poorer. Here we live in better houses, can enjoy a visit with our neighbors, and send our kids to school with their friends. Most of us own cars. Wages stretch twice as far. Food costs are about the same, but we can have fun here without spending a lot of money. In New York it cost me as much to get to the country as taking the wife and kids to the movies and buying a dinner. Here all we have to do is step into the car. And this is a union shop and I'm getting union wages."

He was referring to the wage scale controversy. Men in Merrill knew the eastern union spoke of them as scabs, and they didn't like it.

"I had a chance to learn a new trade and I took it," one said. "I'd have been crazy not to. In New York they'd never have given me a chance to learn to be a cutter. Now I am one. This is America and a fellow has a right to any job he can hold down. What do those men in the east mean when they tell us we can't do fur work in Wisconsin?"

Clearly the Fromms were not the only ones who intended to be stubborn about the right to make fur garments where they pleased. This stubbornness paid off in the fall of 1946 when silver fox declined in price. Now short-haired fur was popular. Standard mink climbed to a new high, and the first auction of Royal Pastel which was held in Seattle brought another muta-

Alwina Fromm with Arthur, Edward, Henry,
John, and Walter.

Photograph taken in 1892 of farmhouse which served family and ginseng crew until 1920.

Country school, 1905. Henry, sitting left; Edward, sitting right; John, standing left; Walter, third from right.

John and Henry with pups caught by Walter in padded trap, May, 1910.

Fromm boys haying.

Litter chopped from hollow log.

John, Henry, and Edward with red fox litter
dug out in 1911.

Picture that won
Funsten $50 prize.

Henry and John bringing home wire fencing
bought with prize money.

Edward with ginseng crop, 1910.

Washing root with family car as power plant.

Ginseng arbor.

Washing with power from their first stationary engine.

Fort Moreland.

Mr. Moreland, center, with red and cross pups
from his silver fox.

First block of pens.

Kaiser.

The Fromm double fox house.

Foxes on range in late twenties.

Range feed cart.

Feeding in the forest.

Walter Fromm, Herbert Kleinschmidt and their washing machine.

Modern method of digging root.

Center of Fromm farm

warehouse in background.

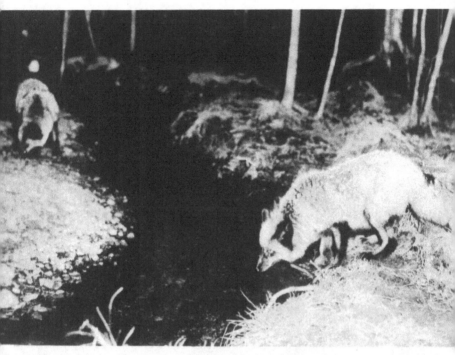

Silver fox of the present day.

Selecting foxes for mating.

The tame fox at Thiensville.

Progress in breeding for silver since 1910.

One of the Fromms' first silverblu mink.

A standard.

A Kohinur.

1947 silverblu.

Edward, Walter, Henry and John in a mink unit, 1947.

One of the mink furring ranges.

Present-day fox when he enters furring range
in September.

Three months later when his coat is prime.

Harvesting fox crop.

Examining pelts.

Grading pelts.

Edward and callers at the 1939 auction,
which was broken off.

Buyers at a Hamburg auction.

Dressing fox pelts in Merrill factory.

"Nailing" mink garment.

Operators working on fox jackets.

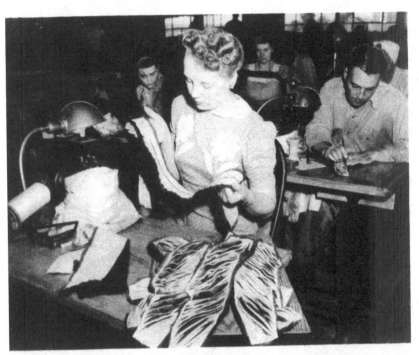

"Letting out" mink.

Johnnie Fromm and the body of first mink coat
made by the Company.

Hamburg farm, office in center.

A few of the thousands of fox pens.

tion favorite to market. The entire offering of 1,850 pelts averaged $115 a skin, and the top bundle sold at $172. It began to be apparent that the subtle, over-all coloring and not the pattern mutations would be preferred by fashion. In the same year 18,656 silverblu skins were sold in New York at an average of $91.83 and a top price of $190 a pelt. In all, more than fifty thousand mutation mink skins were auctioned in the United States. The long gamble of changing the blood strain of a herd to the new colors had proved sound. America liked brighter fur.

The Company continued to build up mutation mink and at the same time redouble efforts to steady the price of silver fox. In this the factory proved its worth. While other ranchers were victims of furriers' reluctance to increase inventories in silver fox pelts, the Fromms were able to sell their crops as jackets. Overhead and manufacturing costs were less in Merrill than in the east, and a finished garment need produce only one profit. This was small but enough, or so the Company then thought, to carry silver fox herds until the fur returned to favor.

That it would return, the Company did not doubt. With the fanatical zeal it had once thrown into the battle for bright silvers, it now prepared to keep the public aware of them. The Company had been the largest producers in the country, had carried promotion, and created styles. In the next two years, single handed, they held silver fox against a falling market. They not only manufactured garments but backed their faith by selling on consignment to make sure those garments would be offered to the public.

Two circumstances made this vigorous campaign possible. The vast herds subsidized manufacture, and again ginseng came to the rescue. For more than forty years the two threads had interwoven, and in 1946 root stored so long in the warehouse could be shipped to China and sold at prices that justified the fifteen-year gamble. Once more ginseng could feed silver foxes. Even Henry, who had never cared for it, became grateful, although for him the vast gardens would never hold the emotional satisfaction of the Company's forests. For several years the ginseng planting had been restricted to ten acres, a mere trifle to Walter and Herbert Kleinschmidt. They had longed for the time when their bed-making machine could really demonstrate its prowess. With a re-opened Chinese market, the Company decided on a twenty-five acre planting, and in a week the machine left twelve hundred beds behind it. Five years must pass before these seeds could be harvested, but to a company that had grown ginseng and silver foxes, five years was only tomorrow.

Renewal of extensive ginseng culture stimulated inventions and discoveries of better methods. Weeds had become a problem. A thousand were coming up in every ten square feet of garden. Pulling these by hand inevitably tore out young plants and if continued half the gardens would be lost. If the Company were to save ginseng culture, a better weed control must be devised. Johnnie experimented with spray. Two years and a hundred tests were necessary to determine the strength and temperature of a solution which would not harm ginseng but would kill weeds. At last he hit it and learned too the sort of weather and the season when it was most effective. Then with weeds defeated the Company felt safe in resuming large plantings.

In 1951 they had eighty-one acres of ginseng under

cultivation. Fourteen of these were one-year old, fifteen were two, twenty-one were three, twelve were four, and twenty were five and ready to be harvested. The first, second, and third year gardens had no blight, and the fourth and fifth had less than ever before in the Company's history. This final rout of their old enemy was the result of two new techniques.

Herbert Kleinschmidt and John Borchard, ginseng straw bosses, had been certain the old method of raking mulch left broken pieces of stems and leaves to act as hosts for disease spores through the winter. They experimented with burning the mulch and burned the ginseng. The idea was fine but the technique bad. It has been perfected, and now each fall, when mulch is changed on all the gardens, the disease spores are killed too.

Dusting was the second innovation and big acreage permitted various experiments. They learned dusting alone was not sufficient but that spraying plus dusting was more effective against blight than spraying had ever been. The Company dusts from mid-May until mid-August and uses 75,000 pounds of chemicals yearly. Edward suggested crews work from five in the afternoon until ten o'clock at night to take advantage of moisture and down currents of air, but the two dusting crews went him one better and proved by trial that if the work were done after dark the results were still more effective. It is now a night job on the farm.

This new weapon against blight brought a fresh problem. Dusting retarded the formation of seed heads, and the seed crop, which must be at least two thousand pounds a year, was the lifeline of the industry. Lack of seed heads had one advantage as it eliminated an extra job in the fall rush. Then a crew of girls must cut all seed heads because seeds held back root development. In ginseng, as in fur farming, it will always be a question of weighing one process against another. Now the Company had to set aside a section which was not dusted and which consequently would have blight but which could produce a seed crop. Everything must be decided by trial and error in the unique job of growing ginseng.

Increased production brought a rash of "patents." Herbert began it in an effort to take the greatest grief out of arbor building. Thousands of posts support the vast stretch of slatted arbor, and because machines must travel only on the dividing paths and never on a bed, postholes had always been dug by hand. Since one man could dig only forty or fifty a day and arbors must be completed in the two or three weeks after the planting season and before the possibility of frost, a crew of twenty-five posthole diggers was required every fall. Herbert welcomed news of a farm model power digger and was sure he could, by using uneven brackets, offset it from the tractor which must travel on the paths. But the farm model digger, then available, had most evidently not been built for digging in the granite subsoil which ginseng plants demanded. Gears were stripped; the augur which must go in as deep as twenty to thirty inches stuck and even broke when it hit large rocks, of which there were plenty. The Company reluctantly decided to return to the manpower method. The frost deadline was drawing near and they'd already wasted almost two weeks fighting the machine. Herbert went to the blacksmith shop, rebuilt the entire contraption, substituted the rear end of a Studebaker for gears, installed a hydraulic lift on the augur, and added heavy springs for elasticity when it hit hard going. Now four men and two machines dig 4,500 postholes in two weeks.

"We just had to do something," Herbert said.

Walter, not to be outdone in taking drudgery out of ginseng culture, contributed a portable revolving screen something like a cement mixer and operated by a gas motor. This eliminated the old manual method. "We can move it to any place on the farm where there's a sieving job to be done," Walter said. "It takes little time to screen the seed crop from the stratifying soil or to strain fine black top earth from forest debris."

Johnnie found bed-marking tedious. This had always been done by a surveyor's method, with corner stakes meticulously set, correct to an eighth of an inch. Two weeks were spent laying out a garden. Johnnie equipped a jeep with dragging chains and a sighting stick set on a swivel so that it was always straight on uneven ground. Starting at a corner post, he could mark out six beds at once. It was as accurate as the former method, and one man could lay out an entire garden in two days.

Herbert began to worry about the root washer which had always been taken to the stream bed. In the heavy fall rains there was a danger they might wake up some morning to find themselves minus this vital equipment. He saw no reason why water couldn't be brought to the washer. When this idea hit him they had only a few days before they must start washing root, but he dug a pit, lined it with planks, detoured stream water, installed a pump, and set the washer in the pit. The scheme worked so well that next year they built a concrete pit under shelter and a larger and improved washer driven by an electric motor. Now the washer, permanently installed in its house, needs no longer to be set up each fall, and the new and larger size can wash ten tons of green root in a day with a crew of three men.

Gradually the hurdles and bottlenecks were taken out of ginseng culture. One process had always been accepted as inevitably tedious and costly. Dried root had to be sorted by grades and the tiny rootlets or fibers, known as prongs in the trade, had to be cut off. These had some value as they were used for tea by the poor in China. At Hamburg the root was prepared for market in the winter. A crew of fifteen could finish a ton of root in five days.

"We'll have to cut the cost on the final process," Edward said to Herbert Kleinschmidt.

No machinery was made in America or elsewhere to perform this highly specialized task, but Herbert shut himself in the big room on the second story of the warehouse. A week later he proudly exhibited his "patent." The defibering and sorting machine stretched through two rooms. Herbert used the old principle of root falling in a revolving cylinder originally employed in the big washer. A series of falls wore off the small fibers, enormous fans blew out the dust, and fibers fell through into boxes below. Then the root was taken by truck to a long table equipped with a moving canvas mounted on rollers. This carried the root twenty feet in one minute, sufficient for a ten-girl crew to pick out the second grade and allow the perfect to fall into shipping boxes. With this machine a ton of dried root could be made ready for market in a day.

Herbert was proud, and justifiably, of the ingenious mechanism. "Now we've got to take the drudgery out of treading seed from the berries," he said. "By next year we'll have that beaten."

Bright With Silver

They'd tried two schemes, both failures. The crush-and-push process between corrugated rubber mats crushed but wouldn't expel the seed. The other scheme, two rollers, merely mashed the fruit. The Company returned to their earliest process, a workman tramping out a bag of fruit with his feet. More than half an hour of hard labor extracted only twenty pounds of seed, an infinitesimal portion of the two thousand pounds which were needed. Herbert and Walter now each have an idea, and the outcome of this competition justifies a pool on the winner. But perhaps in a Company accustomed to long-time gambling with a herd of silver foxes or fifteen years' worth of ginseng harvest so small a stake couldn't arouse interest.

No one has devised a practical method to disinfect the soil so that ginseng may be grown a second time on the same land. Steam is expensive and ineffectual as ground must be disinfected ten inches deep. It proved more economical to buy new land and the Company has purchased ten adjoining farms, each a quarter section. On none has more than sixty to eighty acres been suitable for ginseng which requires a non-alkaline earth with granite subsoil. Ginseng has never been induced to forego its choosy habits.

Nor has it, like silver foxes, ever fallen into disfavor among its customers. It is used in Indonesia, the Malay States, Indo-China, Siam, Burma, Japan, China, Korea, Manchuria, Mongolia, and the western Pacific islands, but the mainland of Asia is the chief consumer. In the past, markets have been cut off by political unrest and extreme depressions, but when the price of rubber or tin is high so is that of ginseng. From the spring of 1946 until October, 1950, when exportation of ginseng root to China was forbidden by the United States, the market was active, with the root bringing fifteen and sixteen dollars a pound. England did not impose an embargo, and ginseng is still sold and shipped by Canadian growers. Now the Company is again storing harvests awaiting the time when American growers have a market. The highest price the Company ever received was twenty dollars a pound. The lowest was one dollar in the thirties when political unrest in China and overproduction in America occurred simultaneously. Today there are not more than a hundred acres of ginseng in the United States, of which the Fromms have eighty. In the past twenty years the Company has had only six of marketing, but the recent government ban has not affected the extent of their plantings. They believe there will always be a market for a root which has been venerated for centuries in China.

Through the fall and winter of 1946 the Company continued to manufacture and promote silver fox despite declining prices. Having proved the success of the factory in Wisconsin, the Fromms were in a position to discuss the strike with the union and offered to reopen in New York on condition the Merrill plant be allowed to continue. The union refused and negotiations were broken off. Compared with other controversies that commanded national attention, the determination of the Company to manufacture in Wisconsin was a mere skirmish on the labor front, but to the Fromms it was tremendously important. It was more than a business obstacle, even more than a weapon in the promotion of silver fox. It was part and parcel of the company idea, as vital to it as was centralization to the union. To them the question was no longer a matter of the rights of an individual or even of a group of individuals. It had become a company right. The battle may have had somewhat the appearance of a slingshot attack on a giant, but with the Fromms it had taken on a terrible earnestness. To an enterprise which had spent almost forty years in building a herd of foxes a C.I.O. union was no more powerful an adversary than others which had attacked it in the past.

Then in December, 1946, the picture changed for each opponent. Raw fur prices suffered the most spectacular decline in history. Silver fox went lower than anyone had believed possible. In a year when they had never been lovelier, when breeding had carried them to a new perfection, skins were selling for less than the cost of production. The manufacture of silver fox garments almost ceased in New York.

Chapter Twenty-Six

THE INDUSTRY WAS IN DISTRESS. FOX HERDS BUILT UP through years of selective breeding were imperiled, but for the first time in its career the Company was prepared to meet a threat. Always before it had been necessary to erect defenses when disaster was already upon it. This time the Company was fortified because it was "dug in" at Merrill, could sell pelts, and revenue from ginseng would carry foxes. Mink prices had tumbled but still permitted profitable farming. The Fromms answered the emergency by enlarging the factory, raising wages, and becoming the only firm in the country to manufacture silver fox jackets in quantity.

In the meantime the fur farmers' organizations appealed to Congress to save the industry by softening the excise tax on fur-trimmed garments to permit a much wider use of fur. Approximately eight thousand fur farms represented an investment of one hundred and thirty million dollars. The pelt value of the two hundred thousand silver foxes, even at the low price of twenty dollars, was four million dollars. Of these the

Fromms produced almost one-fifth. The pelt value of the seven hundred thousand mink at $20 was fourteen million dollars. Forty years of pioneering had made this industry possible. Congress evidently recognized its value and, in February, 1947, granted the asked relief.

This put a new aspect on the battle between the Company and the union. The factory employing two hundred workers was the largest in the country, and Merrill was running full time while New York workers were idle. Also, the Company needed New York outlets. Fur trimming necessitated a return to Seventh Avenue and its complicated network of allied fur industries.

Both contestants wanted peace. The strike had lasted twenty-two months. In March negotiations were reopened. The union retreated from its position of not allowing a "runaway" factory. The Company agreed to maintain an eastern plant equal in size to that in Merrill so long as they manufactured in Wisconsin. The fur workers' union gained an eastern factory, work for members, and a Merrill workshop under C.I.O. charter. It conceded an apprentice rating for inexperienced employees in Merrill. A labor organization which had fought for centralization found itself with two hundred new, if passive, members in a factory more than a thousand miles from Seventh Avenue. The Company gained outlets for pelts and fur garments and wider opportunities to carry on promotion of silver fox.

The outcome of the two-year battle startled observers but did not astonish the Fromms. They had always believed the Company had a right to operate as a complete farm unit, and they needed the Merrill factory in their fight for silver fox. Only by close supervision, known costs, and one-profit merchandising could they hope to keep this fur in retail channels. A four-skin jacket must be sold for $140, far less than the price of a single pelt in the old days. It was a last ditch fight, and they knew they might be facing a real fox disaster. They explored every avenue. They gave away skins. They worked with coat designers. They spent money on selling campaigns. But they didn't cut pelt production, didn't consider retrenchment in the size of herds. Instead, they looked for ways to reduce the cost of raising foxes. Pen care, disease prevention, and furring range life for pelters must all go on. Food costs were rising, with meat more than tripled and becoming scarce, and fox diets required at least two-thirds meat. The mill in Thiensville prepared the cereal, and the formula had been worked out through the years by the pragmatic method of ascertaining what foods made healthy mink and foxes. Now, the Company decided, an enterprise with a crop of 36,000 fox pelts and 29,000 mink skins should take advantage of modern discoveries in nutrition. If cereals were balanced with other proteins, concentrates and vitamins, it might be possible to feed less meat or more fish. Dr. Willard Roberts, who had been specialist in nutrition for a nationally known food distributor, was engaged to explore this question, and in the next two years he carried on the largest scale experiment ever conducted on foxes, mink, and dogs. Hundreds of diets were tested with thousands of animals. The eventual fox formula, a fortified cereal to be fed with 35 per cent meat diet, produced fine-coated foxes and increased fertility.

"But we couldn't have cut the meat so low in the early days when we didn't have enriched cereals," Edward said.

Mink required a higher protein content as they are meat eaters. Their food was worked out on two levels, a fortified cereal to be fed with 68 per cent meat, and another, a complete mink food with the protein included. The last formula is still being improved for a possible future when horse and mule meat is no longer available for fur bearers. It has been tried out on the company farm and is a future bulwark against the common dread of all ranchers.

"We know now that the disappearance of the horse won't mean the extinction of mink ranches," Edward said.

Antibiotics were added, and three years of experiment proved that these, used in lesser proportions than is necessary to combat disease, not only stimulated growth but made better furred animals. Almost simultaneously this same research in use of antibiotics was carried on in nutrition studies for the human race.

In January, 1949, the Thiensville mill was enlarged and Federal Foods established as a separate venture. Dr. Roberts and Loyal Wells, who had deserted fox genetics for nutrition, are partners with Fromm Brothers, who hold controlling interest. The original eight employees have increased to sixty, and the organization supplies food for 25 per cent of mink raised in this country and for many dogs. Dog food was a logical product for an enterprise so aware of the importance of nourishment plus taste appeal in feeding animals. It carries the tag line "Fifty Thousand Foxes Can't Be Wrong" which apparently has convinced canines. The food was put on the market with no special advertising or promotion and now accounts for one third of the annual $2,000,000 sales of the organization.

Mink made a quick recovery from the midwinter slump and prices started up early in 1947. The first offering of Breath of Spring was auctioned and captured the fur world with the delicacy of its color. Man had outdone nature in this first combination of two mutations. Blufrost imparted an elusive shading to platinum, and it was evident this mutation would prove valuable if only for its palette possibilities. Another crossing of mutations had been developed by western breeders and produced a new color called sapphire. While on a buying trip in Colorado, Henry saw them and was rapturous. At last here was a mink truly blue! Hardened mink men spoke like poets in an attempt to describe the elusive shade. Not more than half a dozen existed. Males were valued at $5,000, females at $3,000, and owners said they wouldn't sell at any price. Sapphire had been evolved by crossing two recessives, the aleutian and the platinum.

This new mink made the aleutian strain have sense to the Company. Other farmers had already started on this sapphire project and argued as to whether the Imperial platinum or standard platinum should be used for the crossing. The two looked alike but had a different genetic make-up. The Fromms, one year behind other breeders, with no aleutians in the herd, could not take chances and tried both. The Company spent $25,000 for breeding stock and $35,000 in the following year. They paid $700 for full blood aleutian males, $350 for females, then bought twenty half blood aleutian females and managed to pick up six dihybrid females for $550 each and knew they'd be lucky if half of these would carry the combined factors they sought.

The Company expected trouble with aleutians. Some

breeders doubt if this strain can ever be made a really sturdy mink or a good producer. Litter average was two and a half. For no apparent reason an aleutian may stop eating, become droopy, bleed from the nose, and eventually die. Henry Czech and keepers never worked harder to tempt appetites. Liver, chicken, and squirrel were offered — elaborate menus were lined up before aleutians in the hope they might eat something. They were given "aleutian supplement," a special food high in liver and vitamins. Boys were hired to catch fish and trap mice. Sometimes these delicacies proved successful, and after an aleutian was restored to the habit of eating he could be returned to regular meals. But too often this method didn't work. The Company lost one third of the aleutians before the first breeding season, and two thirds died before the end of the first summer. Keepers marveled that they'd considered platinums hard to raise.

Chef's troubles were as nothing compared to those of the breeder. Preparatory to the project Johnnie drew up a chart of the various crossings and recrossings to produce the midgeneration of carriers which would ultimately lead to the sapphire strain. After the 1948 whelping season, this program became really complicated.

"A thousand animals were involved in the experiment," Johnnie said. "We had kits of twelve different varieties of genetic make-up. We had carriers and possible carriers. We had deadwood which must be discarded and no certain method of telling which were carriers and which were deadwood. We knew the Imperial platinum was headed nowhere. We had a lot of animals of no value, but we knew we had others with degrees of heritability for this ultimate sapphire strain."

The Company also had a windfall. Three of the di-hybrid females produced young. One litter had one sapphire kit and another had three out of four kits. This was better than anyone had dared hope. Four sapphires on the farm a year ahead of expectations! Or so the Company thought. Then one kit died. Two began to pick at their meals in the summer, were wooed by every delicacy known to tempt mink's jaded appetites, but apparently concluded not to go on living. The fourth sapphire was still alive for the next breeding season. Evidently sapphires would be even harder to raise than aleutians.

Next breeding season, procedure was further complicated by two company decisions. First, they determined to lighten pastels and sapphires by working through a third crossing. This could be done by employing Breath of Spring strain or by a short cut, using a new factor called the Stewart. It was a dominant and affected the color of the underfur, giving a subdued lighting to the entire pelt. The Fromms bought Stewart pastels and Stewart platinums, paying $200 each. The Company was now in the project of superimposing the third mutation and to determine the genetic make-up of the various kits in a litter became a matter of higher fractions.

"It makes sense once you understand it," a keeper said, "but it takes study. We knew from the beginning we were bound to get that one-in-sixteen homozygous infertile."

The Company's other decision was to go counter to the judgment of the fur world, and this was emotionally tied up with the old battle for brighter, livelier fur. The trade and auction companies were certain women would

348

prefer darker shades and consider the lighter sapphires unsuitable for daytime wear. The Company disagreed and quoted the history of the silver fox. It had taken years before the brighter fox won general acceptance, but now this palette change was accepted and would dictate the preferences in mink. Since obviously no breeder could pursue two courses in building a herd, it was a question of bright or the more somber, and the Company determined to use the livelier colors in breeding. The wisdom of this decision was confirmed somewhat by results of the introductory sale of the aleutians, 2,600 skins, offered by the New York Auction Company. Every skin was sold, but the competitive bidding which carried the top price to $81 a pelt was for the lightest color. The greater proportion was on the dark side, which made this mutation a slow starter in the race for fashion favor. Only since then has it become a real contestant when further enlivened by selective breeding.

The only comfort to be derived from the position of silver fox in 1938 was the fact that the Company's years of pioneering brighter silver fox could now help them chart their course in mink mutation breeding. Finest fox skins were selling for $15 to $20, half and even less than the $40 it cost to get a silver fox pelt to market. The Company posted up its losses. Foxes had eaten up a million dollars in capital resources in the effort to maintain them as an important fur, but now even Fromm stubbornness was jolted. The Company closed the Merrill and New York factories.

What the C.I.O. union had not been able to accomplish had been done by silver foxes. Manufacture had been a pen-to-wearer idea in promotion, and to the Company it had been an important link in the projection of an enormous fur farm. Thirty-five thousand fox pelts was a tremendous inventory in jacket manufacture. Smaller mink skins, even a big crop, couldn't make enough coats to keep a large factory going, and the Company didn't wish to manufacture the pelts of others. They had steadfastly refused to do so. Essentially the Fromms were not furriers. They were farmers, absorbed in the marketing of their own products. Since the popular mink needed no help in promotion, the Company determined to return to the original concept of raising a fur crop and selling it as did other ranchers.

They also accepted the necessity of cutting the mighty fox herd. In 1949 they pelted heavily. Only 1,250 pairs of breeders were left in the more than 9,000 breeding pens which marched over the rolling landscape. Ironically, this was the year when the herd had shown its greatest increase. Misses, once so deplorable, were at the minimum. Only the choicest of the breeding stock was saved to be the nucleus when long-haired fur returned to favor. The Fromms did not yet accept the fact that the time might not be just around the corner. This remnant herd was carried for three years, until 1952, when even confirmed fox men were convinced short-haired fur would have a long reign. Of 5,000 pups born in the spring, only 750 were kept alive. In the fall pelting season, the breeders were cut to 500 pairs.

Now ginseng must carry foxes as it had in the beginning. The long-time project to develop a finer fox, to immunize against disease, to explore every fact about strains, breeding, nutrition, and the best environment, had been brought to complete perfection when the market no longer warranted production. Foxes had come into their full glory when the only profit lay in emotional satisfaction. But there will always be silver foxes on the Company's farm, both in Hamburg and in Thiensville. Real fox men are die-hards. "I started out with ten pairs and I'm going to end with ten," Edwin Nieman said.

Edward Fromm is more sanguine. "When the silver fox is so rare it's a distinction to possess one, women will be proud to wear it," he said. "Today it's more beautiful than ever. I don't know a finer fur to enhance the loveliness of any woman."

Keepers look away when they pass the great stretches of empty breeding pens. The houses, beginning to lean on rotting corner posts, give the landscape an impression of a ghost village. Scattered inhabitants sit on roofs of their dwellings and stare forlornly as though they knew the era of pampered foxes had come to an end. If old grandfathers are among them they probably tell of the days when foxes received their vitamins, had pans scoured, beds changed often, when even their whims about the color of horses were consulted. As for mutations, and foxes presented owners with startling departures in coat patterns long before ranched mink had thought of it — now a fox couldn't mutate in any way that would raise an owner's eyebrow.

Silver fox, the dream fur of the four brothers, had been swept aside by fashion, but the care of fur bearers still absorbed the Fromms. Knowledge and technique of high production fur farming gained in more than thirty-five years was still theirs to serve the Company. In 1950 they pelted 33,000 mink. Breeders' pens stretched through the forest. The furring range, where pelters grew in size and put on lustrous coats, was enormous. The farm was as busy and as driven as ever in a zeal to give each fur bearer the best possible life. Edward in his five o'clock morning walk visited mink units and examined feeding boards to make sure plates were not too clean. A polished plate is a sign of a scanty night meal.

Mutations added fresh excitement to mink farming. New horizons of what might be accomplished in using nature's palette to develop entrancing shades were appearing with each discovery. The Company now had Stewart kits, pastel kits, platinum kits, sapphire kits, kits of combined mutations — and dreams and hopes for the future.

Even Henry, whose compulsion to raise silver foxes when he was only ten had been the strange beginning of a fur farm, was captured by the possibilities of mutation breeding. To him mink were no longer merely the way to diversified farming but an adventure, and because he couldn't imagine not being surrounded by fur bearers, his forest acres on the Michigan border held a mink ranch. In the twelve years since he had built the first company mink pens many ideas for improvements had occurred to him, and to a man with a fervor for construction an idea demanded action. He built a warehouse with a feedroom which could serve twice his present herd but had so many labor-saving devices one man could operate it. In typical Henry fashion he decided a third story atop the warehouse would make a wonderful home for his and Mamie's old age. From the large living room windows one can look over miles and miles of forest. It is a peaceful room, and the soft colors of the enormous Oriental rugs look so right with the paneled walls of butternut from company trees.

"You like it?" he asked. "Mamie and I could live here

forever. A man's got to have woods to look at. But I haven't half begun the things I want to."

The mink ranch comes first with Henry. He gets up in the night to feed nursing mothers, and when weaning time has come, he knows each mink, young or old, knows whether it is shy or friendly, a light or heavy feeder, and whether it should be the forebear of more exciting shades to come. All Henry's mink are mutations.

Company trucks make long weekly trips to deliver food for his fifteen hundred mink. "And they take the fur crop to the home farm for pelting," he said. The "home farm" will always be Hamburg to Henry, and this new hundred-thousand-dollar venture seems only a natural projection of company substance.

Enormous mink crops produced a fresh "patent." Lawrence Schult never liked the old method of killing mink with a hypodermic shot of ether in the heart. Ether formed a gum on the rubber of the syringe, and even with three syringes and a mechanic to keep them clean, the crew of carriers was often kept waiting with frightened mink. Lawrence bought an ordinary garden sprayer with pressure and a long flexible copper tube. He set a hypodermic needle in a brass plunger so well seated in lead no rubber was required. A valve releases one centimeter of ether. Now he carries this portable equipment through the long aisles between furring pens, a crew of six carriers bring the mink, and 8,000 pelters can be killed in a ten-hour day.

"It's all over in a second before the animal even suspects what's happening to him," Lawrence said. "I hated that old tussle with a mink."

The keepers nodded. Many had been boyhood trappers and knew the tremendous fighting spirit of the weasel family and how often death must be both slow and cruel on a trap line. Keepers like their charges.

"These little fellows think they're only being brought to be looked at or get a treatment like has happened to 'em lots of times," one man said. "That's all they ever know about it."

The first sapphires went to market in 1950 and were auctioned in a midwinter sale. It was a small offering, only 2,500 skins. The introductory sale was well publicized by the Mutation Mink Breeders' Association, now called MMBA, or Emba. Full page advertisements in leading women's magazines told of the years required to distill the essence of full beauty from the crossed mutations. Fur experts agreed the sapphire was one of the loveliest color phases to reach the market and the fur world had great expectations.

The Company did not send a sapphire pelt to the sale. It seemed strange a fur farmer could resist the high prices anticipated. Certainly the Fromms must have held a lengthy and serious conference on such a matter.

"We never even talked it over," John said, astonished at the question. "I knew how the Company felt about building up our herd. We were planning on producing more than a thousand sapphire kits in our next spring's breeding season."

They did.

Prices at the sapphire auction outran all predictions. The top bundles of males brought $350 a skin, the females $165. Nothing like this had been known in mink history. Light and medium light pelts brought the highest prices, and for the 2,359 skins graded as good quality the average price was $118.38. The sale of the latest color phase to reach the market was even more exciting than the auction which introduced mutations.

Man had taken over nature's random experiments, learned which mutation could be used to enliven and purify colors, which would impart an elusive shading or a new delicacy of hue. Now when mink apparently had run out of genes to mutate, man was by no means at the end of his adventure. No longer must a mink farmer pray to be struck by a mutation. He had the material and the knowledge to create his own. Range of colors can be widened, hues be made still more beautiful and subtle.

Another man-made mutation was already underway — the Topaze. This can not be achieved in less than three breeding seasons. At present there are three ways to arrive at a Topaze mink. One is still in the experimental stage and has not been worked out genetically. The two already proven successful are to cross pastel onto the Green-eyed pastel or onto the Ungava pastel. The two latter strains, being of different genetic make-up than that of pastel, will produce in the first generation litters of what appear to be ordinary dark mink but which are carriers of the strains. These mated together will have a one-in-sixteen kit of the famous Topaze with ruby eyes. The one-in-sixteen kits mated will breed true but they are poor producers, averaging two kits to a litter. Obviously the development of a marketable quantity is a slow affair, but the 1952 Topaze crop of all mutation breeders, about 2,500 skins, will reach the market early in 1953. Other improvements in the man-made mutations are being carried on.

"In the next few years sapphires will be still more delicate in coloring as we get the lightening-up factor into them," Edward said. "And look at those mink! They're homozygous Stewart platinums. Not enough in the country to be given a name and probably never will be. They're infertile, but they brought good prices in last winter's auctions."

In the late afternoon sunlight their ice blue coats, vibrant and sparkling, reminded one of glaciers floating in a deep blue sea. Near them were homozygous Stewart pastels, of a warm tone, slightly lighter than a biscuit and alive with a shimmering overlay of silver. They too were infertiles, the one-in-sixteen kit, but their loveliness justified their existence.

These two color phases went to market under the name of homozygous infertiles, which baffled furriers and the public and probably always will. Perhaps mutation breeders had run out of poetical names for color phases or had become discouraged after the government ruling that no fur could be given a geographical name which would mislead the public as to its origin. This meant aleutian could no longer be used in marketing. While MMBA was dealing with this matter, the association decided to protect its membership, which had carried the promotional costs of mutation mink, by copyrighting names they alone were entitled to use and designating the type of mink to which they applied. Non-members must offer furs under type names. This may or may not clear up the confusion. Silverblu may be used by members only, while others will return to the original name of platinum. MMBA members can say Royal Pastel, but others only pastel. MMBA's name for aleutian is now Lutetia. To other fur farmers it's gun metal. Cerulean is used by association members instead of sapphire. Topaze is an MMBA copyright and others must bring this mutation in as Ruby-eyed mink. Homozygous infertile apparently defeated even MMBA's ingenuity and will be offered as homozygous. Breath of Spring is not copyrighted and can be used by anyone to describe the lighter platinum. Starlight is not a real mutation but the hybrid generation of standard mink and platinum.

Perhaps in time these names will not seem important except to the rancher who needs them on his breeding cards to keep a record of the blood strains. Women will undoubtedly dispense with genetics and buy the particular shade they find most captivating, and mink will be wearing more subtle and delicate colors each year. Fur farming has come into its full flower.

Chapter Twenty-Seven

THIRD GENERATION FROMMS WERE NOW GOING TO school and second generation Fromms served on the district school board. The two eldest of Johnnie's four girls went to the little schoolhouse down the road which the Fromm boys had attended. This is now on company property and next to the Fromm cemetery in which the elder Fromms were buried. With young Fromms growing up, education became a live topic. The Company considered this and gave $50,000 for country schools of the county.

The donation caused such confusion between different districts that the county board suggested it be spent on the little schoolhouse down the road. The original structure with belfry and bell was saved intact, but its interior was changed to conform with a large addition in the rear. Specifications for a model country school and community center were followed, and it is now referred to as the finest of its kind in Wisconsin.

Edward made the opening address and described school days as he and his brothers knew them. The children laughed indulgently and undoubtedly didn't believe a word of it. It would have been strange had they done so. Pioneering days, still within the memory of many, seemed centuries distant to youngsters in a school with modern desks, big windows, gymnasium, cafeteria, stage, piano, and a large community room for parties and parents' weekly card club.

Edward's official position is that of janitor, but he delegates his duties to a farm employee. Warm noon dinners are delivered from the company boardinghouse. These were free until the little red schoolhouse was incorporated in the Merrill school district where it is a rule to charge fifteen cents for luncheons. Such a revolutionary change from company policy aroused tremendous indignation among teen-agers suddenly confronted with the high cost of living.

Another major construction of this time was Edward's house when he carried out his desire to live on the site of the original homestead. He and Alice had planned on this for years. The two oldest daughters had finished college, married, and had children. The youngest daughter was in prep school. Edward and Alice could now build for their older years and for young families coming home on visits. The house required a year to build and, unlike Henry, Edward didn't lift a hammer. Like all Fromm homes it bristles with labor saving devices. Early backbreaking work has left a deep respect for motors, and a memory of years when the boys cooked for a crew of ginseng workers has resulted in kitchens which any housewife would envy. But a licensed engineer, not a maid, should be engaged to run them.

Edward's greatest pride is that the house was built entirely by farm labor. The walls are paneled, each room

in different wood—Alleghany white oak, African ma-
hogany, Central American primavera, and India satin
wood—all architectural paneling, done in book match.

"Arnold Haman and Irvin Oefte did it," Edward said.
"I remember when they joined us as general farm labor-
ers and began to work under Bill Cole, construction
straw boss. Now look at their workmanship in those cab-
inets and drawers! Any craftsman could be proud of
them. And those boys have never worked for anyone except the Company."

This is true of a large proportion of the employees.
Edward went through the list, men and women who
joined them in the twenties and early thirties and who
are now straw bosses or heads of the many departments
in the sprawling project—trucking, construction, fur
range, feedroom, ginseng gardens, drying room for root,
boardinghouse, dormitories, blacksmith shop, garage
and repair shop, dairy herd, barns, warehouse, mink
units, pelting room, power plant, and ginseng workers.

"Emma Thiel, boss of the women's ginseng crew,
joined us in the early twenties," Edward said. "We once
thought we needed only young girls with nimble fingers
for ginseng, and now we have grandmothers weeding
ginseng."

The same is true in all departments. An age limit of
nineteen to thirty-five was once the rule in hiring employees. Now many workers are seventy.

"Unless the government raises the draft age to sixty-
five, the Company wouldn't lose many men in another
war," Edward said.

Old age holds no dread on the company farm. One
workman put this feeling into practical terms. "We figure our working days are over when we're too weak to

get to the boardinghouse table." This company policy has paid off. Labor turnover is almost non-existent, and what the Company may lose in speed it more than gains in reliability and little absenteeism. All employees who have worked for the Company more than a year are given a bonus. The farm carries insurance which provides hospitalization for an employee and dependent family, maternity care, and sick leave wages. When asked about severance pay, Edward was astonished.

"Nothing severs an employee from the Company except disinterest in his job — and death," he said. "In the first case, severance pay isn't justified. In the second, it has no meaning."

The work day is still ten hours, and five and a half days a week. Wages are paid on an hourly basis with extra for overtime. Straw bosses, all of whom have come up from the ranks, don't look over any man's shoulder, and there is an impression of leisurely tempo, except in a crisis. Then straw bosses, who have met many in apprentice days, expect each man to speed up. In a very real way the company farm is of community interest. In the last twenty years it has released $10,000,000 in wages. Some of this is paid in rush periods when crews are augmented, and neighbors, men and women who operate nearby farms, count on this extra money.

Some employees live in the boardinghouse, although the majority depart each week end for their own farms. Others live in the Company's farmhouses acquired as the necessity for ginseng land added outlying quarter sections to the holding. These houses are rented for a nominal sum and have the usual company perquisites of maintenance, utilities and perhaps a friendly lift with a bulldozer or power machinery for making a small garden. The Thiensville unit has much the same set-up. It is not so large but has, in addition to a mink farm, the Federal Food plant and biological laboratories.

These two enterprises have been tied more closely into the project by the Company's recent decision to re-enter the auction business in the east. Since the shutdown of the New York factory in 1948, the big floor in the Seventh Avenue building has been empty except for a space rented to Eastwood Holt Inc., a firm of fur brokers. In the fall of 1952 Eastwood Holt, the Fromm Brothers, and the Fur Exchange, a Seattle auction house, formed an auction company with sales to be held in New York. These selling firms have never departed from the traditional methods of the fur trade. As early trade posts gave winter "debt" to trappers, so auction houses now, by a livestock loan operation, enable ranchers to get their crops to market. Federal Food for ranches and the laboratory's biologicals fit into this scheme.

"It's a logical extension of the Company's projects," Edward said. "And there's room for another auction house. Offerings in the past years have been heavy. A sale of 150,000 mink skins is not unusual, and a fur buyer cannot make a pre-sale inspection which will be fair to the pelts of all the producers. The Company has space and refrigerating rooms, and the farm will have pelts to sell. It's a legitimate advance."

The Company's plans for the 1953 season, based on breeders which are being held over, will produce a mink crop of between 35,000 and 40,000 skins. All except a small lot of Kobuk standard will be mutation mink.

Thus this mighty fur farm has evolved from the dream of four farm boys. They have played an important role in two of the great adventures in the history of the fur trade. They have seen the silver fox, once so rare in the wilds, saved from extinction, have seen it domesticated, bred to perfection, and become the glamour fur of a decade. They have brought a precious fur, once worn only by a privileged few, within the reach of every woman. The swift rise of mink was an equally exciting period when fur farming reached its true maturity and man learned to use the fortuitous accidents in nature's breeding to produce entrancing colors and breath-taking hues which never before existed.

The 160-acre homestead, mortgaged to buy three silver foxes, has grown to 17,000 acres. Before the 1952 pelting season the Fromm farm held 70,000 fur bearing animals. Through the years the Company has raised 750,000 foxes and 250,000 mink and is still growing as a mink ranch. It has made a significant contribution to the development of a natural resource. It challenged traditional concepts of beauty in fur and has pioneered acceptance of livelier, brighter pelts. It has ended two great fur farming hazards through medical research. To do all this the Company has spent $2,000,000 in fox housing, $500,000 in mink housing, more than $1,000,-000 in exploration of encephalitis and distemper, and $4,500,000 in farm improvements.

The first small ginseng garden, five by sixteen feet, has culminated in the planting of 500 acres. A farmer who has raised five acres of ginseng in his lifetime is considered a large operator, and if he has raised twenty acres, and few have done so, he is rated as a big producer. At the height of ginseng culture in America the annual crop was never more than 250,000 pounds. The Company has raised almost 9,000,000 pounds.

Such figures do not, however, express the endeavor

which has stretched through more than forty years because its real essence cannot be expressed in foxes, in mink, in pounds of ginseng, or even in dollars in the bank. It was originally a dream to raise silver foxes, and without the dream this great project would never have come into being, but the apex of the idea was set in terms of living. Four farm boys were not content with the ugliness and the drudgery of their lives. They did not talk of spectacular riches, but they knew life could be better. And they made it so.

Sweep of forests, fields, ginseng gardens, fur pens, homes for owners and employees which have cost $500,-000 — these are visible substance of the Company. But to the four Fromm boys it was a Company before it owned a fox or a ginseng plant, and in the forty years of its building "the Company" has become a separate entity, a fusion of them all and yet not the reflection of any one. The Fromms have not owned the Company. It has owned them, and its rights were greater than those of its builders. In many years it was a tyrant, ruthless in its demands on human energy, but it has also been beneficent in gifts and as a symbol inspiring in the fervor of its spirit.

Its future is left to those who follow. The Company isn't an old man of the sea which the young must carry, nor is it a top-heavy structure which will topple with the loss of its builders. It holds a heritage of experience and knowledge in the pioneering of this continent's last natural resource, and whether the fashion is for long- or short-haired fur, or no fur at all, there will always be "the Company."

About

the

Author

Kathrene Pinkerton was born in Minneapolis and graduat
from the University of Wisconsin. Until her marriage she v
Field Secretary of the Wisconsin Anti-Tuberculosis Assoc
tion. She and her husband, a former newspaperman, have c
laborated on many adventure stories for magazines and boo
She has written WILDERNESS WIFE, the account of f
years of living in the Northwoods of Canada, THREE'S
CREW, the story of several years of cruising the coast of Sou
eastern Alaska, as well as a series of adventure stories for you
people about fox-farming in Canada.

Also by KATHRENE PINKERTON

Wilderness Wife
Three's a Crew
Two Ends to Our Shoestring

For Young Peop

Adventure Nortl
Fox Island
Farther North
Windigo
The Silver Strai
A Good Partner
Hidden Harbor